VALENCE

VALENCE

BY

C. A. COULSON

*Rouse Ball Professor of Mathematics
in the University of Oxford*

SECOND EDITION

OXFORD UNIVERSITY PRESS

LLL-3259

Oxford University Press, Amen House, London E.C.4

GLASGOW NEW YORK TORONTO MELBOURNE WELLINGTON
BOMBAY CALCUTTA MADRAS KARACHI LAHORE DACCA
CAPE TOWN SALISBURY NAIROBI IBADAN
KUALA LUMPUR HONG KONG

FIRST EDITION 1952
REPRINTED FOUR TIMES
SECOND EDITION 1961
REPRINTED (WITH CORRECTIONS) 1963
REPRINTED LITHOGRAPHICALLY IN GREAT BRITAIN
AT THE UNIVERSITY PRESS, OXFORD
FROM CORRECTED SHEETS OF THE SECOND EDITION
1965

PREFACE TO SECOND EDITION

IT is now ten years since the first edition was printed. I have therefore taken the opportunity presented by the need for a further reprinting to rewrite considerable parts of the book. During these years some matters previously in dispute have been settled, and in others there is a change of emphasis. Besides this need to bring the book up to date I have felt that a more satisfactory account of d-electrons was required. This has given me the chance to do some sort of justice to the recent remarkable development of the theory of inorganic chemistry. Readers will find a new chapter devoted to ligand-field theory and complex ions. But where possible I have endeavoured to keep the same sequence and even the same wording as in the first edition.

It is a pleasure to express my thanks to many chemists in many different countries who have helped me to correct errors and to avoid obscurities. They are too numerous to mention individually, but such merits as this little book may possess must be ascribed in large measure to them rather than to me.

My thanks are due to Dr. L. E. Orgel and the editors of *Acta Crystallographica* and *Research* for permission to reproduce diagrams.

C. A. C.

January 1961

PREFACE TO FIRST EDITION

In the last twenty-five years the theory of valence has made enormous progress. To a large extent this has been due to the advent of wave mechanics. The result is that a situation has now been reached in which the education of a chemist is not complete unless he knows at least the main lines along which such progress has been achieved. This does not mean that every chemical student should be able to make his own theoretical calculations—this would be ridiculous, and will probably never happen. But it does mean that he should be sufficiently acquainted with the chief ideas and the essential tools that lie behind the modern theory of valence. The splendid and elegant elucidation of so large a part of chemistry which we have seen in the last two decades should not remain unknown to him. No longer ought he to be content with an electronic theory of valence couched in pre-wave-mechanical terms.

This book is written to make this appreciation easier. It is not a text-book of chemistry, and it does not attempt to supplant any of the standard treatises. Rather it is to supplement them, to show the pattern within which much of the contents of these treatises fits; to exhibit the fundamental reasons why molecules are what they are and how the theoretician looks at his problems as they arise. Practically no mathematics is needed for this purpose, since almost everything necessary can be put in pictorial terms. Contrary to what is sometimes supposed, the theoretical chemist is not a mathematician, thinking mathematically, but a chemist, thinking chemically. That is why almost everything in this book should be understandable to a chemist with few mathematical attainments.

Two comments are necessary concerning the layout of the book itself. In the first place, no prior knowledge of wave mechanics is assumed, and all the necessary technique and method is developed in the opening chapters. Experts in wave mechanics will find the 'mixture' here somewhat unusual. This is because the only theory that has been expounded is that which is needed in our later chemical applications. It is surprising how little actually is required.

In the second place a serious attempt has been made to use both of the two main competing theories, usually known as the molecular-orbital and valence-bond methods. Both are approximations, whose range of validity is now sufficiently understood for us to recognize the folly of trusting to either alone. Earlier accounts have tended to emphasize one of these to the exclusion of the other. This will no longer do: and so both have been developed in this book. At first they are treated separately, but in the final third part they are used almost indiscriminately. The subject matter of valence has been, and still is, changing rapidly, as befits a living discipline; but there is now much that seems to have 'settled down'; and we may reasonably claim that most of the material in the first eleven chapters would command universal agreement. The thirteenth and last chapter differs from the rest in that it indicates the present position in several matters where opinion is by no means unanimous, and where further progress is to be expected even now.

In the earlier sections of the book certain paragraphs occur in small type. These may be omitted by those who suffer from an innate fear of mathematics, for they are not essential to the argument.

The greater part of this book was written while I was Professor of Theoretical Physics at King's College, London. I should not wish to end this Preface without an acknowledgement of the friendly contacts and stimulating discussions which I have enjoyed with my group of research students there. Particularly I would like to thank Professor R. D. Brown who has read the proofs and helped me to remove several obscurities. It is too much to hope that none remain. But the responsibility for them is mine, and I should be grateful to be told of places where I could do better.

I have to acknowledge with gratitude permission to reproduce diagrams which I have received from Professor H. Eyring, Professor K. Fajans, Professor N. H. Frank, Dr. G. Herzberg, Professor G. E. Kimball, Dr. Allan Maccoll, Professor N. F. Mott,

Professor Linus Pauling, and Dr. A. F. Wells. I am similarly grateful to the councils of the Chemical Society and the Faraday Society, the editors of *Endeavour, Science Progress*, the *Philosophical Magazine*, the *Journal of Chemical Physics*, and the *Physical Review*. My thanks are also due to Messrs. Blackie, McGraw-Hill, Prentice-Hall, the Cornell University Press and the Delegates of the Oxford University Press.

C. A. C.

1 *November* 1951

CONTENTS

LIST OF TABLES

I

THEORIES OF VALENCE

1.1. Essentials of any theory of valence

THIS book is concerned with the theory of valence. It may be
well, therefore, to start by recalling some of the chief phenomena
which any valid theory has to explain. These phenomena are not
primarily the details of molecular structure, interesting as these
often may be, but rather the main principles of molecular formation; for in so far as the details are significant, they must follow
from the basic principles.

Thus, in the first place, we have to show why molecules form
at all: in its simplest terms this means that we must explain why
for example, two hydrogen atoms will come together to form a
permanent and stable compound, molecular H_2, but two helium
atoms will not form a corresponding He_2. Any molecular helium
that is formed is of so transitory a character that it cannot be
called a chemical species.

Then in the second place we have to show why atoms form
compounds in definite proportions. From the earliest days of
Gay-Lussac and Berzelius the law of multiple proportions has
insisted on the fundamental character of the combining ratio for
different atoms. But the picture of an atom which resulted from
the work of subsequent investigators such as Frankland and
Kekulé was rather like that of a tiny billiard ball on the surface
of which a certain number of fixed knobs (i.e. valences) determined
the number of other atoms that could be directly attached to it.
This picture of chemical behaviour obscures one fundamental
problem—thus, for example, if two hydrogen atoms are able to
attract one another to form a stable union, why should they not
attract a third, or a fourth, one to build up a larger aggregate?
In the same way, why do we find CH_4, but not CH_5 or CH_6? This
may be called the phenomenon of the saturation of valence: it is
evidently quite central to any theory of chemical combination,
even though we have to admit the existence of many exceptions

B

(e.g. CO and CO_2). Indeed we may add to the requirements of our theory an understanding of the reasons why certain atoms do show multiple valences, and of the relationship that these bear to the positions of these atoms in the periodic table.

This leads us to the third section of our field of inquiry. We must ask of our theory of valence that it will adequately explain the stereochemical character of molecules. The subject of stereochemistry may be said to have been started by the brilliant postulate of the tetrahedral carbon atom by van 't Hoff and le Bel: but in more recent times, by availing themselves of many new physical methods such as the study of vibration and rotation spectra and of X-ray and electron diffraction, chemists have been able to give a far more detailed picture of a molecule. For example, we know interatomic distances and angles in many molecules, sometimes with very high precision. Such knowledge places new demands on our theory of valence. A satisfactory theory must, for example, be able to explain not only why in methane the HCH angles all have the characteristic tetrahedral value

$$\begin{array}{cc} H\diagdown & \diagup H \\ & C \\ H\diagup & \diagdown H \end{array}$$

of 109° 28', but also why in chloroform

$$H-C\mathrel{\substack{\diagup Cl \\ -Cl \\ \diagdown Cl}},$$

the three Cl—C—Cl angles are increased to about $110\frac{1}{2}°$, and the three H—C—Cl angles decreased to about 108°. In the same way we must be able to understand why in CO_2 the three atoms lie on a straight line, but in H_2O they form an approximately right-angled triangle.

Our theory of valence must not only be able to deal with the three main aspects of molecular structure which have just been outlined: it must link them together so that they follow naturally from one another. Indeed, the extent to which we are led, almost inevitably, from the reason why two atoms form a molecule, first to the maximum number of groups that a given atom may attach to itself, and then to the geometrical arrangement of these groups around the central atom, will be a measure of the value of our theory.

There is still one further demand to be made. For the prolific and intimate nature of our experimental knowledge of molecular shape and size insists that our interpretation also should be intimate. We can no longer be content with the conventional representation in which, following Odling (1860) and Kekulé (1861), a single bond between two atoms is described by a line and a double bond by two lines, so that H_2 is written H—H and CO_2 as O=C=O. For although such bond-diagrams do tell us something of the relative orientation of the atoms, they say nothing about the length of the bond. Nor do they help us to answer such questions as: what is the shape of a chemical bond, or what is the difference between a double bond and two strained single bonds, or what right have we at all to speak of separate bonds in a polyatomic molecule? To provide answers to these questions and others like them is an essential responsibility of any acceptable theory of valence.

1.2. Electronic character of valence

It is clear that the intimate description of a chemical bond of which we have spoken, must be essentially electronic. It is the behaviour and distribution of the electrons around the nucleus that gives the fundamental character of an atom: it must be the same for molecules. In one sense, therefore, the description of the bonds in any molecule is simply the description of the electron distribution in it.

This fact has been realized for a long time. For example, quite soon after his discovery of the electron in 1897, J. J. Thomson tried to develop an electron theory of valence. He was followed by others, notably G. N. Lewis, Irving Langmuir, and Kossel. All these accounts suffered from one serious disability—they treated the electrons largely as if they were electrical charges at rest. This is particularly well illustrated by the geometrical model of Langmuir, in which each atomic nucleus was surrounded by an imaginary cube with the electrons at the corners. Two atoms in chemical combination would orient themselves so that their cubes were similarly placed, sharing faces of these cubes in such a way that only one electron was at each vertex, and yet each vertex was occupied, so that every atom was surrounded by an octet of electrons. This model was certainly a little more refined than the earlier one of van 't Hoff which applied particularly to carbon and represented the valences of this atom as directed towards the four corners of a tetrahedron with the atom at the centre, and then spoke of a single bond between two carbon atoms as the sharing of a common vertex, a double bond as the sharing of a common side, and a triple bond as the sharing of a common face, of these atomic tetrahedra. But both these models, whether they involve a tetrahedron or a cube, are fundamentally false because they presuppose a static distribution of electrons. They may have emphasized the octet rule, and served for a while to show a relationship with the periodic table developed in 1869 by Mendeléeff; but as we shall see in a later chapter, they almost certainly delayed our understanding of aromatic and other con-jugated molecules. Worse still, these theories did violence to the established rules of electrical behaviour. For whatever may or may not be true about the disposition of charges in an atomic or molecular system, at least we should expect to be able to apply Earnshaw's theorem of electrostatics, which states that no system of charges can be in stable equilibrium while at rest. The stability of an atom or a molecule must be a dynamic and not a static one.

It was precisely this situation which held up the development of a satisfactory theory of valence. For so long as the electrons were at rest, the forces which one atom exerted on another atom were necessarily electrostatic forces of a Coulomb type. Such forces are manifestly unable to describe the covalent bond, as in H_2, though there are chemical systems such as the ionic crystals which we shall discuss in Chapter XI, where they do play a major role. We can see quite easily now why the earliest ideas of a theory of chemical combination, due chiefly to Berzelius (1819), were electrochemical in nature, stressing the electronegative and electropositive character of the combining atoms. There was no other possible alternative if the atoms were static. But even Berzelius himself recognized that such a description could not apply to the elements (e.g. H_2, Cl_2, metallic Na) where, because all the atoms were alike, there could be no compensation of residual charges.

Quite evidently the later theory of G. N. Lewis (1916) which postulated the existence of a shared-electron bond, or electron-pair bond, is in a similar difficulty. It is true that this theory magnificently coordinates a large body of chemical fact. But it is a purely formal description, and tells us nothing about what the sharing of electrons means, or how it arises. If the electrons are in static equilibrium, we have precisely the same difficulties as before; if they are in dynamic equilibrium, we have still to describe their motion and show why the fact of their being shared by the two nuclei leads to a satisfactory solution of the three main problems outlined in § 1—that is, to the existence of a binding energy, to a saturation of combining power, and to an explanation of stereochemistry. No sooner have we stated these requirements than we see how inadequate the theory is in its simplest form. A much more intimate description of the dynamic behaviour of electrons is needed.

A start was made towards such a description by Niels Bohr. In 1913 he introduced the first satisfactory dynamic model of an atom. One of the essentially new elements in this theory was that each electron in an atom, particularly of hydrogen, moved in an orbit under the action of classical (i.e. Newtonian) laws of motion: but certain quantum conditions were introduced to restrict the number of permitted orbits, and hence to allow only a discrete set of energies for the electron. Emission or absorption of light corresponded to a discontinuous electronic jump, or transition, from one allowed energy to another. This is not the place to describe Bohr's theory in any further detail, because although it gave an almost completely satisfactory account of the spectrum of atomic hydrogen, it was only able to make qualitative calculations for systems with more than one electron. In the case of molecular H_2 it was supposed (Fig. 1†) that the two electrons P_1

† The notation for figures is the same as for equations. Thus Fig. 4.2 means the second figure in Chapter IV. If only one number is given (e.g. Fig. 6) the reference is to the current chapter.

and P_2 moved in phase with one another, at opposite ends of a diameter of a circle symmetrically placed with respect to the nuclei A and B. The centrifugal force on each electron is balanced by the attraction to the two nuclei and the repulsion from the other electron. Quantum conditions ('phase integrals') are introduced just as with a single atom to select the permitted orbits, and allow us to calculate the corresponding energy values. The most obvious objections to this model were that although it certainly treats the

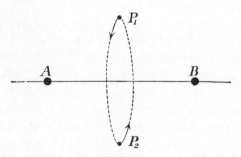

Fig. 1.1. The Bohr model of H_2. P_1 and P_2 are the two electrons which move round the dotted circle between the nuclei A and B.

problem as a dynamic one, it predicts a wrong value for the binding energy and gives a completely fallacious account of the absorption spectrum due to electronic jumps from one level to another.

Bohr's theory represented a great advance because of its dynamic character and the introduction of quantum conditions. It was inadequate chiefly because it gave too definite and measurable a character to the electrons, for it is supposed that the electrons in an atom or a molecule could be individually recognized and located with a precision which we now know to be quite impossible. This lack of precision is not due to any fault or bad design of our apparatus, but is inherent in the very nature of the electron. We shall have more to say about this in the next chapter, when we outline the more recent theory of the electron which has completely replaced that of Bohr. This theory, now called wave mechanics, was started by Schrödinger† in 1926. It is able to give a far more intimate account of the motion of electrons, both

† *Ann. Physik*, 1926, **79**, 361.

in atoms and molecules, than any earlier theory; and, as we shall see in later chapters, it is able to provide us with partial answers to all the questions asked in § 1. Now, for the first time, it is possible to give a coherent and inclusive theory of molecular structure.

Before leaving this paragraph, there is one further comment to make. It is sometimes asked whether ordinary gravitational forces play any part in a chemical bond. The answer is that their effect is quite negligible. In the first place, if they were very significant, we should expect heavier diatomic molecules to be more firmly bound than light ones. So far as there is any tendency of this kind it is in the opposite direction: thus the hydrogen molecule is about three times as strongly bound as is the iodine molecule I_2. In the second place a simple numerical example will show how small gravitational forces are compared with chemical ones. The work required to overcome the gravitational attraction of two hydrogen atoms, each of mass 1.7×10^{-24} gm, and separate them from their equilibrium distance of 0.74 A, is about 2.5×10^{-47} ergs. But the bond strength determined thermochemically tells us that the actual amount of energy required to separate the atoms in H_2 is 6.7×10^{-12} ergs. This shows that gravitational forces play no effective part in chemical combination.

1.3. Importance of the energy

In its widest form we may say that two atoms form a molecule because there is a lowering of the total energy when they come together. For most purposes this energy is effectively the electronic energy, since the energies of rotation and vibration, while sometimes quite significant in absolute magnitude, are small relative to the energy of the electrons. We shall have more to say about this later on, but for the moment we shall assume that the energy relationship between a molecule and its component atoms is primarily that of the electrons.† And we shall find, as we proceed, that this same electronic energy plays the dominant role

† What we are here calling the electronic energy is short for the sum of the kinetic energy and mutual Coulomb energies of electrons with electrons, electrons with nuclei, and nuclei with one another. It is to be distinguished (see later) from vibrational, translational, or rotational energies of the molecule as a whole.

in nearly all molecular phenomena. For example, the fact that hydrogen forms diatomic aggregates such as H_2 rather than triatomic aggregates such as H_3, follows from the fact that the total energy of H_3 is greater than the sum of that of H_2 and H. Similarly the HOH angle in water is equal to $104\frac{1}{2}°$ and the two OH bond lengths are each 0·96 A because it is for these values of the internal coordinates of the molecule that the energy is lowest. A satisfactory theory of valence therefore must be able to show how the electronic energy depends on these variables. Thus, not only do we determine the equilibrium configuration, but we are in the very same process compelled to discuss how the energy changes when the molecule is distorted from this configuration. This means that we obtain the restoring force in any deformation, and have available all the information required for calculating the normal modes of vibration. For this reason we cannot separate the theory of valence from its relation to infra-red vibration spectra and Raman spectra (which are determined by the force constants for vibration) and to the rotational fine-structure (which is determined by the geometry of the molecule).

We have seen that a theory of valence is essentially a theory of the calculation of the energy of a molecule. But we must be careful to distinguish several kinds of energy. Thus in addition to the total electronic energy of a molecule, there is the electronic energy of its component atoms, the difference between the two being the electronic binding energy of the molecule. This is not the same as the dissociation energy (i.e. the energy required to break up the molecule into its constituent atoms) because allowance has to be made for three other effects: (i) the zero-point energy of vibration, which for large polyatomic molecules may reach a total value comparable with the energy of any one bond, though for diatomic molecules the ratio is usually of the order $\frac{1}{10}$ to $\frac{1}{20}$; (ii) the translational energy which is equal to $\frac{3}{2}RT$ per mole both for the original molecule and for each separate fragment; (iii) the energy of rotation of the molecule as a whole, which, except very near 0° K, is $\frac{3}{2}RT$ per mole for a non-linear system, and RT for a linear one. For a diatomic molecule, the dissociation energy may be called the bond energy, since it represents the energy required to break the bond. On account of the effects (i)–(iii), this bond energy depends slightly on the temperature, though of course, the electronic binding energy does not. For a polyatomic molecule, we can still speak of the dissociation energy of any one bond, for this represents the energy needed to break the molecule at this bond into two fragments. But on account of the fact that after the break-up there is often a considerable electronic rearrangement in the two parts, sometimes resulting in the recovery of quite a large amount of energy, the total energy of dissociation of a molecule is not usually the same as the sum of the separate dissociation energies of each bond. A simple example of this distinction between the total binding energy and the sum of the dissociation energies of the separate bonds is found in the water molecule H_2O. The total binding energy is about 219 kcal/mole, so that, if we wished, we could speak of an average bond energy of 109·5 kcal/mole. However, the energy needed to break either of the O—H bonds separately is no less than 119·5 kcal/mole. The explanation of the apparent discrepancy is that after we have broken the first O—H bond, we only require 99·4 kcal/mole to break the second, and the sum of 119·5 and 99·4 is the same as the original 219.

There is yet one further distinction to be mentioned. Bond energies are usually inferred from heats of reaction, adjusted so as to refer to a constant pressure of one atmosphere and a temperature of 18° C. These heats of reaction represent the total heat (sometimes called the enthalpy, or heat content, and written $H = E + pv$) rather than the internal energy E, and if, as usually happens in a dissociation, there is a change of volume, we ought to correct for the presence of the term pv.

Many of these corrections to the original electronic binding energy of the molecule would be unnecessary if all values were extrapolated to zero temperature. But such corrections are usually difficult to make with complete certainty, and when made they do not appear to cause any great relative changes in bond energies. For that reason, tables of bond energies given in the literature are for standard conditions of temperature and pressure, and are not therefore strictly bond energies at all! In very accurate numerical work, care is needed to distinguish between energy and enthalpy;

but it will not be necessary to do so in this book, where we shall be concerned almost entirely with electronic binding energies.

It may serve to emphasize the relative importance of some of these energy terms if we show their values[†] for the particular case of H_2.

Some energy values for H_2

Total electronic energy of H_2	$= 740 \cdot 5 \pm 0 \cdot 1$	kcal/mole	
Electronic energy of two H atoms	$= 631 \cdot 6$	,,	
Electronic binding energy	$= 109 \cdot 5$	,,	
Zero-point vibrational energy	$= 6 \cdot 2$	,,	
Rotational energy of H_2	$= 0 \cdot 6$	,, (at 291° K)	
Translational energy of H_2	$= 0 \cdot 9$	,, ,,	
Correction for pv term	$= 0 \cdot 5$	,, ,,	
Bond energy of H_2	$= 104 \cdot 0$	,,	

Two conclusions follow immediately from these figures. In the first place the corrections for rotation and translation and the pv term are small; but that for the zero-point vibration is more significant. In the second place the electronic binding energy is only a small proportion (here about one-seventh) of the total electronic energy. If we had chosen heavier atoms the fraction would have been even smaller. Thus for Li_2 the ratio is 1 in 14 and for methane it is no more than 1 in 38. The binding energy is thus the difference of two much larger quantities, and if we want to calculate it with a reasonable accuracy, we must be able to compute these other quantities (total electronic energy of the molecule and electronic energy of the separate atoms) with even more precision. As we shall see, this imposes very severe restrictions on *ab initio* calculations of binding energies, though fortunately it does not affect the main basis of our theory of valency.

There is one interesting corollary which follows from the energy values given above. Since the binding energy is a small difference between larger quantities, we must expect it to be very sensitive to the atoms being bonded. There is, in fact, a mutual character about bond energies which is quite absent from most other types of force. This was recognized as long ago as the time of Berzelius, though he could not relate it, as we can do, to subtle differences in electronic behaviour. Two examples will serve to illustrate this

† Taken in part from G. Herzberg and A. Monfils, *J. Molec. Spec.*, 1960, 5, 482.

mutual character. (a) The strongest known single-bond† in a diatomic molecule is the HF bond whose energy (135·1 kcal/mole) greatly exceeds that of either HH or FF (104 and 37·7 kcal/mole respectively). Evidently hydrogen and fluorine are mutually adapted to the formation of a strong bond much better than either of them with another atom of the same kind. An explanation of this will be found in Chapter V. (b) Both phosphorus and nitrogen show single-bond energies P—P and N—N of approximately the same strengths (51‡ and 43§ kcal/mole respectively), and the structure of the atom is much the same in both cases. Yet phosphorus forms a stable tetrahedral molecule P_4, and nitrogen does not. There is at the moment no entirely satisfactory explanation of this difference between apparently similar atoms. It is precisely the existence of mutual effects such as these between pairs of atoms which gives chemistry its intrinsic interest; and it is their elucidation which gives the modern theory of valence its most satisfying quality.

1.4. Potential energy curve for a molecule

A good deal of information about the structure of a molecule is summarized in what is usually called its potential energy curve. Consider, for example, the approach of two atoms A and B with the formation of a diatomic molecule AB. When the internuclear distance is R, the electronic energy may be written $E(R)$. It is usual to choose the zero of energy so that $E = 0$ at infinite separation. Then, if a·stable molecule is formed, E steadily decreases below zero as R decreases, until a minimum value occurs (Fig. 2) at some value $R = R_e$. R_e is called the equilibrium distance, though on account of the inescapable vibration of the nuclei, R oscillates on both sides of R_e. The depth D_e of the minimum of this curve is the electronic dissociation energy. The true dissociation energy D_0 will be rather less than D_e on account of the energy of vibration, for even in the lowest allowed vibrational state there

---

† See Table 12, p. 185, and Johns and Barrow, *Proc. Roy. Soc.* A, 1959, **251**, 504.
‡ F. S. Dainton, *Trans. Faraday Soc.*, 1947, **43**, 244.
§ Skinner, ibid., 1945, **41**, 645. But slightly different values both for P—P and N—N have been suggested by other writers. See Table 12.

still remains the zero-point energy of vibration. Fig. 2 illustrates the relation between these quantities.

At distances less than R_e, the energy curve begins to rise, the physical explanation of this rise being that when the nuclei get close together, they exert a strong repulsion on each other on account of their similar positive charges.

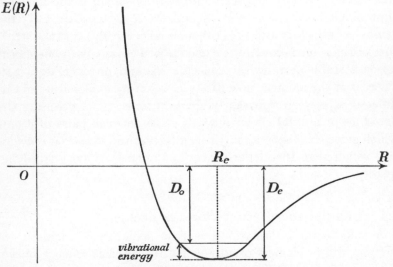

FIG. 1.2. Potential energy curve for a diatomic molecule.

It is one of the major problems for our theory of valence, that it shall be able to calculate the potential energy curve of a given molecule. One of the most convenient empirical representations of such curves is due to P. M. Morse,† and we shall frequently refer to it. It is

$$E(R) = D_e\{e^{-2a(R-R_e)} - 2e^{-a(R-R_e)}\}, \tag{1}$$

where D_e and R_e have the same significance as before, and a is a constant. This expression has a minimum value $-D_e$ at $R = R_e$ and near $R = R_e$ it has the parabolic form

$$E(R) = +D_e\{-1 + a^2(R-R_e)^2 + \ldots\}. \tag{2}$$

With a polyatomic molecule the potential energy curve becomes a surface, because E now depends on several independent variables, e.g. the various bond lengths and angles.

† *Phys. Rev.*, 1929, **34**, 57.

II
ATOMIC ORBITALS

2.1. The Schrödinger wave equation

BEFORE we can profitably discuss the behaviour of electrons in a molecule, we must understand their behaviour in isolated atoms. This is important partly because molecules are built out of atoms, but also because many of the principles which are used in atomic structure apply equally well to molecular structure. There is an advantage in dealing first with atoms. For on account of the single nuclear centre of force, there is an added simplicity not found in molecules where it is of the very essence of the problem that two or more nuclear centres are involved.

The physical picture of an atom that we use is the familiar Rutherford–Bohr one in which the appropriate number of electrons move in orbits around a central nucleus, which we may take to be effectively fixed. In Bohr's early calculations it was supposed that each electron moved in some definite orbit though the orbits slightly disturbed each other on account of the mutual Coulomb repulsion between like charges. Precisely similar conditions are met with in our solar system (except that all the Coulomb forces are attractive), so that this picture could properly be called the planetary atom. However, there are two fundamental objections to this theory when applied to atoms, objections which do not hold when applied to planets. These are the presuppositions

(i) that we are able to define the position and velocity of each electron,

(ii) that, at least in principle, we can follow the motion, or orbit, of each individual electron, just as astronomers follow the motion of each individual planet.

In fact, neither of these presuppositions is valid. For, as Heisenberg showed in 1927 with his Uncertainty Principle,† our

† A full account of this Principle, and of the failure of many conceivable experiments to measure position and velocity simultaneously, may be found in W. Heisenberg, *Physical Principles of the Quantum Theory*, University of Chicago Press, 1930.

knowledge of the behaviour of so minute a particle as an electron can never be as precise as this theory requires. For example, there is no way of measuring exactly the velocity of an electron in an atom, nor is there any way of locating it exactly at any given moment. Indeed, the more closely we attempt to measure its position, the less accurately shall we be able to simultaneously measure its velocity: and *vice versa*. If this is so, we have no right to use such language to describe an atom and we must abandon the hopeless task of trying to follow an electron in its orbit. We must look for some alternative description more in keeping with the kind of information that can be obtained experimentally. Such an alternative description is provided by the wave mechanics with which this book is primarily concerned. This theory, introduced in 1926 by Erwin Schrödinger, rests upon two main lines of evidence. These are:

(i) the wave-character of an electron,

(ii) the probability, or statistical, character of our knowledge.

It is necessary to say a few words about both of these.

The Newtonian, or classical, description of an electron is that it is a point particle completely defined by its coordinates x, y, z. Its motion, or orbit, in an atom is then described by the way in which x, y, z vary with the time. But as early as 1924 de Broglie had shown from some theoretical considerations involving the invariance of certain relativistic formulae, that it was possible to associate waves with a moving particle, and that their wavelength λ would be inversely proportional to the momentum p. The significance of these waves remained obscure until Davisson and Germer in 1927 and independently G. P. Thomson in 1928 showed that a beam of electrons did indeed behave just as if it were a wave and could be diffracted by a suitable grating (here the regular atomic spacing in a crystal). Further the wavelength λ was exactly that which was predicted by the de Broglie relation

$$\lambda = h/p, \tag{1}$$

where h is Planck's constant. Except at very high velocities $p = mv$, where m and v are the mass and velocity of the electron, so that approximately

$$\lambda = h/mv. \tag{2}$$

This relation holds for heavier particles also, though on account of their greater mass, λ becomes so small that there is more ·difficulty in discovering phenomena where the wave-character is important.

Now if there are waves, there must be a wave equation to describe them. This is true for light waves, sound waves, water waves, string waves, etc.: it must also be true for electron waves (or, as they are often called, de Broglie waves). And so we are led at once to the Schrödinger Wave Equation. We shall have something to say about the mathematics of this equation in Chapter III; but there is something that can be said immediately about the interpretation of this equation. This is related to the second point (ii) above, i.e. the probability character of our knowledge. According to Heisenberg's Uncertainty Principle we can never know exactly where a particle is; in such cases the best that we can do is to give the probability that it is in any given region. This means that its position is defined by a probability function. Such a function will vary from place to place according to the probability that the particle will be found in each particular region. If we call this function $\rho(x, y, z)$, then the particle is most likely to be found in those regions where ρ is greatest. In fact $\rho\, dxdydz$ ($\equiv \rho\, d\tau$) is the probability that the particle is in the small volume $dxdydz$ ($\equiv d\tau$) surrounding the point x, y, z. For that reason ρ is sometimes called the *probability density*. Since the particle must be somewhere, the total probability is unity, so that

$$\int \rho\, d\tau = 1. \tag{3}$$

This introduction of probability density takes account of the fundamental law of nature, that our knowledge of the position of a particle can never be absolute.

We have still to connect our wave equation with the density ρ. Here we may appeal to the physical interpretations of other equations of wave motion. It is usually the square of the amplitude of a wave that has significance, rather than the amplitude itself. For example, in an electric field where **E** and **H** are the electric and magnetic vectors the energy density is $(\mathbf{E}^2 + \mathbf{H}^2)/8\pi$; and in a progressive wave along a stretched string, the total energy is proportional to the square of the amplitude. This suggests that we should make a similar association for electron waves and other particle waves. Thus, let the solution of the wave equation for a single particle be a function which we write $\psi(x, y, z)$ and which we call a wave function. Then we may anticipate that

$$\rho(x, y, z) \propto \psi^2(x, y, z). \tag{4}$$

The wave equation itself does not determine ψ absolutely, for we shall see later that we may always multiply any one solution by an arbitrary constant and it still remains a solution of the equation. We generally choose the constant in such a way that the proportionality in equation (4) is replaced by an equality:

$$\rho(x, y, z) = \psi^2(x, y, z). \tag{5}$$

Equation (3) then reads $\quad \int \psi^2 \, d\tau = 1$.

Such wave functions are said to be *normalized*. If ψ is not already normalized, it may be made so on multiplication by N, where

$$N^{-2} = \int \psi^2(x, y, z) \, d\tau.$$

There are occasions in which ψ is a complex quantity and then we replace ψ^2 in the above expressions by $|\psi|^2$. An entirely equivalent form is $\psi\psi^*$, where ψ^* is the complex conjugate to ψ.†

There is a simple reason why the square of ψ, and not ψ itself, must be associated with the probability density. When we solve the wave equation, we usually find some regions of space in which ψ is positive, and others in which it is negative. But the probability must always be positive or zero; and we are therefore forced to abandon ψ in favour of ψ^2 when trying to relate the wave function and the density.

Let us suppose that we want to find the behaviour of a certain particle moving under the influence of given forces. Our procedure is as follows:

    (i) we write down the wave equation in the form appropriate to the given conditions;

---

† If ψ is a complex quantity equal to $f+ig$, where $i = \sqrt{(-1)}$, then $\psi^* = f-ig$, and $|\psi|^2 \equiv \psi\psi^* = f^2+g^2$.

(ii) we solve this equation to find a wave function $\psi(x, y, z)$;

(iii) the probability density is then

$$\rho = \psi^2(x, y, z).$$

We shall not go into the details of this technique now, because that will be the subject-matter of Chapter III. For the present we shall be satisfied with a qualitative account of the procedure and its results when applied to the study of atomic structure. The pictorial character of these results can easily be appreciated before we give the theoretical justification for them. But before going any further, we must point out one very important factor that has so far been omitted. The wave equation has an infinite number of solutions, though by no means all of them correspond to any physical or chemical reality; we call such solutions unacceptable. Acceptable wave functions must satisfy certain conditions. In the case of an electron which is bound to an atom or a molecule we can state that ψ is to be everywhere finite, single-valued, and continuous; and its gradient must also be continuous. It must also be such that the integral $\int \psi^2 \, d\tau$ is finite, so that the wave function may be normalized. These conditions seem very simple and obvious, but in fact they are very far-reaching in their effects. For the wave equation contains in one of its terms the total energy E of the electron, and therefore its solutions themselves depend on E. We have already stated that only certain of these possible solutions are acceptable wave functions. This means that it is only for certain values of the energy that there exist physically significant probability functions. We call these *stationary states* since they arise from a constant energy, and in such cases it may be shown that $|\psi|^2$ is independent of the time. These are the only states in which we shall be interested. The energies are sometimes called eigenvalues, and the corresponding wave functions eigenfunctions, but we shall be content usually to refer to them simply as the allowed energy levels and wave functions.

It was one of the major triumphs of the wave equation that the existence of discrete energy levels followed inevitably, without the need to introduce certain quantum conditions, as Bohr had been compelled to do in his earlier theory. If we may anticipate a little, it was particularly gratifying to discover that in the case of the hydrogen atom, where in fact Bohr's theory gave energy levels in agreement with experiment, the new theory gave exactly the same agreement; and in the case of the helium atom, where Bohr's theory gave wrong energy values, the new theory gave energies as accurate as they could be measured experimentally. It is in this sense that we may say that the wave equation has been 'proved'.

2.2. The charge-cloud interpretation of ψ

According to the wave equation a moving particle is represented by a wave function ψ such that $\psi^2 \, d\tau$ is the probability that it is found in the volume $d\tau$. There is, however, an alternative and more pictorial (though less strictly accurate) interpretation of ψ which may be given as follows. Let us deal with the case in which the moving particle is an electron. Then we suppose that this electron is spread out in the form of a cloud—we refer to it as a charge-cloud—the density of this cloud at any point being proportional to ψ^2. In places where ψ^2 is largest, the charge-cloud is densest and most of the negative charge is to be found.

The essential difference between this interpretation and our earlier one is that instead of speaking of the probability density (i.e. the chance of finding the electron in any given region) we speak of the actual particle density. Now if a single electron is a particle, it cannot possibly be distributed over regions of the size of an atom or molecule, which are of the order of 10^{-8} cm in each direction, so that the charge-cloud picture, though very useful, is not strictly correct. Only the statistical, or probability, interpretation is really valid. A link between the two viewpoints may be found in the following way: let us suppose that at a particular moment we were able by some means to determine exactly where the electron was, and that we represented this position by a minute dot in a space of three dimensions. Let us now repeat the observation a very large number of times (perhaps a million times) and put a similar dot in the appropriate place in this space. If the dots are so small that we cannot distinguish individual ones from their neighbours, the general effect of this diagram will be exactly the same as a cloud; the densest parts of the cloud will be those where there are most dots, and these are precisely the places where our individual observations are most likely to discover the electron. So the density of the charge-cloud is a direct measure of the probability function.

Despite its lack of validity we shall find the idea of a charge-cloud most useful, and shall frequently employ it. For example, the wave functions of an electron in an atom are not strictly confined, but ψ stretches to infinite distance from the nucleus. This implies that there is a finite chance of finding the electron even at large distances. This chance is very small if the distance exceeds about 2 or 3×10^{-8} cm, so that not much significance attaches to that part of the probability outside a certain region. Using the charge-cloud picture we might say that there is a certain contour for each ψ such that 90 per cent. (or if we wish, 99 per cent.) of the charge lies within this contour. We shall shortly describe some typical contours and find characteristic patterns. We could refer to one of these as the boundary surface for an electron in this allowed stationary state. The significance of the shape of the various boundary surfaces can hardly be exaggerated; for we shall see later that these shapes largely determine the stereochemical disposition of the atoms in a polyatomic molecule.

2.3. Hydrogen atom, ground state

The ideas that we have just been describing are very nicely illustrated by the example of the ground state of the hydrogen atom. We have only one electron to deal with, and this moves round the nucleus which we may take to be fixed at the origin of coordinates. In such a case there are many allowed wave functions and corresponding energies; the lowest of these is called the ground state.

According to the Bohr theory the electron moves round the nucleus in a circle whose radius is called the radius of the first orbit, or more simply 'the Bohr radius', and which is written a_0. It is found that this radius is related to the mass m and charge e of the electron by the formula

$$a_0 = h^2/4\pi^2 m e^2 = 0 \cdot 529 \times 10^{-8} \text{ cm.} \qquad (6\,a)$$

Similarly the allowed energy is

$$E = -\frac{2\pi^2 m e^4}{h^2} = -\frac{e^2}{2a_0} = -13 \cdot 60 \text{ eV.\dag}$$ (6 b)

The minus sign here means that this is the energy, or work, that we have to do in order to separate the proton and the electron to infinite distance apart. The whole of the motion takes place in one plane.

But according to the wave mechanical theory this electron is described by a suitable wave function. It is found‡ that

$$\psi = \sqrt{\left(\frac{1}{\pi a_0^3}\right)} e^{-r/a_0},$$ (7)

where r is the distance from the origin. From this it follows that the probability density is

$$\rho = \frac{1}{\pi a_0^3} e^{-2r/a_0}.$$ (8)

It will be noticed at once that the motion takes place in three dimensions, and that ρ is spherically symmetrical around the origin. Further, the wave function (7) is already normalized since

$$\int \psi^2 \, d\tau = \int_0^\infty \psi^2 4\pi r^2 \, dr = \int_0^\infty 4a_0^{-3} r^2 e^{-2r/a_0} \, dr = 1.$$

There are several ways in which we can exhibit graphically the nature of (7) or (8). We could for example:

(a) plot a graph showing how ψ and ψ^2 ($\equiv \rho$) vary with r;

(b) draw contours of constant value of ψ. In this case the contours are concentric spheres, and at all points on any one sphere ψ has the same value;

(c) draw the charge-cloud (or, in this case, a section of it by some plane through the origin);

(d) draw the boundary surface. This is that particular one of the contours referred to in (b) such that the total charge outside the contour is some definite small percentage (e.g. 10 per cent.) of the total electronic charge.

† 1 electron-volt (eV) is the energy acquired by an electron in falling through a potential of 1 volt, and is numerically equal to 23·06 kcal/mole.

‡ See § 3.4 for a verification of these results.

All these possibilities are illustrated in Fig. 2.1. Of these diagrams (a) and (b) are very detailed, and require an exact knowledge of ψ; (c) is able to give us a very good general impression of the charge distribution even if we are not able to represent the density

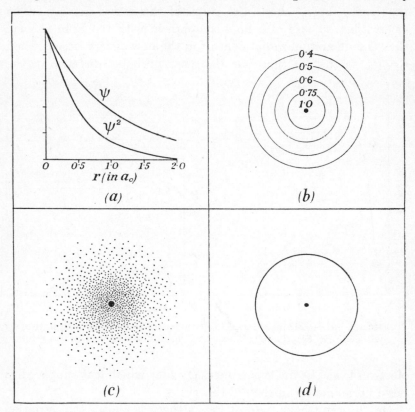

FIG. 2.1. Representation of the wave function for the ground state of a hydrogen atom.

(a) graph of ψ and ψ^2.   (c) charge-cloud.
(b) contours of ψ (units of $(\pi a_0^3)^{-\frac{1}{2}}$).   (d) boundary surface.

of the cloud with complete precision; (d) is much the simplest, but for many purposes it provides a surprisingly adequate pictorial representation, and we shall make frequent use of it.

There is yet another method of representing the charge density which is often used for atoms. Since the atom is spherically symmetrical ρ is here a function only of the radial distance r. So, instead of plotting the density $\rho(r)$, we plot what is called the radial density $4\pi r^2\rho(r)$. Since $4\pi r^2\,dr$ is the volume lying between the two spheres r, $r+dr$, it follows that $4\pi r^2\rho(r)\,dr$ is the total probability that the electron is at a distance between r and $r+dr$ of the origin. Fig. 2 shows the graph of this radial density. It is interesting, by way of a final comparison with the Bohr theory, that the maximum radial density in the new theory occurs when $r = a_0$, so that in this case the most probable distance of the

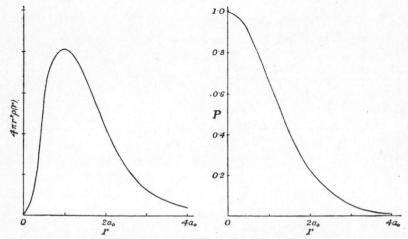

FIG. 2.2. (a) Radial distribution function or density for the ground state of hydrogen. (b) Fraction of charge-cloud outside a sphere of radius r for the ground state of atomic hydrogen.

electron from the nucleus is precisely that which it is supposed to have permanently in the old theory.

On the right-hand side of Fig. 2 there is shown the variation of $P(r)$, where $P(r)$ is that fraction of the total charge-cloud which lies outside a sphere of radius r. Evidently $P(0) = 1$, and $P(\infty) = 0$. It will be noticed that $P(r)$ falls off rapidly with r. If, for example in (d) above, we chose the boundary surface for which 10 per cent. of the charge lay outside, its radius would be $2\cdot6a_0 = 1\cdot4$ A. The analytical expression for $P(r)$ is

$$P(r) = \int_r^\infty \psi^2 4\pi r^2\,dr = e^{-2r/a_0}\left\{1+\frac{2r}{a_0}+\frac{2r^2}{a_0^2}\right\}.$$

2.4. Atomic orbitals

The wave function (7) may be said to describe the motion of the electron. In a rather loose way we could speak of it as describing the orbit, though of course we have now abandoned the hopeless attempt to follow the electron in its path; in fact we believe that even the idea of a path has no meaning. But on account of its relationship to the distribution of the electron we call it an *atomic orbital*. It will be convenient to abbreviate this to a.o.

The a.o. drawn in Figs. 1 and 2 is not the only one for hydrogen. It is the ground state orbital and for that reason it is the most important one chemically, since an atom is normally in its state of lowest energy. However, there are plenty of other allowed energies and corresponding wave functions. Fig. 3 shows some of the more frequently used a.o.'s, including our previous one, now referred to under its spectroscopic name of 1s. It is absolutely essential to have a clear mental picture of the more common a.o.'s, and in particular, to recognize and remember their symmetry properties.

For this purpose the most significant classification is into the types s, p, d,..., examples of which are shown in Fig. 3. s-type a.o.'s are all spherically symmetrical so that the charge-cloud density is a function only of r. All the other types are unsymmetrical. For example, there are three p-type a.o.'s in which the boundary surface consists of two regions together resembling a 'dumb-bell'. If we exclude that part of the electron-cloud which is very near the origin, and not effective in molecular formation, then in one half of the dumb-bell ψ is positive and in the other it is negative. There is a very marked directional character in these orbitals, which we exhibit by means of a suffix p_x, p_y, p_z. Fig. 4 shows approximate boundary surfaces for these a.o.'s; each of them is symmetrical around the direction shown by its suffix. These three p-type orbitals are entirely equivalent except for their directions, and they are all linearly independent. There are only three such which are linearly independent. This means that any other similar p-type orbit which points in a different direction can be regarded as the superposition of certain amounts of the three basic ones. In actual fact, the resolution is exactly analogous to the resolution of a vector into its three components in mutually perpendicular directions. Thus, if l, m, n denote the direction cosines of the direction in which the additional dumb-

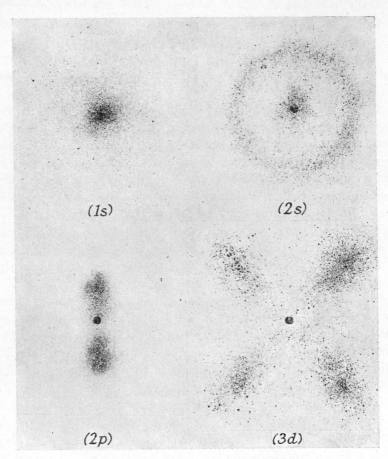

(1s)

(2s)

(2p)

(3d)

Fig. 2.3. Some atomic orbitals for hydrogen.

bell is to point, its wave function is $\psi(p_{lmn})$, where in an obvious notation

$$\psi(p_{lmn}) = l\psi(p_x) + m\psi(p_y) + n\psi(p_z). \tag{9}$$

We shall require this formula later on.

An important characteristic of these a.o.'s is that the regions where ψ is of opposite sign are separated by a 'nodal plane', over which $\psi = 0$. For example, in the orbital p_x, this is the plane $x = 0$, a fact which is obvious at once if we are told that for p_x-type a.o.,

$$\psi(p_x) = x \times \text{some function of } r. \tag{10}$$

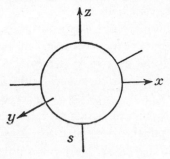

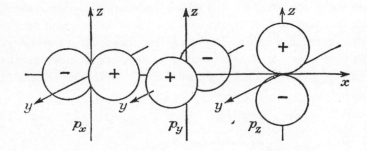

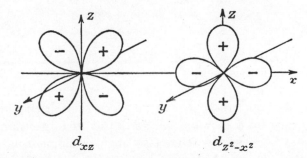

Fig. 2.4. Types of atomic orbital; approximate boundary surfaces.

It is convenient, when drawing the boundary surface, to insert $\pm$ signs, as in Fig. 4, in those regions where ψ is positive or negative.

There is, of course, no physical significance whatever in the sign: we can, for example, multiply ψ by -1, which reverses the signs but leaves the physically significant ψ^2 unchanged. But particularly when considering the overlap of two neighbouring ψ functions (e.g. Figs. 3.6 and 4.1), a knowledge of the relative signs of different regions is of great help.

In the same way there are five d-type orbitals, two of which are shown in Fig. 4. In some respects (but by no means all) a d orbit is like the superposition of two p orbitals, for there are four similar regions of alternating sign, separated by two nodal planes.†
Further discussion of these d orbitals is reserved for § 9.

In the same way there are f-type and g-type a.o.'s, but these are rather more complicated to visualize. As we shall not make much use of them in this book, they have not been included in Fig. 4.

When there are several a.o.'s which are completely equivalent, but still independent, it is obvious that they correspond to the same allowed energy value. In such a case we speak of the energy level as degenerate and the number of equivalent a.o.'s as the degree of degeneracy. Table 1 shows the degeneracy with different types of a.o.

TABLE 1. *Degeneracies of a.o.'s*

s	non-degenerate
p	triply degenerate
d	fivefold degenerate
f	sevenfold degenerate

2.5. Further quantum numbers

The division into s, p, d,... orbitals is quite clear-cut; there is nothing intermediate between an s and a p, or between a p and a d orbital. For that reason we call it a quantum distinction, and label the types by a *quantum number*. This quantum number is called l, and is related to the total angular momentum of the moving electron (to be distinguished from the magnetic quantum number, which is the subscript referred to later in § 9 and usually

† For more exact diagrams of these orbitals see H. E. White, *Phys. Rev.*, 1931, **37**, 1416.

called m, or m_l). The relation between the value of l and the s, p, d,... type is shown in Table 2 below.

TABLE 2. *Relations between quantum numbers*

Type of orbital . .	s	p	d	f
l-value . . .	0	1	2	3
Lowest value of n .	1	2	3	4

For our purposes the geometrical character associated with the labels s, p,... is more important than the l-value, and for that reason we shall almost always use the former rather than the latter.

There are two other quantum numbers with which we shall be concerned. They are (i) the principal, or total, quantum number, and (ii) the spin. Now it is evident from Figs. 3 and 4 or from the analytical expressions such as (10) that the division into s, p, d,... types governs the shape of the orbital, as, for example, whether it is spherically symmetrical or dumb-bell shaped In much the same way the principal quantum number governs the overall size of the charge-cloud. This implies that it also chiefly governs the energy, a conclusion that may be seen as follows. The total energy E of any allowed state is the sum of the average kinetic energy T and potential energy V. Further it may be shown by the Virial Theorem that if, as here, all the forces are inverse square law forces, then T and V are in constant ratio.† Thus E is itself proportional to V. But in the case of an electron moving round a given central nuclear charge, the potential energy depends on the average distance of the electron from the nucleus. The closer the electron is to the nucleus, the greater numerically is V. Now if the charge-cloud is compressed within a small boundary surface, the average distance is small and hence the binding energy is great. But if the charge-cloud is diffuse, then the mean distance between electron and nucleus is large and the binding energy is less. This general principle, that contraction of charge-cloud implies greater. binding energy, is important both for molecules and for atoms. It follows from all this that if the principal quantum

---

† More precisely $T = -\frac{1}{2}V = -E$, a result which is true both in classical and in quantum mechanics. E is here measured from a zero in which the electron is at rest at infinity, so that if the electron is bound to the atom, E is negative.

number, which is called n, and which is always a positive integer, is large, the spread of the charge-cloud is also large and the binding energy is small.

We can illustrate this by a few formulae which we shall merely quote without proof. For a single electron moving around a central positive nuclear charge Ze in an orbit whose quantum numbers are n, l it may be shown that

$$E = -\frac{Z^2 e^2}{2a_0 n^2},\tag{11}$$

mean value of $1/r = Z/n^2$, in units of a_0^{-1}, (12)

$$\text{mean value of } r = \frac{n^2}{Z}\left[1 + \tfrac{1}{2}\left\{1 - \frac{l(l+1)}{n^2}\right\}\right], \text{ in units of } a_0.\ (13)$$

Equations (12) and (13) show that the size of the orbit is roughly proportional to n^2. In this simple case the energy values depend solely on the value of n and not at all on the s, p, d,... type of orbital; but when there is more than one electron present in the atom, this ceases to be rigorously correct, though it still remains true that the n-value is more significant than the l-value in determining the energy.

There are two further comments to be made concerning the principal quantum number. In the first place it turns out that $n - l$ must always be positive. This means that for s-type orbitals (where $l = 0$) the allowed values of n are $n = 1, 2, 3,...$; but for p-type orbitals ($l = 1$) $n = 2, 3, 4,...$ and for d-type orbitals $n = 3, 4, 5,...$. When labelling the states it is customary to write the n-value first, followed by the designation s, p,... . Thus the ground state is $1s$, and in order of increasing energy, i.e. decreasing binding energy, the sequence of levels is

$$1s < 2s = 2p < 3s = 3p = 3d < 4s \dots .$$

This sequence of energies applies only to hydrogen. The case of other atoms is dealt with in § 7.

Our second comment concerns the influence of the quantum number n on the nodes. We have already seen that the s, p, d,... character determines the number of nodal planes through the origin, this being respectively 0, 1, 2,...; it turns out that there are also radial nodes, that is, concentric spheres at all points of which $\psi = 0$ and that the number of these is given by $n-l-1$. Thus the $1s$ has no radial node and the $2s$ has one, as shown in Fig. 3. Similarly the $2p$ has no radial node, but the $3p$ has one. These radial nodes do not greatly concern us because they are nearly always so close to the nucleus as to be relatively ineffective for chemical purposes. Indeed for our purposes their very existence may usually be neglected. It will be recognized that the total number of nodes, counting both planes and spheres, is $n-1$.

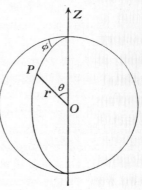

The student who is interested in the mathematical aspect of this work will easily verify the truth of the statements made above when the complete wave function is written down.

It is convenient to use spherical polar coordinates r, θ, ϕ as shown in Fig. 5. In terms of these coordinates the a.o. which is defined by the three quantum numbers n, l, m_l has the analytical expression

FIG. 2.5. Spherical polar coordinates r, θ, ϕ.

$$\psi_{nlm_l} = NR_{nl}(r)P_l^{|m_l|}(\cos\theta)e^{\pm im_l\phi}, \tag{14}$$

where N is a normalizing factor, $P_l^{|m_l|}(\cos\theta)$ is the associated Legendre polynomial, and $R_{nl}(r)$ is a function

$$R_{nl}(r) = e^{-\frac{1}{2}\rho}\rho^l L_{n+l}^{2l+1}(\rho). \tag{15}$$

In this latter equation, $L_{n+l}^{2l+1}(\rho)$ is an associated Laguerre polynomial and ρ is a subsidiary variable proportional to r and defined by

$$\rho = \frac{2Z}{na_0}r. \tag{16}$$

The number of radial nodes is determined by the number of zeros of (15); the number of the other nodes is determined by the angular terms in θ and ϕ, or in the linear combinations that are taken in order to get the real and equivalent a.o.'s used in §§ 4 and 9. The division into radial nodes and non-radial nodes arises because of the factorizing of ψ into the product of a function of r and a function of θ and ϕ.

We still have to discuss the fourth and last quantum number, i.e. the spin. In 1925 it was shown by Uhlenbeck and Goudsmit from a careful consideration of the spectra of alkali atoms such as Li, Na, that in addition to its orbital motion, an electron must be regarded as spinning about some axis through its centre. This motion gives it an angular momentum and (because the electron is an electrically charged body) a magnetic moment. The peculiarity about this motion is that if we choose any arbitrary direction the component of the angular momentum in this direction can have only two values $\pm h/4\pi$. The customary units in which angular momentum is measured are $h/2\pi$, so we could describe the spin as m_s, where m_s is the spin quantum number, and can only assume the values $\pm\frac{1}{2}$. There is no need for us to suppose that the 'spinning' is a real rotation; indeed it almost certainly is not, since, as Dirac showed in 1928, it appears automatically as soon as the Schrödinger equation is made relativistically satisfactory. What matters for us is that there are two values for the spin, and that the interaction between the spin motion and the orbital motion is usually so small that it may be neglected. We conventionally represent the spin by an extra factor in the wave function; this is α if $m_s = \frac{1}{2}$, and it is β if $m_s = -\frac{1}{2}$. Thus (see equation 7) the ground state of the hydrogen atom is twofold degenerate, and is represented by either one or the other of the two wave functions

$$\psi_{100\frac{1}{2}} = \sqrt{\left(\frac{1}{\pi a_0^3}\right)} e^{-r/a_0}\, \alpha, \qquad \psi_{100-\frac{1}{2}} = \sqrt{\left(\frac{1}{\pi a_0^3}\right)} e^{-r/a_0}\, \beta. \quad (17)$$

Two electrons with the same spin wave function are said to have parallel spins; otherwise they have opposed, or antiparallel, spins.

2.6. Spectrum of atomic hydrogen

We have just shown how to describe the allowed orbitals of the electron in a hydrogen atom. As much of what we have said applies to other atoms, it will be convenient to summarize our discussion in the form of a set of properties. These are:

(a) The electron is described by a wave function ψ and associated energy E, which are found as acceptable solutions of the wave equation. The wave function may be called an atomic orbital, and ψ^2 measures the probability of finding the electron in any region.

(b) These atomic orbitals are designated in terms of quantum numbers. Of these the l-value gives the s, p, d,... type and tells us the geometrical shape and degeneracy; the n-value tells us the size; and the m_s-value tells us the spin, which must be $\pm\frac{1}{2}$.

(c) Transitions are allowed between different energy levels, as a result of absorption or emission of light. The relation between the energy change E_1-E_2 and the frequency of the light ν_{12} is the familiar Planck law

$$E_1-E_2 = h\nu_{12}.$$

(d) Not all transitions are allowed but selection rules operate to limit the permitted jumps. These selection rules are that while n may change arbitrarily, m_s does not change at all and l changes by ± 1. This means that allowed transitions are:

$$s \rightarrow p,$$
$$p \rightarrow s \quad \text{or} \quad d,$$
$$d \rightarrow p \quad \text{or} \quad f, \quad \text{etc.}$$

All this is in complete agreement with experiment, allowance being made for certain small relativistic and other effects.

2.7. The self-consistent-field model of an atom†

The method of dealing with an atom containing several electrons has already been stated on p. 16. We are to write down the appropriate wave equation and then solve it. Now it is easy to write down the equation (see Chapter III) but quite impossible to solve it in the same sort of exact way that was possible for the hydrogen atom with only one electron. The fundamental difficulty is, of course, that each electron repels every other electron with an inverse-square-law force, so that the motion of any one electron is dependent on the motion of all the others. It is this non-separability of the individual electron orbits which introduces the real complexity into this problem, and at the same time suggests a way out of the difficulty. Let us suppose that when dealing with one of the electrons we disregard its instantaneous interactions with the other electrons, and imagine it to move in an effective electric field which is obtained by a suitable average over all positions of all the other electrons. In such a case each electron would be described by a wave equation which involved only its own coordinates, and not the coordinates of any other electron;

† A complete account of this theory is in D. R. Hartree, *The Calculation of Atomic Structures*, John Wiley, 1957.

the effect of all the other electrons would be shown by the existence of a potential energy function for the first electron. Such a wave equation is vastly easier to deal with than the more strictly accurate one, and can always be solved by numerical methods. On account of the fact that the average potential due to the other electrons has spherical symmetry,† the *s*, *p*, *d*,... classification still remains, so that the wave functions resemble quite closely the functions previously described for hydrogen.

Of course this does not solve our problem. For according to this scheme we can only write down the wave equation for any one electron if we already know the wave functions for all the others! But we can approach our complete solution in stages, as suggested first by Hartree,‡ to whom this model of an atom is due. Suppose that there are *n* electrons in our atom. Then let us first guess plausible wave functions for each of these electrons; this process is nothing like so difficult as it may at first appear, for after a little experience quite good wave functions may be guessed without much trouble. Now choose one of the electrons and find the average field provided by all the others. This average field is simply the field that would be provided if each of these electrons was a charge-cloud as in § 2. If necessary we average this field over all angles to make it spherically symmetrical. This process allows us to write down, and then to solve, the wave equation for our chosen electron. We obtain what may be called a first-improved wave function for this electron. This new function may next be used to calculate the average field for a second electron, and enables us to get a first-improved wave function for this electron also. The process is continued until we have a complete bunch of first-improved orbitals. In the same way starting with these we may improve them, one by one, and calculate second-improved a.o.'s. This technique is continued until successive iteration makes no appreciable difference to the orbitals. We may

---

† This is not strictly true, but it is always assumed.

‡ D. R. Hartree, *Proc. Camb. Phil. Soc.*, 1928, **24**, 89. A list of atoms for which wave functions have been obtained up to 1943 is given in N. F. Mott and I. Sneddon, *Wave Mechanics*, Oxford, 1948, p. 141. More recent results are listed by D. R. Hartree, *Reports on Progress in Physics*, Physical Society, 1946–7, **11**, 113: and by R. S. Knox, *Solid State Physics*, ed. F. Seitz and D. Turnbull, Academic Press, N.Y., 1957, **4**, 413.

then say that the set of a.o.'s are self-consistent; this means that
if we choose any one electron, its charge-cloud is precisely that
which comes from solving the wave equation in which the potential
field is due to the charge on the nucleus and the sum of the charge-
clouds of all the other electrons. This is true whichever electron
we choose. For this reason it is called the method of the self-
consistent field.

Naturally enough, there are certain errors in the above procedure. These arise chiefly from 'smoothing-out' the distribution
of all electrons except the one being considered. However, it may
be shown that these errors are not serious and, if we are prepared
to spend sufficient time, the wave functions obtained in this way
may be used as a very good basis for more accurate calculations
in which no such 'smoothing-out' occurs. It turns out that the
resulting charge distribution is usually only altered by a few per
cent. of its maximum value, so that the simpler procedure is quite
adequate for most purposes.

The 'smoothing-out' process referred to above is likely to be
more satisfactory in heavy atoms than in light ones. For in atoms
with a large nuclear charge the field arising from this is more important than the field from any individual electron, so that to
average the latter is not so serious an approximation as when the
central nuclear charge is smaller.

In view of its later applicability to molecules, it may be desirable at this stage to summarize the principles which we use for
describing the electronic structure of an atom. It will be recognized at once that these principles are natural extensions of those
principles listed on p. 30 for atomic hydrogen. They are:

(a) Each electron is represented by wave function ψ, called an
atomic orbital; this orbital is found by solution of the appropriate
Schrödinger wave equation, obtained by the Hartree procedure,
or some similar technique, and is such that ψ^2 measures the density
of the charge-cloud for this electron.

(b) Each a.o. is designated in terms of a set of quantum numbers. First there is the principal quantum number n, which chiefly
determines the energy and also the size of the orbital, so that
electrons in orbitals with the same value of n are said to be in the

same shell. Next there is the geometrical shape, given by the quantum number l, or the label s, p, d,... with an appropriate suffix, e.g. p_x, p_y, p_z, to show which of the degenerate orbitals of this symmetry we are actually using. Finally there is the spin quantum number m_s which has the value $\pm\frac{1}{2}$.

(c) Each a.o. has a characteristic energy which is found from the wave equation. This energy measures very approximately the

FIG. 2.6. Energy levels and cells for atoms. Each cell will hold not more than two electrons.

work required to remove this particular electron, i.e. to ionize the atom. Each type of electron has its own ionization potential. The usual order of energies is (see Fig. 6)

$$1s < 2s < 2p < 3s < 3p < 3d \sim 4s \ ...,$$

and the order of ionization potentials is, of course, just the reverse of this. The total energy of an atom is now the sum of the energies of all the a.o.'s which are occupied by electrons, corrected for their mutual interaction. Without this correction, this interaction would, in fact, have been counted twice over, because the Coulomb repulsion e^2/r_{ij} between electrons i and j has been included in the wave equations—and hence in the energy values—of both electrons separately.

(d) Transitions take place between one a.o. and another, accompanied by emission or absorption of light, the frequency of which is related to the difference of the two energies by the Bohr frequency relation $E_1 - E_2 = h\nu_{12}$. Selection rules operate to allow certain transitions and forbid others.

(e) When assigning electrons to the various allowed a.o.'s, we must take account of the Pauli Exclusion Principle. This states that under no circumstances whatever may two electrons have precisely the same set of quantum numbers. Two electrons may indeed have the same space ψ, i.e. orbital wave function, but only if their spins are opposed; i.e. $+\frac{1}{2}$ and $-\frac{1}{2}$. In this case we speak of them as paired. Such electrons usually exert a repulsion upon other electrons near them.

2.8. The *aufbau* principle

The principles (a)–(e) listed at the end of § 7 lead us at once to an *aufbau*, or building-up process, when giving the electronic state of an atom. This means that we first determine the allowed orbitals and then feed the electrons one at a time into these levels, beginning with 1s which is the lowest, and satisfying the exclusion principle by allowing only two electrons to each of the orbitals just described. Thus hydrogen is represented in its ground state by (1s), helium by $(1s)^2$, lithium by $(1s)^2(2s)$, nitrogen by $(1s)^2(2s)^2(2p)^3$, etc. The method is very simply portrayed on a diagram if we adopt the procedure of Fig. 6, in which each orbital is represented by a small rectangle, and energy is plotted upwards. Each of these 'cells' represents a possible orbital; if it is unoccupied in a given state of the atom, this cell is left empty; if it is singly-occupied, we place one arrow inside it, pointing upwards or downwards according as the spin is $\pm\frac{1}{2}$; if it is doubly-occupied we place two arrows in the cell, one up and the other down. Diagrams of this kind for the first ten atoms of the periodic table are shown in Fig. 7. In drawing these diagrams we have had to use Hund's rules† to decide, in the cases of nitrogen and oxygen, and all other

† See, e.g., G. Herzberg, *Atomic Spectra and Atomic Structure*, Blackie, ch. iii.

atoms containing incomplete groups of electrons, just which of the equivalent orbitals (here the $2p_x$, $2p_y$, $2p_z$ orbitals) are filled. These rules are that for equivalent orbitals:

(i) electrons tend to avoid being in the same space orbit, or cell, so far as is possible, and

(ii) two electrons, each singly-occupying a given pair of equivalent orbitals (e.g. $2p_x$, $2p_y$) tend to have their spins parallel in the state of lowest energy.

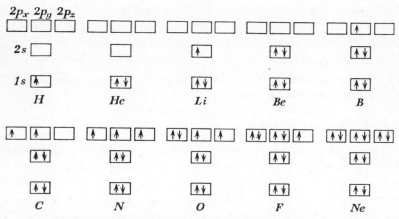

FIG. 2.7. Cell diagrams for the electrons in simple atoms.

These rules show us at once that in nitrogen the $1s$ and $2s$ orbitals are doubly filled, and each of the $2p_x$, $2p_y$, $2p_z$ orbitals singly filled, the three electrons concerned having parallel spins; and that oxygen, with one more p-electron, has one p-orbital (say $2p_z$) doubly filled, the other two being singly occupied, with parallel spins, as shown in Fig. 7. The $(2p_z)^2$ group, which as we shall see later make no contribution to the divalent character of the oxygen atom, are sometimes called the 'lone-pair' electrons. A similar name is used for the nitrogen $(2s)^2$, or for any other similar group of two mutually-paired electrons in the outer electronic shell.

According to the above, any description of an atom, whether in its ground state or an excited state, requires that we know which atomic orbitals are occupied, and by how many electrons. Such information provides us with what is usually called a configuration. For example, $1s^2 2s^2 2p^2$ is a configuration for a neutral carbon atom (written C I by spectroscopists), and $1s^2 2s^2 2p^6 3s^2 3p^6 3d^2 4p$ would be an excited configuration for the titanium ion Ti⁺ (written Ti II) in which the $1s$, $2s$, $2p$, $3s$, and $3p$ shells were closed, and there were two electrons in the $3d$ shell

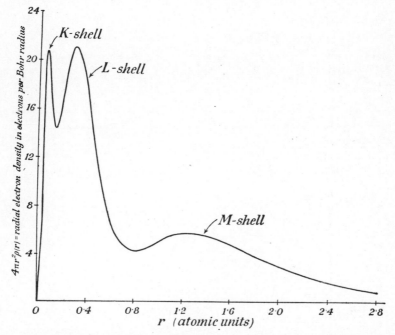

Fig. 2.8. Charge distribution in Argon, according to Hartree. The area under the curve is equal to the total number of electrons, here 18.

and one in the $4p$ shell. The inner completed shells are sometimes omitted, and then the two configurations above would be written $s^2 p^2$ and $d^2 p$.

This *aufbau* principle gives an immediate demonstration of the Periodic System of the elements. Thus the group of two electrons $(1s)^2$ completes what we might call the inner, or K-shell; a further group of eight electrons $(2s)^2(2p)^6$ completes the L-shell; eight more complete the next sub-group of the M-shell, and so on. The details are very familiar, and we do not need to repeat them.†

† See Herzberg, loc. cit., for further information.

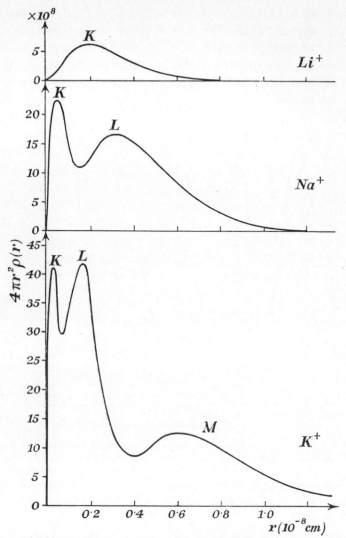

FIG. 2.9. Radial density curves for the ground states of Li+, Na+, and K+, drawn according to the work of Pauling and Goudsmidt, and Hartree. The curves are all drawn to the same scale.

But we can see why the groups we have mentioned are referred to as shells if we use the calculated a.o.'s to draw the electronic density functions. Fig. 8 shows the particular case of A,† and

† D. R. Hartree and W. R. Hartree, *Proc. Roy. Soc.* A, 1938, **166**, 450.

the way in which the complete charge distribution is built up by addition of the contributions from $(1s)^2$, $(2s)^2(2p)^6$, and $(3s)^2(3p)^6$. Quite evidently the K-, L-, and M-shells are here almost distinct,[†] and the outer part of the atom is dominated completely by the outer shell, here the M-shell. It is clear that in so far as the size of an atom has any meaning, it is determined entirely by this outer shell. Indeed, calculations such as these are the basis of any theoretical estimates of the atomic radius of an atom or ion. This radius varies according to the number of electrons present, and the nuclear charge. As the nuclear charge is increased each individual shell moves in towards the origin so that the rare-gas atoms, which properly come at the end of each row of the Periodic Table, have the smallest atomic radii, and the alkali atoms which start each new row have the largest. This is well illustrated in Fig. 9 which shows the radial density function for the ground states of a series of ions, plotted on the same scale. These ions all have a rare-gas structure of completed shells, and are relatively small. It will be noticed, however, that the heavier atoms tend to be larger than the lighter ones.

Full self-consistent-field calculations are quite complicated and lengthy. The final a.o.'s thus obtained are also rather unwieldy because the results are given in a numerical table and not by means of an analytical function. Approximate analytical functions have been devised[‡] which represent the true a.o.'s with considerable accuracy. In principle, these wave functions are wave functions for a single electron in a central field provided by an 'effective' charge Ze. Rules are given for writing down the value of Z for each electron in any given atom. The difference between this Z and the true nuclear charge is called the screening constant for this electron; as its name implies, it measures the degree to which the other electrons in the atom are able to screen the nucleus from the electron considered. When Z is known, formulae such as (15) and (16) soon enable the atomic radius to be determined. In particular (16) shows that for orbits with the same principal quantum number, the size of the orbital varies inversely as the effective nuclear charge.

'Slater's rules' for writing down approximate analytic wave functions are so frequently used that it is desirable to give them here. Atomic orbitals

---

† This distinction is not quite so clear if $\rho(r)$ is plotted instead of $4\pi r^2\rho(r)$.

‡ J. C. Slater, *Phys. Rev.*, 1930, **36**, 57; P. M. Morse, L. A. Young, and E. S. Haurwitz, ibid., 1935, **48**, 948; corrected by W. E. Duncanson and C. A. Coulson, *Proc. Roy. Soc. Edin.*, 1944, **62**, 37; P.-O. Löwdin, *Phys. Rev.*, 1956, **103**, 1746.

are assumed to be of the forms

$$\psi(1s) = N_{1s}e^{-cr}, \qquad \psi(2s) = N_{2s}re^{-cr/2}, \qquad \psi(3s) = N_{3s}r^2e^{-cr/3},$$

$$\psi(2p_x) = N_{2p}xe^{-cr/2}, \qquad \psi(3p_x) = N_{3p}xre^{-cr/3}, \qquad \psi(3d_{xy}) = N_{3d}2xye^{-cr/3},$$

$$\psi(3d_{x^2-y^2}) = N_{3d}(x^2-y^2)e^{-cr/3}, \qquad \psi(3d_{z^2}) = N_{3d}\frac{3z^2-r^2}{\sqrt{3}}e^{-cr/3}, \qquad (18)$$

with similar expressions for $\psi(2p_y)$, $\psi(3d_{y^2-z^2})$, etc. The constants N are normalizing factors chosen so that $\int \psi^2 \, d\tau = 1$, and distances are measured in Bohr radii a_0. The appropriate values of N are:

$$N_{1s} = (c_3/\pi)^{\frac{1}{2}}, \qquad N_{2s} = (c^5/96\pi)^{\frac{1}{2}}, \qquad N_{3s} = (2c^7/5.3^9.\pi)^{\frac{1}{2}},$$

$$N_{2p} = (c^5/32\pi)^{\frac{1}{2}}, \qquad N_{3p} = (2c^7/5.3^8.\pi)^{\frac{1}{2}}, \qquad N_{3d} = (c^7/2.3^8.\pi)^{\frac{1}{2}}. \qquad (19)$$

The values of c, which is the effective nuclear charge, are found by use of the following rules:

(1) $c = Z - S =$ atomic number Z of the element minus a screening (or shielding) constant S.

(2) To determine the shielding constant, electrons are divided into the following groups, each having a different shielding constant: $1s$; $2s$, $2p$; $3s$, $3p$; $3d$; $4s$, $4p$; $4d$; $4f$; $5s$, $5p$; etc. Thus the s and p of a given shell are grouped together, but the d and f are separated. The shells are considered to be arranged from inside out in the order named.

(3) The shielding constant S is formed as the sum of the following contributions:

(a) nothing from any shell outside the one considered;

(b) an amount 0·35 from each other electron in the group considered (except in the $1s$ group, where 0·30 is used instead);

(c) if the shell considered is an s, p shell, an amount 0·85 from each electron in the next inner shell, and 1·00 from all electrons still further in; but if the shell is a d or f, an amount 1·00 from every electron inside it.

Two examples will illustrate these rules. Helium, with atomic number 2, has two electrons in a $(1s)$ orbit, so that the effective nuclear charge is just $c = 2 - 0·30 = 1·70$. Carbon, with atomic number 6, has two $1s$ electrons and four $2s$, $2p$ electrons. The effective nuclear charges are

$$1s: \qquad 6 - 0·30 = 5·70,$$

$$2s, 2p: \qquad 6 - 3 \times 0·35 - 2 \times 0·85 = 3·25.$$

These rules work equally well even if some of the inner electrons are missing, as in X-ray spectra. They do, however, become somewhat unreliable as soon as orbitals with total quantum number 4 are reached, and must then be used with caution.

For the sake of our later discussion on hybridized orbitals (Chapter VIII) it is necessary to say a few words about the order of magnitude of the energy differences between the orbitals shown in Fig. 6. If the electrons in question are in the valence, or outer,

shell of the atom, then the difference E_p-E_s between a p-type
and s-type orbital with similar principal quantum number is
usually in the region of 2 to 4 eV† for elements in the first column
of the Periodic Table, and increases steadily as we move to later
columns. For example, the familiar sodium D lines at 5,890 A
arise from a transition $3p \to 3s$, with energy 2·10 eV, but in
chlorine the corresponding transition has energy about 10 eV.
Similarly, the difference E_d-E_p is usually a little larger than
E_p-E_s, so that a d orbital for principal quantum number n has
an energy in the same region as an s orbital for quantum number
$n+1$. In potassium, for example, the energies of $4s$, $4p$, and $3d$
are nearly equal, and in that order. E_f-E_d is also large, with the
result, shown in Fig. 6, that $4f$, $5d$, and $6s$ are comparable in
energy. In all these numerical values it is assumed that the lower
level is one which is actually occupied in the ground state of the
atom in question. If neither orbital is occupied in the ground
state, the energy differences involved may be considerably
reduced.‡

2.9. d orbitals

In Figs. 3 and 4 we showed some diagrams of certain d orbitals.
We also said that there were exactly five linearly independent
d functions with the same principal quantum number n. At first
sight this is a little confusing, because, by analogy with Fig. 4, we
might expect to have orbitals

$$d_{xz}, d_{xy}, d_{yz}, d_{x^2-y^2}, d_{y^2-z^2}, d_{z^2-x^2}. \tag{20}$$

It is obvious that all these functions would be equivalent in shape,
and have four similar regions of alternating sign, separated by
nodal planes. In the case of d_{xz}, d_{xy}, d_{yz} these planes are the
coordinate planes, but in the case of the other three orbitals,
which are obtained by rotating the first group through 45°, the
nodal planes are also rotated. Equation (18) shows that explicit
forms for these orbitals are

$$\psi(d_{xy}) = 2xy \times \text{some function of } r,$$
$$\psi(d_{x^2-y^2}) = (x^2-y^2) \times \text{the same function of } r. \tag{21}$$

† For the definition of electron-volt, see footnote on p. 20.
‡ A useful table of s, p, d energies is given by J. C. Slater, *Phys. Rev.*, 1955, **98**, 1039.

We can now see that the three orbitals in the second group in (20) are not independent. For, from (21),

$$\psi(d_{x^2-y^2})+\psi(d_{y^2-z^2})+\psi(d_{z^2-x^2}) \tag{22}$$

is identically zero. The vanishing of this sum can also be seen by superposing the three diagrams similar to $\psi(d_{z^2-x^2})$ shown in Fig. 4, and taking account of the sign of ψ in each lobe. Thus any pair from the three orbitals in (22), together with the previous $d_{xy},...$, make a total of exactly five independent, and spatially equivalent, d-type orbitals.

Even now, however, the situation is not really satisfactory. For, as we shall see later, it is nearly always desirable that the orbitals which we choose should be orthogonal (see p. 203). This means that if we integrate the product of any two of these functions throughout all space, the result must be identically zero. Now it is not difficult to show that if we take the first four of the functions in (20) they are all mutually orthogonal. But the fifth and sixth ones, while orthogonal to the first three, are not orthogonal to the fourth. However, if we have chosen the first four d functions, we only need one additional function to complete the required total of five. Since neither $\psi(d_{y^2-z^2})$ nor $\psi(d_{z^2-x^2})$ is acceptable by itself, it may be that some combination of them can be found which will permit all five functions to be orthogonal. In fact the combination

$$\psi(d_{z^2}) \equiv \frac{1}{\sqrt{3}}\{\psi(d_{z^2-x^2})-\psi(d_{y^2-z^2})\} \tag{23}$$

does achieve this, while at the same time preserving the normalization of (18). The function (23) may be written

$$\psi(d_{z^2}) = \frac{3z^2-r^2}{3} \times \text{same function of } r \text{ as in (21)}.$$

It is usual, now, to take

$$d_{xy},\ d_{yz},\ d_{zx},\ d_{x^2-y^2} \text{ and } d_{z^2} \tag{24}$$

as the five basic d orbitals. But of course we are at liberty to choose the direction of the z-axis to be what we wish. So if the stereochemical situation around our central atom suggests one particular direction, or if there is an applied electric or magnetic field, we shall often choose this direction for the axis of z.

On account of their great importance—particularly when dealing with molecular complexes in Chapter X—we show in Fig. 10
further diagrams of these five orbitals. $\psi(d_{z^2})$ is the only one with
axial symmetry. This symmetry appears almost accidentally as
a result of the combination (23). But in the more mathematical

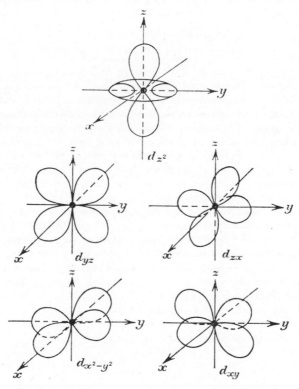

Fig. 2.10. Schematic diagrams for the five d orbitals.

formulation (14) this symmetry appears quite naturally. It is
important to realize that all five functions correspond to the same
energy (in the absence of any applied field). The fact that $\psi(d_{z^2})$
looks different from the others does not mean that its energy is
different.

There are, of course, other choices of combinations of the
original six orbitals (20) which we could have taken instead of (24).
But (24) is the simplest orthogonal set.

One of the most important of the alternative choices arises when we have a magnetic field present. It turns out to be best to replace the purely real p and d functions of (18) by complex combinations of them. Since this new representation consists of suitable linear combinations of the old a.o.'s, it leaves the degeneracy unaltered. It also maintains orthogonality. Pictorially it corresponds to replacing the purely stationary electron waves that we have so far used by running waves. For example, the combinations $p_x + ip_y$ are equivalent (see equation 10) to

$$(x \pm iy) \times \text{some function of } r.$$

If we use ρ and ϕ as polar coordinates in the (x, y)-plane this is equivalent to

$$\rho e^{\pm i\phi} \times \text{a function of } r.$$

These are waves running round the z-axis in a clockwise and anticlockwise direction. We could say that there are tiny electric currents. For that reason we call them $p_{\pm 1}$ and replace p_x, p_y, p_z by the alternative set p_0, $p_{\pm 1}$, where p_0 is merely another name for p_z. These currents will give rise to tiny magnetic moments. In terms of the fundamental unit of magnetic moment $eh/4\pi mc$ (called the Bohr magneton), the component of this moment in the direction of the z-axis has a magnitude that is given by the suffixes 0, ± 1. This representation is particularly useful in magnetic problems, for in the presence of an external magnetic field directed in the z-direction the degeneracy is destroyed and the energies change by amounts proportional to 0, ± 1, etc. In a similar way there are d_0, $d_{\pm 1}$, $d_{\pm 2}$, which could be used to replace our previous five d-type orbitals. It is worth mentioning that just as we found the running waves by combining together two or more stationary waves (e.g. $p_{\pm 1} = p_x \pm ip_y$), so we could regard the stationary waves themselves as the result of superposing two or more progressive waves, in different directions and with suitable phase differences. Electron waves are in this respect no different from other types of waves. The student will recognize that this new set is precisely the set previously described in (14), and obtained by straightforward mathematical solution of the wave equation.

III
WAVE-MECHANICAL PRINCIPLES

3.1. The wave equation

THE last chapter was devoted chiefly to a review of the conclusions that followed from the application of wave mechanics to atomic structure. This chapter will show how these results were obtained, and prepare the ground for our subsequent discussion of molecules. Naturally enough, our chief concern is with the wave equation. We cannot attempt to derive this equation—indeed there is no derivation, any more than there is a derivation of Newton's equations of motion—but there are analogies between wave mechanics and classical mechanics, which are worth describing because they 'carry over' a great deal of the latter, which is well known, to the former, which is less familiar.

We can think of the wave equation for stationary states as representing, in appropriate terms, the classical law of the conservation of energy. This latter law is conveniently written:

$$T + V = E, \tag{1}$$

where T and V are the kinetic and potential energies of the system being considered. Thus, for a single particle of mass m moving along the x-axis in a potential field $V(x)$, equation (1) would read:

$$\tfrac{1}{2}m\dot{x}^2 + V(x) = E. \tag{2}$$

The integration of this equation gives the classical orbit, or motion. Since the momentum $p = m\dot{x}$, we could write (2) in the form:

$$\frac{p^2}{2m} + V(x) = E. \tag{3}$$

The rule for converting such an equation as this into a wave equation is as follows: wherever p appears, replace it by a differentiation $\dfrac{h}{2\pi i}\dfrac{d}{dx}$, where h is Planck's constant, and $i = \sqrt{(-1)}$. We might write this symbolically[†]

$$p \to \frac{h}{2\pi i}\frac{d}{dx} \tag{4}$$

[†] This is sometimes written $p \to \dfrac{\hbar}{i}\dfrac{d}{dx}$, where $\hbar$ stands for $h/2\pi$ and is read 'crossed-h'.

In this symbolic notation

$$p^2 \to \frac{h}{2\pi i} \frac{d}{dx}\left(\frac{h}{2\pi i} \frac{d}{dx}\right) = -\frac{h^2}{4\pi^2} \frac{d^2}{dx^2}. \tag{5}$$

Equation (3) then becomes

$$-\frac{h^2}{8\pi^2 m} \frac{d^2}{dx^2} + V(x) = E.$$

Quite clearly such an equation as this is meaningless, as it stands, for the left-hand side is what we call an operator—here a differential operator, since it tells us to differentiate twice with respect to x. So there must be something on which we operate, i.e. an operand. Let us call it the wave function ψ. In this case ψ is only a function of x, and the wave equation is

$$\left(-\frac{h^2}{8\pi^2 m} \frac{d^2}{dx^2} + V\right)\psi(x) = E\psi(x). \tag{6}$$

This is usually written in the more familiar form

$$\frac{d^2\psi}{dx^2} + \frac{8\pi^2 m}{h^2}(E-V)\psi = 0. \tag{7}$$

The wave equation is thus a differential equation of the second order.

It is not difficult to generalize this to the case where our single particle moves in a field which depends on all three space coordinates $V(x, y, z)$. For the kinetic energy is

$$T = \tfrac{1}{2}m(\dot{x}^2 + \dot{y}^2 + \dot{z}^2) = (p_x^2 + p_y^2 + p_z^2)/2m,$$

where p_x, p_y, p_z denote the components of momentum. We follow (5) in making the symbolic replacement:

$$p_x \to \frac{h}{2\pi i} \frac{\partial}{\partial x}, \qquad p_y \to \frac{h}{2\pi i} \frac{\partial}{\partial y}, \qquad p_z \to \frac{h}{2\pi i} \frac{\partial}{\partial z}, \tag{8}$$

in which the differentiations are all partial differentiations. Equation (7) becomes the wave equation for one particle in a general potential field:

$$\frac{\partial^2\psi}{\partial x^2} + \frac{\partial^2\psi}{\partial y^2} + \frac{\partial^2\psi}{\partial z^2} + \frac{8\pi^2 m}{h^2}(E-V)\psi = 0. \tag{9}$$

This is often abbreviated to

$$\nabla^2\psi+\frac{8\pi^2m}{h^2}(E-V)\psi = 0, \tag{10}$$

where ∇^2 is the so-called Laplacian operator:

$$\nabla^2 \equiv \frac{\partial^2}{\partial x^2}+\frac{\partial^2}{\partial y^2}+\frac{\partial^2}{\partial z^2}. \tag{11}$$

The advantage of this latter way of writing the equation is that there are definite rules† for converting ∇^2 into an equivalent operator using other variables such as the spherical polar coordinates shown in Fig. 2.5; and these are more suited to a general discussion of atomic wave functions on account of the central nuclear charge from which the radial distance is measured.

It is obviously important to be able to write down the wave equation quickly for all sorts of problems. The following examples will show how easy this is.

Simple harmonic motion. A particle of mass m moves along the x-axis under a restoring force equal to k times its displacement. Its potential energy is $\frac{1}{2}kx^2$ and its kinetic energy is $\frac{1}{2}m\dot{x}^2 = p^2/2m$. The wave equation is:

$$\frac{d^2\psi}{dx^2}+\frac{8\pi^2m}{h^2}(E-\tfrac{1}{2}kx^2)\psi = 0. \tag{12}$$

This is generally referred to as the wave equation of a harmonic oscillator.

Hydrogen atom. The electron moves in three dimensions so that its kinetic energy is $\frac{1}{2}m(\dot{x}^2+\dot{y}^2+\dot{z}^2)$. Its potential energy is $-e^2/r$, for the nuclear charge is $+e$, the electronic charge is $-e$, and r is the distance between the two. The wave equation is:

$$\nabla^2\psi+\frac{8\pi^2m}{h^2}\left(E+\frac{e^2}{r}\right)\psi = 0. \tag{13}$$

If the effective nuclear charge had been Ze, this would have been:

$$\nabla^2\psi+\frac{8\pi^2m}{h^2}\left(E+\frac{Ze^2}{r}\right)\psi = 0. \tag{14}$$

† See, e.g., D. E. Rutherford, *Vector Methods*, Oliver & Boyd, Edinburgh, 1939.

Helium atom. There are now two electrons P_1 and P_2 (Fig. 1),

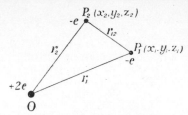

FIG. 3.1. Coordinates for atomic helium. P_1 and P_2 are the two electrons, O is the nucleus.

with coordinates $(x_1\ y_1\ z_1)$ and $(x_2\ y_2\ z_2)$, which move around a fixed nuclear charge $2e$ at the origin. Using the notation of this figure it follows that:

$$T = T_1 + T_2$$
$$= \frac{1}{2m}(p_{x_1}^2 + p_{y_1}^2 + p_{z_1}^2 + p_{x_2}^2 + p_{y_2}^2 + p_{z_2}^2),$$
$$V = -\frac{2e^2}{r_1} - \frac{2e^2}{r_2} + \frac{e^2}{r_{12}}.$$

The wave equation is now:

$$(\nabla_1^2 + \nabla_2^2)\psi + \frac{8\pi^2 m}{h^2}\left(E + \frac{2e^2}{r_1} + \frac{2e^2}{r_2} - \frac{e^2}{r_{12}}\right)\psi = 0, \tag{15}$$

where ∇_1^2 denotes the Laplacian operator (11) in terms of the coordinates $(x_1\ y_1\ z_1)$ and ∇_2^2 in terms of $(x_2\ y_2\ z_2)$. This latter equation is a partial differential equation in all six variables $x_1, y_1, z_1, x_2, y_2, z_2$. There are only six independent variables because the other quantities $r_1,\ r_2,\ r_{12}$ may all be expressed in terms of the original six.

Hydrogen molecule ion H_2^+. Let us next write down the wave equation for the simplest of all molecules, the hydrogen molecule ion, where there is only one electron moving in the presence of two fixed attracting centres A and B (Fig. 2). We may then write

$$T = \frac{1}{2m}(p_x^2 + p_y^2 + p_z^2), \qquad V = -\frac{e^2}{r_a} - \frac{e^2}{r_b} + \frac{e^2}{R_{ab}}.$$

So the wave equation is

$$\nabla^2\psi + \frac{8\pi^2 m}{h^2}\left(E + \frac{e^2}{r_a} + \frac{e^2}{r_b} - \frac{e^2}{R_{ab}}\right)\psi = 0. \tag{16}$$

The validity of supposing that we may take the nuclei as fixed is a question to which we shall return in § 5.

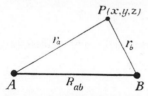

FIG. 3.2. Coordinates for the hydrogen molecule ion H_2^+.

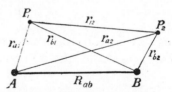

FIG. 3.3. Coordinates for the hydrogen molecule H_2.

Hydrogen molecule H_2. There are now two electrons $P_1(x_1\,y_1\,z_1)$ and $P_2(x_2\,y_2\,z_2)$, so that with the notation of Fig. 3:

$$T = \frac{1}{2m}(p_{x_1}^2+\ldots)+\frac{1}{2m}(p_{x_2}^2+\ldots),$$

$$V = -e^2\!\left(\frac{1}{r_{a1}}+\frac{1}{r_{a2}}+\frac{1}{r_{b1}}+\frac{1}{r_{b2}}\right)+\frac{e^2}{r_{12}}+\frac{e^2}{R_{ab}}.$$

The wave equation is

$$(\nabla_1^2+\nabla_2^2)\psi+\frac{8\pi^2m}{h^2}(E-V)\psi = 0. \tag{17}$$

After we have written down the wave equation, our subsequent task is always the same, viz. to find those particular values of the energy E for which acceptable wave functions exist. As we stated in Chapter II, an acceptable wave function is one which is finite, single-valued, and continuous, whose gradient is continuous, and which can be normalized.

It must not be supposed from the above that we have given anything in the nature of a 'proof' of the wave equation. As we have said, there is none. But it may be made plausible by the following argument. The argument itself is suggestive rather than logical, and some of the details must not be pressed too closely. The correspondence that we gave in (8) between the momentum and a certain differential operator suggests strongly that the de Broglie relation $\lambda = h/p$ must be our starting-point. If we use the fact that

$$\frac{p^2}{2m} = T = E-V,$$

it follows that

$$\lambda^2 = \frac{h^2}{2m(E-V)}. \tag{18}$$

Now if ψ is any quantity which vibrates with a harmonic motion of frequency ν and wavelength λ, we can write

$$\psi = A \cos 2\pi\left(\frac{x}{\lambda} - \nu t + \varepsilon\right),$$

where A is the amplitude and ε is an arbitrary phase angle. Clearly ψ satisfies the differential equation:

$$\frac{d^2\psi}{dx^2} = -\frac{4\pi^2}{\lambda^2}\psi.$$

This is one form of the standard equation of wave motion† common to almost all types of wave. If we substitute the value (18) of λ^2 appropriate to de Broglie waves, we recover the Schrödinger equation (7) in one dimension

$$\frac{d^2\psi}{dx^2} + \frac{8\pi^2 m}{h^2}(E - V)\psi = 0.$$

The extension to three variables is obvious.

3.2. Application to the Hartree self-consistent field for atoms

The application of all this to the calculation of self-consistent-field atomic orbitals is quite straightforward. In its simplest form we suppose that the electrons $1, 2, ..., N$ occupy orbitals $\psi_1, \psi_2, ..., \psi_N$. Several of these will be identical in pairs, though on account of the Exclusion Principle, not more than two may be precisely the same. The wave equation for electron 1 in its a.o. ψ_1 can be written down if we know the potential field V_1 in which it moves. But V_1 is simply a combination of the nuclear potential energy $-Ze^2/r$ (where Z is the true nuclear charge) and the potential due to the series of charge-clouds $\psi_2^2, \psi_3^2, ..., \psi_N^2$. This latter potential may be found by a quite straightforward integration. Thus consider a point P (Fig. 4) distance r_1 from the nucleus, and let ρ_2 be the charge-cloud density due to ψ_2^2 at a small volume element $d\tau_2$. Then the charge in $d\tau_2$ is $\rho_2\, d\tau_2 = -e\psi_2^2\, d\tau_2$, and its potential energy with respect to the charge $-e$ at P is $e^2\psi_2^2\, d\tau_2/r_{12}$. So the complete charge-cloud ψ_2^2 contributes a potential energy

$$e^2 \int \frac{\psi_2^2\, d\tau_2}{r_{12}}.$$

† See, e.g., C. A. Coulson, *Waves*, Oliver & Boyd, Edinburgh, 1941.

Contributions such as these are summed, the nuclear potential is added, and the whole is averaged over all angles to provide the

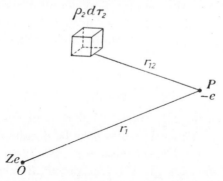

FIG. 3.4. Calculation of potential energy between electron 1 at P and charge-cloud of electron 2.

spherically symmetrical potential energy V_1 in which electron 1 is supposed to move. The wave equation for this electron is

$$\nabla_1^2 \psi_1 + \frac{8\pi^2 m}{h^2}(E - V_1)\psi_1 = 0. \tag{19}$$

In practice this equation has to be solved numerically, but when this has been done we have what in § 2.7 was called a first-improved ψ_1. In such a way the whole process described in § 2.7 is carried through until further iterations yield no effective alterations in any of the ψ. At this stage we have obtained a truly self-consistent field.

3.3. Hamiltonian form of wave equation

Our derivation of the wave equation started with the fact that for stationary states the expression $T + V$ was constant and equal to the energy. Now for problems in which the potential energy V is independent of the time, $T + V$ is identical with what has been known in classical mechanics as the Hamiltonian.† Thus the conservation of energy would be written in classical mechanics as

$$H = E, \tag{20}$$

† After W. R. Hamilton, who introduced it. For some examples and further applications in wave mechanics, see L. Pauling and E. B. Wilson, *Introduction to Quantum Mechanics*, McGraw-Hill Co., New York, 1935.

and in wave mechanics as

$$H\psi = E\psi. \tag{21}$$

Equation (21) is the neatest and simplest form of the wave equation. To use it, all that we need to do is to express the kinetic energy part of H in a form involving the various momenta and then make the operator-substitution

$$p_x \to \frac{h}{2\pi i} \frac{\partial}{\partial x}, \quad \text{etc.}$$

We shall often use (21), and shall find, somewhat surprisingly, that a good many general results may be obtained even if we do not know the exact Hamiltonian for any given problem. This might occur if, for example, the true potential energy was known only approximately.

The classical Hamiltonian is a function of the various coordinates and the momenta. But by virtue of the substitution of p_x by a differentiation with respect to x, the quantum Hamiltonian is an operator. That is to say, it tells us to do something; and the operation takes place on the wave function ψ.

Our description of the wave equation only applies to stationary states, in which the particles are bound together, and do not escape to infinity. As such it cannot deal with all the scattering phenomena, of X-rays or of electrons, which provide us with such a large proportion of our experimental knowledge of molecular structure, nor with the rates of chemical reactions. To do this we require a more general wave equation, the so-called time-dependent equation, which differs from our previous so-called amplitude equation in that the energy term E is replaced by a differential operator $-\frac{h}{2\pi i}\frac{\partial}{\partial t}$. The resulting wave equation is

$$H\psi = -\frac{h}{2\pi i}\frac{\partial\psi}{\partial t}. \tag{22}$$

3.4. Some special solutions of particular wave equations

It will help to familiarize us with the way in which allowed wave functions and energies satisfy the wave equation if we describe two or three particular examples.

The harmonic oscillator. According to (12) the wave equation is

$$\frac{d^2\psi}{dx^2} + \frac{8\pi^2 m}{h^2}(E - \tfrac{1}{2}kx^2)\psi = 0.$$

It may be verified by direct substitution that this equation is satisfied by

$$\psi = e^{-\alpha x^2},$$

provided that the constant α has the value

$$\alpha = \frac{\pi}{h}\sqrt{(mk)},$$

and in such a case

$$E = \frac{h}{4\pi}\sqrt{\frac{k}{m}} = \tfrac{1}{2}h\nu_0,$$

say, where

$$\nu_0 = \frac{1}{2\pi}\sqrt{\frac{k}{m}}$$

is the frequency with which the particle would vibrate if it obeyed classical equations of motion with the same potential energy. As a matter of fact this is the ground state, but this cannot be proved from the analysis we have given. The reader may care to verify that there is another solution

$$\psi = xe^{-\alpha x^2},$$

in which the energy is three times as great as before. This is the first excited state.

In general the energy levels may be shown to be

$$E_n = (n+\tfrac{1}{2})h\nu_0. \qquad n = 0, 1,\dots .$$

The hydrogen-like atom. According to (14) the wave equation is

$$\nabla^2\psi + \frac{8\pi^2 m}{h^2}\left(E + \frac{Ze^2}{r}\right)\psi = 0.$$

If we use the fact that

$$\frac{\partial r}{\partial x} = \frac{x}{r},$$

it may be verified that this equation is satisfied by

$$\psi = e^{-kr}, \tag{23}$$

provided that

$$k = \frac{4\pi^2 Z m e^2}{h^2} = \frac{Z}{a_0} \quad \text{(from 2.6),}\dagger \tag{24}$$

and then

$$E = -\frac{h^2 k^2}{8\pi^2 m} = -\frac{2\pi^2 m Z^2 e^4}{h^2} = -\frac{Z^2 e^2}{2a_0}. \tag{25}$$

---

† This notation means 'equation (6) of Chapter II', and will be used throughout the book. When the chapter number is not given, the reference is to the current chapter.

This is the ground state of the atom, and in the particular case of hydrogen, for which $Z = 1$, these are precisely the equations (7) and (8) of Chapter II, which were there given without proof. Equation (23) gives us, when normalized, the 1s a.o. of an atom with nuclear charge Ze.

In the same way it may be verified that there is a solution

$$\psi = xe^{-\frac{1}{2}kr}, \tag{26}$$

where k is still given by (24). By symmetry there are also $ye^{-\frac{1}{2}kr}$ and $ze^{-\frac{1}{2}kr}$. These are the $2p_x$, $2p_y$, $2p_z$ a.o.'s described in equations (2.10) and (2.19).

The student who is interested in the mathematical aspect of the wave equation will soon recognize the significance of the s, p, d,... classification, as follows. In spherical polar coordinates the wave equation (19) for an electron in a central field $V(r)$ is

$$\frac{\partial^2 \psi}{\partial r^2} + \frac{2}{r} \frac{\partial \psi}{\partial r} + \frac{1}{r^2 \sin\theta} \frac{\partial}{\partial\theta}\left(\sin\theta \frac{\partial\psi}{\partial\theta}\right) + \frac{1}{r^2 \sin^2\theta} \frac{\partial^2\psi}{\partial\phi^2} + \frac{8\pi^2 m}{h^2}\{E - V(r)\}\psi = 0. \tag{27}$$

This differential equation is separable† in all three variables r, θ, ϕ; this is the basis of (2.14) for the case when $V(r) = -Ze^2/r$. An important fact about (27) is that, whatever the particular form of $V(r)$, provided only that it depends on r, and not on θ or ϕ, there are solutions which are spherically symmetrical, i.e. are functions only of r. These satisfy the equation

$$\frac{d^2\psi}{dr^2} + \frac{2}{r} \frac{d\psi}{dr} + \frac{8\pi^2 m}{h^2}\{E - V(r)\}\psi = 0, \tag{28}$$

and are what we have previously called s-type orbitals. Similarly there are solutions of the form required by (2.10), viz.

$$\psi = z \times \text{some function of } r,$$
$$= \cos\theta \times f(r) \quad \text{(say)}, \tag{29}$$

where $f(r)$ satisfies the equation

$$\frac{d^2f}{dr^2} + \frac{2}{r} \frac{df}{dr} + \left\{\frac{8\pi^2 m}{h^2}\{E - V(r)\} - \frac{2}{r^2}\right\}f = 0. \tag{30}$$

These are what we have called p_z-type a.o. There are equivalent p_x, p_y orbitals, and, in the same manner, d-type a.o.'s, etc.

3.5. Need for an effective approximate method of solving the wave equation

Only for certain rather special forms of the potential function V is the wave equation completely soluble in closed terms. For

† See, e.g., C. A. Coulson, *Waves*, chap. I. Oliver & Boyd, Edinburgh, 1941.

example, it is insoluble for all atoms except those of hydrogenic character in which each electron is supposed to move in the presence of a single effective nuclear charge: this is the case *a fortiori* for molecules. A simple example will show the complexity of the problem. In methane CH_4 there are five nuclei and ten electrons, so that the complete wave equation involves a total of $3 \times 15 = 45$ independent variables. A partial differential equation in as many variables as this is utterly outside the range of exact solutions, even if we are able to reduce it somewhat by the use of symmetry.

Fortunately we may reduce it considerably without trouble. On account of their heavier mass (the mass of a proton is about 1,836 times as great as the mass of an electron) the nuclei move much more slowly than the electrons. In fact, using classical language to make the matter clearer, during the time that the nuclei make one vibration around their equilibrium positions, each electron has made some hundreds of circuits of its particular orbit. This means that when calculating the energies of the electrons we may treat the nuclei as fixed. The argument has been put in wave-mechanical terms by Born and Oppenheimer,[†] but the conclusion is just the same. It means that the vibrational and rotational motions of a molecule are effectively quite separate from the electronic motions. Corresponding to any given positions of the nuclei, there is a definite energy (or set of energies) for the electrons. Further, we can obtain these energies by treating the nuclei as fixed and solving the appropriate wave equation. This is our justification for writing the wave equation for H_2^+ and H_2 in the forms (16) and (17).

This approximation reduces the complexity of the complete molecular wave equation by removing from it terms involving the motion of the nuclei. It is known as the fixed-nucleus approximation, and is astonishingly accurate. Thus, the error for H_2^+ has been shown[‡] to be not more than 0.0075 eV; this may be com-

---

[†] *Ann. der Phys.*, 1927, **84**, 457. See also A. Dalgarno and R. McCarroll, *Proc. Roy. Soc. A.*, 1956, **237**, 383.

[‡] J. H. Van Vleck, *J. Chem. Phys.*, 1936, **4**, 327; V. A. Johnson, *Phys. Rev.*, 1941, **60**, 373. But the error may be somewhat larger if the atoms are not in S states.

pared with a total electronic energy at the equilibrium configuration of about 32 eV. But quite apart from this accuracy, the significance of the approximation itself is of the utmost importance. For the validity of this separation of electronic and nuclear motions provides the only real justification for the idea of a potential curve, or potential energy curve, of a molecule. Thus, if E now denotes simply the electronic energy, together with the nuclear repulsion energy, then E may be regarded as a function of the relative positions of all the nuclei. In the particular case of a diatomic molecule, E is a function simply of the internuclear distance R and, at least in principle, the wave equation enables us to determine the function $E(R)$. The graph of $E(R)$ against R is the potential energy curve of the molecule, such as was discussed in § 1.4.

In case our use of the phrase 'potential energy curve' is liable to mislead the student, it may be well to list the contributions that are involved in it, and reveal themselves as separate terms in the wave equation. These are (i) the Coulomb forces of attraction between the electrons and the various nuclei, (ii) the Coulomb repulsions between the various electrons, (iii) the Coulomb repulsions between the nuclei, and (iv) the kinetic energies of the electrons. The sum-total of (i)–(iv) is only to be regarded as a potential energy in so far as it plays the part of a potential energy in determining the vibrations of the nuclei.

This fixed-nucleus approximation certainly simplifies our wave equation. But it is still far too complex. In methane there still remain thirty variables, and even in H_2 there are six. Quite clearly, if any progress is to be made, we must have some technique for finding approximate solutions of the wave equation, and corresponding approximate energies. If by some means we knew the true ψ, we could easily determine the true energy: in fact we know neither, so that we are faced with two interlocking problems:

(i) How can we get the most suitable approximate ψ?
(ii) How can we use this approximate ψ to calculate an approximate E?

It is for the solution of these two problems that the Variation Method has been found to be the most effective technique.

3.6. The Variation Method

We must return to the original formulation (21) of the wave equation

$$H\psi = E\psi.$$

If we multiply both sides of this equation by ψ and integrate over all the coordinates involved, represented† simply by $d\tau$, we have the result‡

$$E = \int \psi H\psi \, d\tau \bigg/ \int \psi^2 \, d\tau. \tag{31}$$

In such cases as those where ψ is complex, this becomes

$$E = \int \psi^* H\psi \, d\tau \bigg/ \int \psi^*\psi \, d\tau. \tag{32}$$

This extremely important formula enables us to calculate E if we know ψ. We can either make an outright guess at ψ—and we shall see later that this may often be done with great effectiveness, if we bring sufficient chemical intuition to bear on the choice—or we may use the theorem known as the Variation Principle.§

The nature of (31) suggests that even if ψ is not a correct wave function, we should nevertheless consider the quantity $\mathscr{E}$, with dimensions of energy, which is related to ψ by the equation

$$\mathscr{E} = \int \psi H\psi \, d\tau \bigg/ \int \psi^2 \, d\tau, \tag{33}$$

and which we may call the energy function. Now suppose that we guess a particular ψ; it is most unlikely to be a correct wave function. But, calling it ψ_1, it gives a value $\mathscr{E}_1$, by the use of (33). Now let us guess another function ψ_2, leading to $\mathscr{E}_2$. The Variation Principle tells us that if E_g is the true energy of the ground state, both $\mathscr{E}_1$ and $\mathscr{E}_2$ are always necessarily greater than E (unless we happen to have guessed the true wave function), and that if

---

† We shall adhere to this convention throughout the book. Unless the contrary is stated, $\int \ldots d\tau$ will imply an integration over all the coordinates represented in the integrand.

‡ We must be careful to write $\psi H\psi$ and not $H\psi\psi$ or $H\psi^2$ because H is an operator, and (21) shows that it is only to operate on ψ.

§ See, e.g., L. Pauling and E. B. Wilson, *Introduction to Quantum Mechanics*, 1935, for a proof and further discussion. In classical mechanics the Principle is no less important. See G. Temple and W. G. Bickley, *Rayleigh's Principle*, Oxford University Press, 1933.

$\mathscr{E}_2 < \mathscr{E}_1$, then $\mathscr{E}_2$ is the better approximation to the energy and ψ_2 to the wave function.

There is no reason why we should limit ourselves to two guesses. We can choose as many functions ψ_n as we wish, and calculate the corresponding $\mathscr{E}_n$. If we choose the lowest of all the $\mathscr{E}_n$—which we may call $\mathscr{E}_i$—then

(i) $\mathscr{E}_i$ will be the closest of all to the true energy E_g,

(ii) $\mathscr{E}_i$ will always be at least a little greater than E_g,

(iii) ψ_i will be the closest approximation of all the ψ to the true ψ_g.

It is rather ineffective to guess isolated ψ's: and unnecessarily tedious. So as far as possible we deal with a whole family of ψ at the same time. This may be done by choosing a trial function with one or more variable parameters. If we call these $c_1, c_2,...$ then $\mathscr{E}$ is a function of $c_1, c_2,...$. We now choose the values of $c_1, c_2,...$ so that $\mathscr{E}$ is minimized. These values give us the best approximate wave function consistent with the type of function originally used. Naturally, the more arbitrary parameters c we are able to introduce, the more flexible is our trial function, and the better our final ψ. If we have enough parameters, we can get as near as we like to the true ψ, though except in very rare instances we never quite get there. In practice the introduction of additional parameters adds considerably to the labour, so that some compromise is necessary between accuracy and convenience.

The question is sometimes asked: why, starting with the original wave equation (21), is it necessary to multiply both sides by ψ and integrate in order to obtain (31): why can we not deal at once with the equally accurate equation

$$E = \frac{H\psi}{\psi}?$$

The answer is simple. First, there is no easy minimum property for the expression $H\psi/\psi$. Second, unless ψ happens to be a true wave function the expression $H\psi/\psi$ will be a function (usually quite complicated) of the coordinates of the system, and, as such, it varies from place to place and cannot possibly be equated to a constant E. Indeed, the allowed wave functions are precisely those for which $H\psi$ is simply some constant multiple of ψ, so that $H\psi/\psi$ is a constant and not a variable function of position.

The Variation Method can also be applied to excited states, but the technique is a little more involved. We shall make very little use of it except for the ground states, which are of far the greatest interest chemically.

3.7. Variation Method for the ground state of the hydrogen atom

The Variation Method is so important a tool that it is worth illustrating at once, even though the example that we choose happens to be one where the wave equation can be solved exactly, and for which therefore no approximate methods are necessary. We choose the hydrogen atom, for which (see (13)) the Hamiltonian is

$$-\frac{h^2}{8\pi^2 m}\nabla^2 - \frac{e^2}{r}. \tag{34}$$

We are to look for acceptable wave functions. In this case it is quite obvious that $\psi \to 0$ at large distances. A plausible hypothesis would be that it has spherical symmetry and that ψ dies away exponentially with r. Let us, in fact, try a hypothetical wave function

$$\psi = e^{-cr}, \tag{35}$$

with one arbitrary parameter c. Only positive values of c are physically acceptable. It is soon verified that

$$\nabla^2 \psi = \left(c^2 - \frac{2c}{r}\right)e^{-cr},$$

so that the relation (33) gives us

$$\mathscr{E}(c) \equiv \int \psi H\psi \, d\tau \Big/ \int \psi^2 \, d\tau = \frac{h^2}{8\pi^2 m}c^2 - e^2 c. \tag{36}$$

The graph of $\mathscr{E}(c)$ against c is shown in Fig. 5. It appears that the lowest value of $\mathscr{E}$ occurs at M, where $\dfrac{\partial \mathscr{E}}{\partial c} = 0$, and thus

$$c = \frac{4\pi^2 m e^2}{h^2}, \qquad \mathscr{E}_{\min} = -\frac{2\pi^2 m e^4}{h^2}.$$

It will be recognized from (2.6) that $c = 1/a_0$ and $\mathscr{E}_{\min} = -e^2/2a_0$.

In this particular case we have managed to obtain the true ground-state function and energy, as given in (2.7) and (2.11) though this could not be recognized from the analysis that we have made. It arose from the particularly fortunate choice of an exponential function in (35).

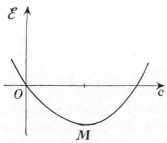

Fig. 3.5. Variation of energy function $\mathscr{E}(c)$ with parameter c.

We might not have chosen so fortunately. For example, we might have tried a Gaussian type of function, similar to that (§ 4) which appears in the harmonic oscillator. Now, if we try

$$\psi = e^{-cr^2},$$

we find that

$$\mathscr{E}(c) = \frac{3h^2}{8\pi^2 m}c - \frac{2e^2\sqrt{2}}{\sqrt{\pi}}c^{\frac{1}{2}},$$

with a minimum value when

$$c = 8/9\pi a_0^2.$$

The corresponding $\mathscr{E}_{\min}$ is $-\dfrac{4}{3\pi}\dfrac{e^2}{a_0} = -0.424 e^2/a_0$, which does not differ greatly from the true value $-0.5 e^2/a_0$.

It would have been possible to introduce greater flexibility in our trial function. If we had expected an exponential variation, but did not know what power of r was involved, we could have tried

$$\psi = e^{-cr^n},$$

containing c and n as parameters. We should have found the lowest value of $\mathscr{E}(c, n)$ when n was equal to 1 and c had the value previously given.

The only significance to be attached to these figures when $\psi = e^{-cr^2}$ is that unless we choose as our trial function an expression of the right form, we cannot hope, by using the Variation Method, to obtain the true energy. But even though we try a wave function which differs quite appreciably from the true one— e^{-cr^2} tends to zero at large distances very much quicker than e^{-cr} —we may still obtain a fairly good approximation to the energy. In the example chosen the approximate value is about 15 per cent. too high, and with only a little more labour we could appreciably decrease the error.

Our conclusion from this special case is quite general. It may be shown that the energy calculated by a variation process is nearly always good; the percentage error in the energy being much less than that in the wave function. This peculiarly happy circumstance largely explains why any quantitative calculations of molecular energies are possible at all.

3.8. The method of linear combinations

There is one particular form of the Variation Method which is outstandingly convenient to use. It is also important and is worth a separate description, because, as will appear later, it includes the essence of what is commonly referred to as resonance, and it represents one of the most powerful ways in which chemical intuition may be introduced into the finding of a suitable wave function.

Suppose first that we have grounds for believing that the true wave function ψ has characteristics typical of two known functions ψ_1 and ψ_2. It is not necessary that ψ_1 and ψ_2 should themselves be solutions of any particular wave equation. For example, if an electric field acts in the x-direction on an electron in an s-type a.o., it will tend to pull the electron away from the nucleus preferentially in the x-direction, and give a polarity to the atom. We could imagine the true ψ as having at the same time characteristics both of the original s-type orbital ψ_1 and of some directed orbital ψ_2 related to the direction of the field, and here perhaps one of the p_x a.o.'s. In a case like this we should naturally try to describe the complete wave function as a sum of contributions from each separate orbital: i.e. we might write

$$\psi = c_1\psi_1 + c_2\psi_2, \tag{37}$$

where c_1 and c_2 are constants to be chosen so that the energy expression is minimized. In the example mentioned above, presumably when the field was zero, c_2 would vanish; and if the field was large, c_2 would be relatively more important. Alternatively, if we may anticipate some of the analysis in Chapter IX, ψ_1 and ψ_2 might represent alternative ways of pairing electrons to form the bonds of a molecule. However, provided that we choose a linear combination of the known functions ψ_1 and ψ_2, it does not matter much what they separately correspond to, in any chemical sense: it is not even necessary that they should correspond to anything at all of chemical significance.

Trial wave functions such as (37) are particularly well suited to the Variation Method. The energy function $\mathscr{E}$ is given by

$$\mathscr{E} = \int \psi H \psi \, d\tau \bigg/ \int \psi^2 \, d\tau$$

$$= \frac{c_1^2 \int \psi_1 H \psi_1 \, d\tau + 2 c_1 c_2 \int \psi_1 H \psi_2 \, d\tau + c_2^2 \int \psi_2 H \psi_2 \, d\tau}{c_1^2 \int \psi_1^2 \, d\tau + 2 c_1 c_2 \int \psi_1 \psi_2 \, d\tau + c_2^2 \int \psi_2^2 \, d\tau}. \qquad (38)$$

We have used the very important relation, that

$$\int \psi_1 H \psi_2 \, d\tau = \int \psi_2 H \psi_1 \, d\tau.$$

The only difficulty in proving this lies in the differential terms such as ∇^2 in the Hamiltonian H. But a typical element $\partial^2/\partial x^2$ may be dealt with by twice integrating by parts, as follows:

$$\int \psi_1 \frac{\partial^2 \psi_2}{\partial x^2} \, dx = \left[\psi_1 \frac{\partial \psi_2}{\partial x} \right] - \int \frac{\partial \psi_1}{\partial x} \frac{\partial \psi_2}{\partial x} \, dx$$

$$= \left[\psi_1 \frac{\partial \psi_2}{\partial x} \right] - \left[\psi_2 \frac{\partial \psi_1}{\partial x} \right] + \int \psi_2 \frac{\partial^2 \psi_1}{\partial x^2} \, dx.$$

For acceptable functions ψ_1 and ψ_2 vanish at infinity, so that the terms in square brackets both vanish, making the rest of the proof very easy.

Equation (38) is much simplified if we adopt the following notation:

$$H_{rs} = \int \psi_r H \psi_s \, d\tau, \qquad S_{rs} = \int \psi_r \psi_s \, d\tau. \qquad (39)$$

Then $H_{rs} = H_{sr}$, and $S_{rs} = S_{sr}$. If ψ_1 and ψ_2 are separately normalized—which is often useful, but by no means necessary—then $S_{11} = S_{22} = 1$. We refer to H_{rs} as the matrix component of H with respect to ψ_r and ψ_s. In the same way we could call S_{rs} the matrix component of unity, but it is more usual to refer to it as an overlap integral. It may be shown that if ψ_1 and ψ_2 are normalized $|S_{12}| \leqslant 1$, the equality sign only holding when ψ_1 and ψ_2 are identical.

There is a special reason for calling S_{12} the overlap integral.

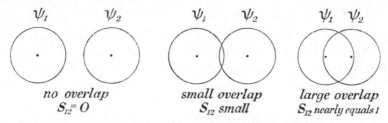

FIG. 3.6. Overlap integral for two identical orbitals.

Suppose that we draw the two boundary surfaces (§ 2.4) of the separate orbitals ψ_1 and ψ_2. The significance of these surfaces is such that we may effectively neglect those parts of each ψ which lie outside the appropriate surface. Thus the product $\psi_1\psi_2$ is to be neglected except where the two surfaces overlap one another: it is only such regions that make any effective contribution to the integral $\int \psi_1\psi_2\, d\tau$. If (Fig. 6) the two boundary surfaces are separate from each other, there is no overlap and $S_{12} = 0$: as they approach closer S_{12} increases. Indeed a very good judgement regarding the magnitude of S_{12} may be made by qualitative consideration of the two boundary surfaces, without any detailed knowledge of the orbitals themselves. When doing this, however, some care is needed to distinguish those distinct regions where one or another of ψ_1 and ψ_2 changes sign.

We can now proceed with the development of our Variation Method. Using (39) we write (38) as

$$\mathscr{E} = \frac{c_1^2 H_{11} + 2c_1 c_2 H_{12} + c_2^2 H_{22}}{c_1^2 S_{11} + 2c_1 c_2 S_{12} + c_2^2 S_{22}}. \tag{40}$$

The only variables are the parameters c_1 and c_2. We are asking ourselves the following question: what are the values of c_1 and c_2 which make a function of the general type $c_1\psi_1+c_2\psi_2$ the best possible approximation to the true wave function? The answer is given by the general Variation Principle that $\mathscr{E}$ must be stationary (in the ground state a minimum) with respect to c_1 and c_2. If we write down the conditions

$$\frac{\partial\mathscr{E}}{\partial c_1} = 0, \qquad \frac{\partial\mathscr{E}}{\partial c_2} = 0,$$

we obtain what are known as the Secular Equations

$$c_1(H_{11}-ES_{11})+c_2(H_{12}-ES_{12}) = 0,$$
$$c_1(H_{12}-ES_{12})+c_2(H_{22}-ES_{22}) = 0. \tag{41}$$

In (41) we have written E instead of $\mathscr{E}$, because for these values of c_1 and c_2, $\mathscr{E}$ is the closest approximation to the true energy.

These equations (41) may be solved to give the energy E and also the ratio of the coefficients c_1 and c_2.

This particular form of the Variation Method is sometimes known as the Rayleigh–Ritz, or Ritz, method because it was developed long before wave mechanics to deal with a wide variety of problems in classical mechanics and wave motion. It is easily extended to introduce more than two component functions. Thus with a trial wave function ψ compounded out of three functions ψ_1, ψ_2, ψ_3 and of the form of a linear combination:

$$\psi = c_1\psi_1+c_2\psi_2+c_3\psi_3, \tag{42}$$

the secular equations are three in number, and have the form entirely analogous to (41):

$$c_1(H_{11}-ES_{11})+c_2(H_{12}-ES_{12})+c_3(H_{13}-ES_{13}) = 0,$$
$$c_1(H_{12}-ES_{12})+c_2(H_{22}-ES_{22})+c_3(H_{23}-ES_{23}) = 0,$$
$$c_1(H_{13}-ES_{13})+c_2(H_{23}-ES_{23})+c_3(H_{33}-ES_{33}) = 0. \tag{43}$$

These equations give the ground state energy and the corresponding coefficients c_r, and provide us with a wave function of greater accuracy than does (41). If we eliminate the c_r from (43) we obtain† a cubic equation in E, so that there are three roots. It may be

† Details of the procedure are given, e.g., by L. Pauling and E. B. Wilson, loc. cit. The result of eliminating the c_r is a determinant, here of three rows and columns, called the secular determinant. Determinants of this kind have been known for a long time in calculating the periods (hence the word secular) of the planets and of other vibrating systems.

shown that these are all real. The upper ones correspond to excited states, which they describe somewhat less accurately than the ground state.

The advantages of the Ritz method are that it is easily extended to as many component functions as we want, and that the process of minimizing the energy function (33) leads very simply to a set of linear equations (the secular equations). This is usually much easier than minimizing ψ with respect to other types of parameter such as, for example, the coefficient c in an exponential function e^{-cr}. There is a further advantage, that the component functions ψ_1, ψ_2,... are at our free choice, and we may, therefore, follow chemical intuition by introducing just those functions which correspond to behaviour to be expected chemically. If we have made a mistake, and introduced an unnecessary function ψ, it will make no difference (except in the additional computations involved) because the corresponding coefficient c_r will automatically be small, showing that this particular ψ_r really is unimportant. Alternatively, if we have introduced what we believe to be suitable components, and have then calculated their coefficients c_1, c_2,..., we may argue in the opposite way, and interpret our calculated wave function in chemical terms appropriate to the components used. Such an interpretation is often very interesting. In the case of the three-component wave function (42) the argument would be as follows: since it is ψ^2 rather than ψ itself which has physical significance, we could say that the electronic distribution (42) is built up out of the separate distributions ψ_1^2, ψ_2^2, and ψ_3^2 in the ratio $c_1^2 : c_2^2 : c_3^2$. Such an interpretation is not quite correct because it neglects the cross-products $\psi_1 \psi_2$, etc., but it is qualitatively true, and from time to time we shall use it.

On the other hand, there is an alternative interpretation which is often given, but which is definitely not true. This is that the system exists in states ψ_1, ψ_2 and ψ_3 for fractions of the total time proportional to c_1^2, c_2^2, and c_3^2. This is not a valid interpretation for several reasons, sufficiently important to be worth listing:

(i) the system is in one definite stationary state, independent of the time, and does not oscillate from one to another state ψ_1, ψ_2,... ;

(ii) adding more components ψ_3, ψ_4,... changes the coefficients of the previous function, so that these coefficients have no absolute significance;

(iii) the linear combination (42) represents one way of breaking up a true and highly complicated wave function into components. But it is by no means unique, and other sets of component functions could be used, giving the same (or nearly the same) energy value, but a quite different interpretation in terms of fractional times.

The significance of these comments will become very much clearer when we study the resonance effect in Chapters V and IX.

3.9. Simplifying features

When using variation methods there are two simplifying features which deserve comment.

(a) Often we do not need to go through the process of minimizing (Ritz or variation methods) the complete wave function, because we may have physical or chemical grounds for supposing that certain electrons have orbits relatively unchanged from their nature in some known situation. An example is provided by the inner-shell electrons of atoms which, because their charge-clouds are so near to the nucleus, are practically unaffected by chemical combination. Excellent confirmation of this is found from X-ray analysis of the energies required to remove them from the atom or the molecule by ionization.

(b) Since the energy function $\mathscr{E}$ is a minimum for the best ψ of the type we are considering, it does not change much when we select a ψ which is nearly, but not quite, the best. This is shown quite clearly in Fig. 5 on p. 60, where, if we choose a value of the exponent c which differs only a little from the best value $1/a_0$, the energy $\mathscr{E}$ is scarcely affected. This singularly fortunate chance enables us to get many useful results which would be quite impossible if we had to introduce every possible kind of component in our trial function. For it justifies us in selecting a ψ which we have good chemical grounds for believing to be plausible, and in using this to determine $\mathscr{E}$. It is true that we shall not thus get the absolutely right energy, but we shall get a pretty close approximation to it; we shall be able to make reasonably simple calculations and yet give reasonably valid answers to the fundamental questions of molecular structure mentioned in § 1.1. For as we stressed at the time, the answers to the questions depend almost entirely on energy, and much less on the details of a particular wave function.

There is one other simplifying feature that must be mentioned here. When we write down the complete Hamiltonian for a molecule, in addition to a kinetic energy term for each electron, we have electron-electron repulsion terms and electron-nucleus attractions. There is also a nucleus-nucleus repulsion. In the case of a diatomic molecule we might write

$$H = H_{elec} + \frac{Z_A Z_B e^2}{R_{AB}}, \tag{44}$$

where H_{elec} is a Hamiltonian solely concerned with the electrons and the last term represents the Coulomb repulsion energy between charges $Z_A e$ and $Z_B e$ at a distance R_{AB} apart. Thus the energy function $\mathscr{E}$ defined in (33) as

$$\mathscr{E} = \int \psi H \psi \, d\tau \bigg/ \int \psi^2 \, d\tau$$

is itself the sum of two parts. The first part is evidently the energy associated with the electrons: the second part is the nuclear repulsion term

$$\int \psi \frac{Z_A Z_B e^2}{R_{AB}} \psi \, d\tau \bigg/ \int \psi^2 \, d\tau = Z_A Z_B e^2 / R_{AB}.$$

Thus wave mechanics makes no difference to the separation of the total energy of the molecule into parts, and we may write

$$E = E_{elec} + E_{nucl}, \tag{45}$$

where E_{nucl} is the classical potential energy of the nuclei at internuclear distance R_{AB} due to their positive charges, and E_{elec} is the allowed energy associated with the Hamiltonian H_{elec}. Thus calculations of the energy of a molecule may be made without consideration of the nuclear term, which may be incorporated at the very end. This is the method that we shall normally adopt in this book. In addition we shall not usually bother to insert the suffix so that, unless it is expressly stated otherwise, the Hamiltonian for a molecule will be the H_{elec} of (44) rather than the full Hamiltonian.

3.10. Mutual repulsion of two energy curves: the non-crossing rule

There is an important further point which emerges in the particular case where we use a Ritz-type variation method with just two functions ψ_1 and ψ_2. Let us suppose, for convenience, that ψ_1 and ψ_2 are each separately normalized, so that

$$S_{11} = S_{22} = 1.$$

The energy function $\mathscr{E}$ associated with the component ψ_1 by itself is simply

$$\frac{\int \psi_1 H \psi_1 \, d\tau}{\int \psi_1^2 \, d\tau} = \frac{H_{11}}{S_{11}} = H_{11}.$$

It will be convenient to call this E_1; similarly H_{22}, which is the energy associated with the component ψ_2 by itself, is written E_2. The secular equations (41) become

$$c_1(E_1 - E) + c_2(H_{12} - ES_{12}) = 0,$$
$$c_1(H_{12} - ES_{12}) + c_2(E_2 - E) = 0.$$

If we eliminate $c_1 : c_2$ we find that E is a root of the quadratic equation

$$(E - E_1)(E - E_2) - (H_{12} - ES_{12})^2 = 0. \tag{46}$$

Let us call the left-hand side of this equation $f(E)$; the graph of $f(E)$ is drawn in Fig. 7 for the particular case in which $E_1 < E_2$. The curve is a parabola whose ordinate has a positive value when E is large, either positive or negative: and which has a negative value when $E = E_1$ or E_2. Evidently the values of E for which $f(E) = 0$ lie outside the region between E_1 and E_2. This result is quite independent of the relative magnitudes† of E_1, E_2, H_{12}, and

---

† A simple discussion of this principle, and some applications, is given by C. A. Coulson, *Proc. Camb. Phil. Soc.*, 1937, **33**, 111. The case of more than two components is dealt with by L. Pauling and E. B. Wilson, loc. cit.

S_{12}. Thus, when we combine two functions ψ_1 and ψ_2, we find two possible combinations, and two possible energies; one of the original energies has gone downwards, the other has gone up. It is as though the two separate energies repelled one another.

A very important application of this law occurs in diatomic molecules. We have already seen in § 5 that the energy of the molecule depends on the separation R of the two nuclei. This

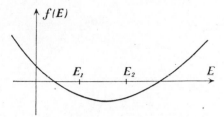

FIG. 3.7. Graph of the function $f(E)$.

means that E_1 and E_2 are themselves functions of R, where E_1 and E_2 are the energies that would be calculated if the wave function were ψ_1 or ψ_2 respectively. The energies which we obtain when we allow combinations of ψ_1 and ψ_2 always lie above and below the energies E_1 and E_2, with the result that even if the curves of E_1 and E_2 against R cross one another, the energies of the combination can never cross. Two possible situations are illustrated in Fig. 8 which shows the apparent repulsion between the two original energy curves. A similar rule applies to polyatomic molecules also.

The fact that the two final curves do not cross one another is referred to as the non-crossing rule. It is of the greatest importance, as we shall see, in correlating molecular states with the products of dissociation.

Lest any confusion should result from a possible misunderstanding of the non-crossing rule, it should be emphasized that it only applies to component wave functions ψ_1 and ψ_2 that may be combined together in the form $c_1\psi_1 + c_2\psi_2$. It will appear later that certain symmetry conditions must be satisfied without which there can be no possible linear combination of this kind. Thus the non-crossing rule only applies to states of the same type, or symmetry. The potential curves of states with different symmetries are quite independent of each other, and may cross freely. The non-crossing rule is also valid only on the condition that the fixed-nuclei approximation (§ 5) is adequate. There is still some doubt about what happens when this approximation does not hold. In such cases the whole conception of potential energy curves breaks down.

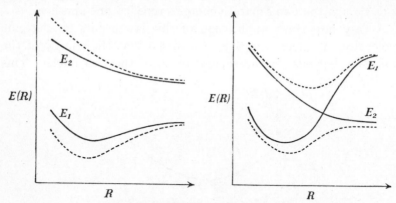

FIG. 3.8. Two possibilities in the non-crossing rule. Thick lines denote the energies E_1 and E_2 before combination. Dotted lines denote the final combined energies.

The above discussion of linear combinations of two functions may be extended to three or more. Each time that we add a new component we obtain a new set of secular equations, with one more energy value. It may be shown that between any two consecutive energies in the new series there lies just one of the previous series.

We have now completed our development of the general principles of wave mechanics, so far as they concern their application to atomic and molecular structure. The time has now come when we may apply these tools to the chief object of our study.

DIATOMIC MOLECULES, MOLECULAR-ORBITAL THEORY

4.1. The two chief theories of molecular structure

WE have seen that even for atoms the wave equation is impossibly difficult to solve exactly; it is much more difficult for molecules. For that reason rather more drastic approximations are needed than those which were involved with atoms. There are two chief types of approximation which are most commonly used, known respectively as the molecular-orbital and the valence-bond approximations. It has frequently been the custom for the supporters of one or the other of these theories to claim a greater measure of chemical insight and quantitative reliability for the method of their choice. This is a pity because neither method is complete or fully satisfactory. Fortunately in most of their conclusions the two theories agree, though they reach these conclusions in quite distinct ways. This means that we must not arbitrarily reject one or the other, and in this book we shall develop them both. There is, in fact, a good deal of interest attaching to a comparison of their interpretations of chemical binding.

The molecular-orbital theory attempts to treat a molecule from the same point of view as that which we described in Chapter II for atoms: the valence-bond, or electron-pair, theory regards a molecule as composed of atoms, which to some extent preserve their distinct character even when chemically bonded. There is little doubt but that the molecular-orbital theory is conceptually the simplest. Historically it was developed after the other theory was already established, and for that reason has been a little slower in gaining acceptance. Its present status, however, especially in dealing with excited states, is fully equal to that of the valence-bond theory. On account of its essential simplicity we shall devote this chapter entirely to a development of the molecular-orbital theory of diatomic molecules. The following chapter similarly describes the valence-bond theory.

4.2. Molecular orbitals

The molecular-orbital theory starts by supposing that the main ideas of the self-consistent-field method for atoms may be applied equally well to molecules. This means that we may adopt a large proportion of §§ 2.7 and 2.8, and enunciate the following set of fundamental principles:

(i) Each electron in a molecule is described by a certain wave function ψ, which, because it represents the orbit of the electron in the molecule, is properly called a molecular orbital (abbreviated to m.o.). These orbitals are essentially polycentric, and not monocentric, as in the case of an atom. The interpretation of ψ is that $\psi^2\, d\tau$—or $\psi\psi^*\, d\tau$ if ψ is complex—measures the relative probability that this electron is in the small volume element $d\tau$. If ψ is normalized, so that $\int \psi^2\, d\tau = 1$, then $\psi^2\, d\tau$ measures the exact probability, and not just the relative one. Alternatively we may speak (§ 2.2) of the charge-cloud associated with this orbital. The density of the charge-cloud is ψ^2 in electrons per unit volume. We may represent the orbital by drawing contours of constant ψ (or ψ^2), or we may draw a boundary surface, which is such that effectively all the charge-cloud lies within this surface.

(ii) Each ψ is defined by certain quantum numbers, which govern its energy and its shape.

(iii) Each ψ is associated with a definite energy value, which represents, very closely, the energy required to remove it from the molecule by ionization. The total energy of the molecule is the sum of the energies of the occupied m.o.'s, corrected for the mutual interaction between the electrons. For rough purposes, this latter is often neglected. Such a neglect is not really justified because (section (c) in § 2.7) in calculating the energy of any one m.o. we take account of the repulsion between it and all the other electrons. This means that when we add together the various m.o. energies, we do in fact count each electronic repulsion term twice over. Those terms (see Table 4 on p. 91) are sometimes as large as, or even larger than, the total binding energy.

(iv) Each electron has a spin, which, just as in the case of an electron in an atom, has to have a value $\pm\frac{1}{2}$, and which may be labelled by its spin quantum number m_s.

(v) When building a molecule we determine the allowed orbitals and then adopt the *aufbau*, or building-up process of § 2.8, in which the electrons are fed into the allowed orbits one at a time, taking due account of the Pauli Exclusion Principle, so that not more than two electrons have the same ψ. Even then they must have opposed spins.

All this is almost identically word for word the same as for atomic electrons. But before it is very much use to us, we must be able to describe the m.o.'s in some detail, and show in what ways new features appear on account of their molecular character. What then can we say in general terms about the nature of these m.o.'s?

4.3. LCAO approximation

The most obvious characteristic of a m.o. for a diatomic molecule is that it is bi-centric. It is this which distinguishes it from an a.o. The most appropriate physical description is that the electron moves in an orbit which extends to the neighbourhood of both nuclei.

But there is a further point to be made here. When the electron is in the region of one of the nuclei, the forces on it are those due chiefly to that nucleus and the other electrons near that nucleus. This may be put in a form useful for later calculations if we return to the Hamiltonian H introduced in § 3.3. We shall adopt the simplification suggested at the end of § 3.9 in which we omit the Coulomb repulsion between the nuclei, and introduce it only at the end of the calculations. We may say that in the region of one nucleus A, the most significant parts of H are precisely those terms which would comprise the Hamiltonian of an electron in an isolated atom A. The other terms, associated with atom B, are not exactly zero, but they are small. Thus the wave equation here resembles the wave equation of the isolated atom: so also must its solution. This means that in the neighbourhood of one nucleus, e.g. A, the m.o. resembles an a.o. ψ_A. Similarly in the neighbourhood of the other nucleus B, the m.o. resembles ψ_B.

Since the complete m.o. has characteristics separately possessed by ψ_A and ψ_B, it is a natural step to adopt the method of linear combinations described in § 3.8 and write

$$\psi = c_A\,\psi_A + c_B\,\psi_B.$$

This is most conveniently written

$$\psi = N(\psi_A + \lambda\psi_B), \tag{1}$$

where N is a normalizing factor. The value of N is given (see 3.39) by

$$N^{-2} = S_{AA} + 2\lambda S_{AB} + \lambda^2 S_{BB}$$
$$= 1 + \lambda^2 + 2\lambda S_{AB}, \tag{2}$$

if we suppose that ψ_A and ψ_B are each separately normalized. For most purposes we may omit the normalizing factor, and write (1) in the simple form

$$\psi = \psi_A + \lambda\psi_B. \tag{3}$$

The constant λ measures the polarity of the orbital, and may have any value ranging from $+\infty$ to $-\infty$, according to the nature of the combining atoms. According to the Ritz variation method this value of λ must be chosen to minimize the energy function

$$\int \psi H \psi \, d\tau \Big/ \int \psi^2 \, d\tau.$$

The approximation represented by (3) is called the approximation of Linear Combinations of Atomic Orbitals,[†] usually abbreviated to LCAO.

We have still to decide which orbitals ψ_A and ψ_B of the two atoms may be combined together in the form (3). In order that there may be an effective combination between a given ψ_A and ψ_B it is necessary:

(a) that the energies of ψ_A and ψ_B in their respective atoms should be of comparable magnitude;

(b) that the charge-clouds of ψ_A and ψ_B should overlap one another as much as possible;

(c) that ψ_A and ψ_B should have the same symmetry relative to the molecular axis AB.

[†] The orbital terminology was introduced by R. S. Mulliken, *Phys. Rev.*, 1932, **41**, 49, and the LCAO notation by the same writer, *J. Chem. Phys.*, 1935, **3**, 375.

If these conditions are not fulfilled, then ψ_A and ψ_B combine together either to a very minute degree, or not at all. The proof of these conditions is not difficult; we must go back to §§ 3.8 and 3.10 where the method of linear combinations was developed. Let us introduce a slightly different notation more convenient for our present purposes. Let E_A ($\equiv H_{AA}$) denote the energy associated with the a.o. ψ_A, etc., and let β be written instead of H_{AB}. Then the form taken by the secular equations (3.41) is

$$(E_A - E) + \lambda(\beta - ES) = 0,$$
$$(\beta - ES) + \lambda(E_B - E) = 0. \qquad (4)$$

We have dropped the suffix AB in S_{AB}, since there are only two orbitals involved, and no confusion can result. Now E_A and E_B are not quite the same as the energies of electrons in the orbitals ψ_A and ψ_B of isolated atoms, but, from what we said at the beginning of this section, they do correspond quite closely. The quantity S is known as the *overlap integral* of the orbitals ψ_A and ψ_B, and β is known (see later) as the *resonance integral* between ψ_A and ψ_B.

If we eliminate λ from (4), we have the equation analogous to (3.46), viz.:

$$(E - E_A)(E - E_B) - (\beta - ES)^2 = 0. \qquad (5)$$

In this equation E denotes the energy of the 'best' linear combination of ψ_A and ψ_B. There are two roots of (5) so that there are two such combinations. The arguments developed in § 3.10 show that one of the two energy values lies below the smaller of E_A and E_B; the other lies above the larger of E_A and E_B.

In order to prove condition (a) above, let us suppose that E_A and E_B are very different, and that $E_A \ll E_B$. We have already seen that E_A determines the size of the atomic orbital ψ_A. Hence ψ_A is much smaller than ψ_B and so the overlap integral S will be small; so also will be the resonance integral β. Thus the term $(\beta - ES)^2$ in (5) is small. But this is only possible if either $E - E_A$ or $E - E_B$ is small. If we consider the case where $E - E_A$ is small, we may obtain a good approximation very simply by just putting $E = E_A$ in all the terms of (5) except those that would vanish identically if we did. Thus, very nearly,

$$(E - E_A)(E_A - E_B) = (\beta - E_A S)^2.$$

This means that the solutions of (5) are approximately

$$E = E_A - \frac{(\beta - E_A S)^2}{E_B - E_A},$$ (6)

$$E = E_B + \frac{(\beta - E_B S)^2}{E_B - E_A}.$$ (7)

If we substitute (6) in the first equation of (4), we obtain, with the same degree of approximation,

$$\lambda = \frac{-(\beta - E_A S)}{E_B - E_A},$$ which is small.

Thus in the m.o. corresponding to (6), λ is small so that this m.o. is practically the same as the a.o. ψ_A: and the m.o. corresponding

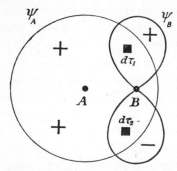

to (7) has a very large value of λ, so that when normalized it is almost entirely ψ_B. In neither case is there any effective combination between ψ_A and ψ_B.

Condition (b) follows from equation (4) by recognizing that if the a.o.'s ψ_A and ψ_B do not overlap at all (Fig. 3.6) then $S_{AB} = 0$ and also β. E is then equal either to E_A or E_B, and no effective combination of ψ_A and ψ_B occurs. This important condition is often referred to as the 'criterion of maximum overlapping'.

Fig. 4.1. Diagram to illustrate the vanishing of S_{AB} when ψ_A and ψ_B are of different symmetry type. Here ψ_A is an s-type orbital, ψ_B is a p_z-type orbital.

It will play a large part in most of our later work.

We shall have more to say later about the symmetry condition (c). But, as the last paragraph shows, there is no combination of ψ_A and ψ_B if, for any reason, $\beta = 0 = S_{AB}$. This will happen if the two orbitals do not overlap (condition (b)), or it may happen because of certain symmetries in ψ_A and ψ_B which enable us to separate each of the integrals S_{AB} and β_{AB} into two parts of equal magnitude and opposite sign. When this occurs, we can say that ψ_A and ψ_B are of the wrong symmetry type to be combined together in a m.o. An example of this occurs if ψ_A is an s-type a.o., and ψ_B is a p_z-type a.o. (Fig. 1) where the z-axis is directed perpendicular to the molecular axis AB. It is clear from Fig. 1 that in the integral $S_{AB} = \int \psi_A \psi_B \, d\tau$, on account of the difference in sign in the two lobes of a p_z orbital, to every small volume element $d\tau_1$ there is a corresponding element $d\tau_2$ such that the values of the integrand in $d\tau_1$ and $d\tau_2$ are equal and opposite. We can therefore say that the integral vanishes by symmetry; in fact $S_{AB} = 0$, whatever the detailed form of ψ_A and ψ_B when they are of s and p_z types respectively. It is evident at once that a p_z on one atom cannot be combined with a p_y or a p_x or an s on the other atom. Allowed combinations for the s-, p-, and some of the d-type orbitals are shown in Table 3 (page 78).

When the integral $\int \psi_A \psi_B \, d\tau$ is identically zero, we say that the wave functions ψ_A and ψ_B are orthogonal. It is often a matter of the greatest importance to know whether two given functions are or are not orthogonal. The following rules will help us to decide:

(i) If ψ_A and ψ_B are a.o.'s belonging to different symmetry types s, p, d,... of the same atom they are orthogonal.

(ii) In the same orbital type, p_x is orthogonal to p_y and p_z, and each of the five fundamental d-type orbitals is orthogonal to the rest.

(iii) If ψ_A and ψ_B are *accurate* (as opposed to approximate) solutions of the wave equation, they are necessarily orthogonal if the corresponding energies E_A and E_B differ.

(iv) Any two wave functions found by the Ritz method of linear combinations (§ 3.8) will be orthogonal if they are built up out of the same basic units.

In Chapter VIII it will appear that there are occasions when a given atomic ψ_A is associated with two or more ψ_B simultaneously. Possible combinations must be from among those labelled 'allowed' in Table 3. Since the molecular axis is the x-axis, we have chosen for the five fundamental d orbitals (see § 2.9) d_{xy}, d_{yz}, d_{zx}, d_{z^2}, $d_{y^2-z^2}$.

We can easily illustrate these three conditions for effective combinations of a.o.'s in the LCAO method by a consideration of

HCl. In the first place the condition (*a*) of comparable energies tells us that the $(1s)^2$, $(2s)^2$, $(2p)^6$, $(3s)^2$ electrons of Cl are not able to combine with any orbital of the H atom, for their energies are much too low. The only other possibilities among the next group are the chlorine $(3p_x)$, $(3p_y)$, and $(3p_z)$. Now the lowest a.o. of hydrogen is the $(1s)$, and so, according to Table 3, the symmetry

TABLE 3. *Allowed combinations of a.o.'s in LCAO method*

ψ_A	ψ_B	
	allowed	forbidden
s	s, p_x, d_{z^2}	$p_y, p_z, d_{xy}, d_{yz}, d_{xz}, d_{y^2-z^2}$
p_x	s, p_x, d_{z^2}	$p_y, p_z, d_{xy}, d_{yz}, d_{xz}, d_{y^2-z^2}$
p_y	p_y, d_{xy}	$s, p_x, p_z, d_{yz}, d_{xz}, d_{z^2}, d_{y^2-z^2}$
d_{xy}	p_y, d_{xy}	$s, p_x, p_z, d_{yz}, d_{xz}, d_{z^2}, d_{y^2-z^2}$
d_{z^2}	s, p_x, d_{z^2}	$p_y, p_z, d_{xy}, d_{yz}, d_{xz}, d_{y^2-z^2}$
$d_{y^2-z^2}$	$d_{y^2-z^2}$	$s, p_x, p_y, p_z, d_{xy}, d_{yz}, d_{xz}, d_{z^2}$

condition only allows a m.o. to be formed by combination of H(1s) and Cl($3p_x$).† There are possible m.o.'s of higher energy which do not concern us at the moment. It follows from this discussion, and by application of the *aufbau* process, that the ground state of HCl could be described as

$$\text{HCl,} \quad \{\text{Cl}(1s)^2(2s)^2(2p)^6(3s)^2(3p_y)^2(3p_z)^2\}\{\text{H}(1s)+\lambda\text{Cl}(3p_x)\}^2. \quad (8)$$

There is a particular significance in the LCAO relation between a m.o. ψ in a molecule AB and its component a.o.'s ψ_A and ψ_B. This is seen most clearly when the two electrons that occupy the orbital ψ are valence electrons contributing to the bonding between A and B. Normally one of these electrons comes from each atom, and in these atoms they would occupy orbitals ψ_A and ψ_B. Thus the m.o. ψ, which will accommodate two electrons, is correlated with the two a.o.'s into which we might expect the molecular electrons to go when the atoms were separated to infinite distance. In a loose kind of way we could therefore speak of 'the electron originally in state ψ_A' and 'the electron originally in state ψ_B' being paired to form molecular electrons in state

† There are solid grounds for believing that a small amount of Cl(3s) enters the combination, but this does not seriously affect the description given above. See Chapter VIII.

ψ ($=\psi_A+\lambda\psi_B$) for the molecule $A-B$. We could, in fact, imagine ourselves bringing up the atoms A and B towards one another, but without allowing interaction; and then pairing together suitable electrons in A and B. This rather crude, and certainly not completely accurate, description of molecule formation reveals a link between m.o. theory and both the Lewis shared-electron-pair bond and the Langmuir octet theory.

4.4. Significance of the resonance integral

The quantity β_{AB} (or β) is of great importance in this theory. It is called the resonance integral for two reasons. In the first place it is an integral, for by definition:

$$\beta_{AB} = \int \psi_A H \psi_B \, d\tau. \qquad (9)$$

Secondly, it may be shown by an argument which we shall not reproduce, that if, by some means, we were able to start an electron in the orbital ψ_A and compel its wave function at later times to have the form $C_A\psi_A+C_B\psi_B$, then C_A and C_B would be periodic functions of the time. This means that after a certain time interval the wave function would be ψ_B, and after another time interval it would again be ψ_A. Thus the electrons would be changing from ψ_A to ψ_B and back again just as, in the well-known physical experiment of two almost equal pendulums swinging from the same horizontal bar, the energy of the system resonates from one pendulum to the other.

In some ways this analogy is quite close. Thus consider the case of two pendulums with different natural frequencies, independent of each other except for the coupling between them arising from the small movements of their common horizontal axis. Ordinary mechanics tells us that this combination of pendulums has two normal modes of vibration, and two corresponding frequencies. Unless the original natural frequencies are of comparable magnitudes, the two pendulums oscillate almost independently of each other. But if they are comparable, then there is considerable mutual interaction, leading to two new frequencies, one greater and the other less than either of the originals. The reader will notice at once how closely these conditions are parallel to the ones we listed in § 4.3 for an effective LCAO combination of ψ_A and ψ_B, if we make use of the Planck relation $E = h\nu$ between frequency and energy. But the analogy may be taken further. For if the two original pendulums have comparable frequencies, then in the new normal modes the energy flows from one pendulum to the other with a frequency depending on the coupling coefficient which we mentioned a moment ago. Now in the quantum mechanical problem the resonance from ψ_A to ψ_B similarly depends in a simple way upon β_{AB}, which therefore plays the role of a coupling coefficient. Thus a large β_{AB} implies a large coupling and hence considerable changes in the frequencies (energies) of the normal modes (LCAO wave functions), and a quick oscillation backwards and forwards. Considerations of this kind justify us in calling β_{AB} the resonance integral. It is important to realize that the analogy itself is not complete, and the justification is not perfect, for the interchange between ψ_A and ψ_B is not a phenomenon that actually occurs in molecule formation. This is because we are concerned only with stationary states, in which there is one single molecular wave function, independent of the time, and such an oscillatory behaviour could not in general be regarded as a stationary state. Furthermore, there is no conceivable physical mechanism whereby we could start an electron in ψ_A and subsequently compel its wave function to be a linear combination of ψ_A and ψ_B. So our quantum-mechanical resonance does not have the objectivity of mechanical resonance. Considerable confusion has arisen because of a tendency to regard resonance, both of this LCAO type and of other types which we shall meet in later chapters, as a phenomenon which actually takes place. It should be clear from the above discussion that the justification for using the word resonance is only by analogy: mathematically it has arisen here because of our use of the LCAO type of approximation in expressing m.o.'s as linear sums of a.o.'s. There are other alternative ways of 'breaking down' the accurate m.o. into parts, and to each way we should have to ascribe a different set of resonating structures—in our case ψ_A and ψ_B. That consideration alone should be sufficient to show that we have no right whatever to speak of the 'resonance phenomenon'. Resonance has appeared because of our own quite arbitrary choice of the type of approximation to a complete m.o.

4.5. Hydrogen molecule ion H_2^+

The LCAO approximation takes a particularly simple form for homonuclear diatomics, i.e. molecules where both atoms are of the same kind, as H_2, O_2, N_2, etc. It will be convenient to begin with the simplest of all such systems, H_2^+. On account of the fact that there is only one electron, this problem has the same central significance for molecules as the H atom has for atomic structures.

We are to form m.o.'s from the various a.o.'s, using the principles of § 3. These m.o.'s will be of the form (3), viz. $\psi_A + \lambda\psi_B$, where ψ_A and ψ_B denote identical a.o.'s except for their different origins A and B. By symmetry ψ_A and ψ_B must appear with equal weight so that (§ 3.8)

$$\lambda^2 = 1.$$

This shows us at once that the two allowed† m.o.'s are

$$\psi_A \pm \psi_B. \tag{10}$$

The same result follows from the secular equations (4), on introducing the condition that $E_A = E_B$. Equation (5) shows that the energies associated with these two orbitals are

$$E_\pm = \frac{E_A \pm \beta}{1 \pm S}. \tag{11}$$

These are conveniently written‡ as

$$E_\pm = E_A \pm \frac{\beta - E_A S}{1 \pm S}. \tag{12}$$

In approximate work, S is sometimes put equal to zero, and then

$$E_\pm = E_A \pm \beta. \tag{13}$$

Equations (12) and (13) show how the original pair of degenerate energies E_A and E_B is split into two, of which one is greater and

---

† L. Pauling, *Chem. Rev.*, 1928, **5**, 173, but the significance of the symmetry or antisymmetry in ψ_A and ψ_B was first stressed by J. E. Lennard-Jones, *Trans. Faraday Soc.*, 1929, **25**, 668.

‡ Here, and elsewhere, when the symbols $\pm$ and $\mp$ are used, either the top symbol or the bottom symbol must be used throughout.

the other is less than before. It also shows that the extent of this splitting depends very intimately on the magnitude of the resonance integral β. We could represent it on an energy diagram as in Fig. 2, where energy is plotted upwards and the levels for the

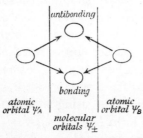

separate atoms A and B are at the sides, those for the molecule AB being in the middle. Since β is negative, the lowest energy is associated with the $+$ signs in (12) and (13). Also, on account of the term $1 \pm S$ in the denominator it follows that the top energy exceeds E_A by a greater amount than the bottom energy lies below it.

Fig. 4.2. The formation of molecular orbitals from atomic ones.

We have so far left undecided the particular choices of ψ_A and ψ_B. If we are interested in the ground state, this will arise by choosing

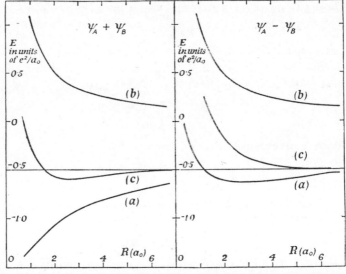

Fig. 4.3. Energy curves for H_2^+. On the left the m.o. is $\psi_A + \psi_B$, on the right it is $\psi_A - \psi_B$. On both diagrams (a) is the electronic energy; (b) is the nuclear Coulomb repulsion energy; (c) is the total energy curve of the molecule.

for ψ_A and ψ_B the lowest a.o.'s for a hydrogen atom. These are the wave functions of (2.7), from which β and S may be calculated for any chosen internuclear distance R. In this way the electronic energy is obtained, and so, by adding the nuclear Coulomb energy e^2/R, we determine the energy curve for the molecule. The results are shown in Fig. 3; on the left is the energy curve for the m.o. $\psi_A + \psi_B$ and on the right for $\psi_A - \psi_B$. The first of these is the energy curve of the molecule in its ground state.

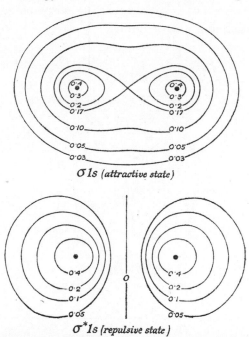

$\sigma 1s$ *(attractive state)*

$\sigma^* 1s$ *(repulsive state)*

Fig. 4.4. Contours of constant density ψ^2 for (top) the attractive $\sigma 1s$ state, and (bottom) the repulsive $\sigma^* 1s$ state of H_2^+.

Several features emerge from these energy curves. In the first place the curve for $\psi_A + \psi_B$ shows a minimum at a nuclear separation of about 2 Bohr radii (approximately 1 A). This proves that the ion H_2^+ must be stable. It also shows how the type of potential curve for a molecule which has been found experimentally (cf. § 1.4) can be calculated theoretically. It is true that H_2^+ is not a chemical species, but it has been found in the discharge tube and the mass spectrometer. Any criticism that we have been using approximate wave functions and therefore getting only approximate energies is met by the observation (§ 3.6) that better wave functions would in fact give us a lower energy and therefore greater stability.

In the second place the final energy curve for $\psi_A - \psi_B$ shows no minimum, so that the molecule would be unstable in such a level, breaking up spontaneously into $H + H^+$ with emission of energy. Potential energy curves of these two kinds are called attractive and repulsive respectively: the corresponding orbitals are called bonding and anti-bonding.

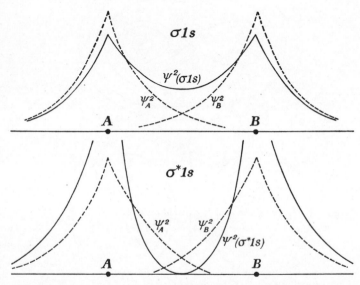

FIG. 4.5. The density ψ^2 at points along the nuclear axis for the attractive $\sigma 1s$ and the repulsive $\sigma^* 1s$ states of H_2^+. [No screening constant introduced here.]

The distinction between attractive and repulsive molecular orbitals is so fundamental that it is worth further discussion. Fig. 4 shows contours of constant ψ^2, i.e. charge-cloud density, or probability. The plane of the paper is any plane through the nuclei A and B. Even though more accurate wave functions would change the shapes of these contours slightly, these diagrams are substantially correct. Fig. 5 shows the value of ψ^2 at points along the nuclear axis, and also the values of ψ_A^2 and ψ_B^2 for comparison, though these latter are drawn to half scale. This is to enable us to compare the 'true' density ψ^2 with the sum of the atomic densities $\frac{1}{2}(\psi_A^2 + \psi_B^2)$. These curves show that

(i) in a bonding orbital the charge is concentrated rather more between the nuclei than would be expected by superposition of the component a.o. densities;

(ii) in a bonding orbital the lateral spread is not very great so that the effective thickness of the charge-cloud is less than the internuclear distance. The outer contours of constant density resemble in general appearance a set of confocal ellipses with the nuclei as foci;

(iii) in an anti-bonding orbital the charge is pushed away from between the nuclei so that there is actually a node along the mid-plane of AB. In view of this it is not surprising that this orbital is less binding than the other one, for our study of a.o.'s in Chapter II suggested that increasing the number of nodes increased the energy;

(iv) the m.o. $\psi_A + \psi_B$ is symmetrical with respect to the centre of the molecule, but $\psi_A - \psi_B$ is antisymmetrical. They are sometimes referred to in these terms, and sometimes by g and u (short for *gerade* and *ungerade*, German for even and odd respectively). The full description of this is: even or odd with respect to inversion in the centre of symmetry.

As a result of all this we can give the following qualitative explanation of the bonding that occurs when an electron occupies the m.o. $\psi_A + \psi_B$. The total energy with which we are concerned is the sum of the potential and kinetic energies of the electron and the nuclear repulsion e^2/R_{AB}. Concerning the potential energy we may say that the electron is being simultaneously attracted to both nuclei, and is correspondingly concentrated in the region between them. This means that its potential energy is much larger numerically—though of course, negative in sign—than it would be around one single nucleus. But the kinetic energy, which is necessarily positive, is not so much increased. As a result there is a gain in energy sufficient to offset the nuclear repulsion. The dominant effect, from the energy point of view, is the increase in magnitude of the electronic potential energy. With the m.o. $\psi_A - \psi_B$ the concentration of charge between the nuclei does not occur, so that there is not sufficient gain in potential energy to overcome the nuclear repulsion, and an anti-bonding state results.

It is sometimes said that one reason for molecule formation is that when the available space for an electron is increased, by bringing two nuclei towards each other, the kinetic energy is lowered. It is certainly true that if we calculate the kinetic energy of a particle in a box of given size, we find that this energy diminishes when the size of the box is increased. But this argument is a little too simplified to be applied to molecules. For as a result of the two nuclear attractions, the electron in H_2^+ is concentrated into an effective volume which is actually less than that of an isolated atom. This implies that its de Broglie wavelength λ is decreased, and, since $\lambda = h/p$, its momentum p and its kinetic energy are increased. This increase is only about 20 per cent., which is less than one-third of the percentage change in electronic potential energy. Evidently it is this latter change which is dominant. In the case of the completely accurate wave function, we can prove from the Virial theorem that at the equilibrium distance the change in potential energy when a molecule is formed is twice as large as the change in kinetic energy.

It is worth while carrying the calculations represented by (12) for the ground state of H_2^+ a little further. The resonance integral β is defined in terms of the Hamiltonian, which (see 3.16, omitting the nuclear Coulomb term e^2/R_{AB}) is

$$H = -\frac{h^2}{8\pi^2 m}\nabla^2 - \frac{e^2}{r_a} - \frac{e^2}{r_b}. \tag{14}$$

ψ_A is an a.o. for the hydrogen atom and satisfies

$$\left(-\frac{h^2}{8\pi^2 m}\nabla^2 - \frac{e^2}{r_a}\right)\psi_A = E_0\psi_A, \tag{15}$$

where E_0 is the energy of the ground state of hydrogen

$$E_0 = -\frac{e^2}{2a_0}$$

(as in 3.25). The quantity E_A in (12) is

$$E_A = \int \psi_A H\psi_A \, d\tau$$

$$= \int \psi_A\left(E_0 - \frac{e^2}{r_b}\right)\psi_A \, d\tau, \quad \text{from (14) and (15)},$$

$$= E_0 - \int \frac{e^2}{r_b}\psi_A^2 \, d\tau. \tag{16}$$

Similarly the resonance integral β is

$$\beta = \int \psi_A H \psi_B \, d\tau = \int \psi_B H \psi_A \, d\tau$$

$$= \int \psi_B \left(E_0 - \frac{e^2}{r_b} \right) \psi_A \, d\tau$$

$$= E_0 \, S - \int \frac{e^2}{r_b} \, \psi_A \, \psi_B \, d\tau. \qquad (17)$$

The electronic energy (12) may therefore be written

$$E_+ = E_0 - \frac{\int e^2/r_b) \psi_A^2 \, d\tau + \int (e^2/r_b) \psi_A \psi_B \, d\tau}{1 + \int \psi_A \psi_B \, d\tau}. \qquad (18)$$

The other energy E_- has just the same form as (18) except that the two $+$ signs are replaced by $-$ signs. Since from (3.23),

$$\psi_A = \left(\frac{1}{\pi a_0^3} \right)^{\frac{1}{2}} e^{-r_a/a_0}, \qquad \psi_B = \left(\frac{1}{\pi a_0^3} \right)^{\frac{1}{2}} e^{-r_b/a_0}, \qquad (19)$$

the calculation of $E_\pm$ is reduced to the evaluation of three integrals.[†] Since all these integrals are obviously positive, it follows at once that $E_+ < E_-$. It was from (18) that the curves in Fig. 3 were calculated.

The wave function which we have been using may be improved in two ways. First we may realize from Fig. 4 that the electron-cloud is contracted in the molecule as compared with the atom. This suggests that for ψ_A and ψ_B we should use a.o.'s similar to (19), but with an effective nuclear charge ce. In the language of the variation method, we take a trial wave function[‡]

$$\psi = \psi_A \pm \psi_B,$$

where

$$\psi_A = \left(\frac{c^3}{\pi a_0^3} \right)^{\frac{1}{2}} e^{-cr_a/a_0}, \quad \text{etc.} \qquad (20)$$

According to the argument of § 3.6 we must now calculate the energy function $\mathscr{E}(c)$ and choose that value of c which makes $\mathscr{E}$ stationary. This value will vary with the internuclear distance, and will in fact be different for the two cases $\psi_A \pm \psi_B$. The way in which c varies with R is shown in Fig. 6. At the observed equilibrium distance $R = 2 \cdot 0 a_0$, and the effective nuclear charge for the bonding orbital is $ce = 1 \cdot 24e$.

† Expressions for these and other integrals have been collected by C. A. Coulson, *Proc. Camb. Phil. Soc.*, 1942, **38**, 210. See also R. S. Mulliken, C. A. Rieke, D. Orloff, and H. Orloff, *J. Chem. Phys.*, 1949, **17**, 1248.

‡ C. A. Coulson, *Trans. Faraday Soc.*, 1937, **33**, 1479.

The second improvement is to say that when the electron is in the vicinity of A it is not adequately described even by a wave function (20), because this is spherically symmetrical, and we may expect a polarization, or distortion, of the orbit depriving it of its spherical symmetry. We may

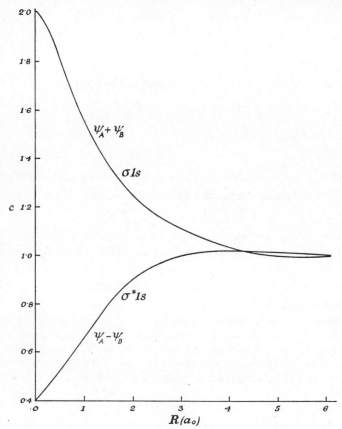

Fig. 4.6. Variation of effective nuclear charge for the molecular orbitals of H_2^+.

say that ψ_A should contain some term representing this local polarity. Omitting the normalization factor we might write[†]

$$\psi_A = e^{-cr_a/a_0} + \lambda x e^{-cr_a/a_0}, \qquad (21)$$

in which the x-axis lies along AB and λ is an additional variation parameter. For given R we have to minimize the energy function with respect to both λ and c. Fig. 7 shows how the energy is improved by these processes. Other improvements can be made and, as a check, a completely

[†] B. N. Dickinson, *J. Chem. Phys.*, 1933, **1**, 317.

accurate calculation can be made† in terms of the coordinates $r_a \pm r_b$ and an azimuthal angle about AB. This curve differs inappreciably from the curve (iii) associated with (21).

Before concluding this account of H_2^+ there are two further comments to make. The first is concerned with our choice of wave functions. The wave functions we have used are all of the LCAO type. This is because we shall shortly want to generalize our results to other molecules. But such a choice is by no means

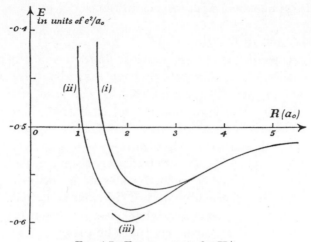

FIG. 4.7. Energy curves for H_2^+.

    (i) Simple form $\psi_A + \psi_B$ using hydrogenic ψ_A, ψ_B.
    (ii) Introduction of screening constant c into ψ_A and ψ_B.
    (iii) Introduction of polarization terms in ψ_A and ψ_B.
       The true energy differs inappreciably from (iii).

necessary. For example, James‡ has shown that extremely good wave functions and energies for H_2^+ may be obtained from a function

$$\psi = e^{-c_1(r_a + r_b)}\{1 + c_2(r_a - r_b)^2\}, \qquad (22)$$

where c_1 and c_2 are chosen to minimize the energy function, as in § 3.6. With a wave function of this kind there is no trace of resonance, and no resonance integral appears corresponding to our previous β.

† E. A. Hylleraas, *Z. Phys.*, 1931, **71**, 739; S. K. Chakravarty, *Phil. Mag.*, 1939, **28**, 423; D. R. Bates, K. Ledsham, and A. L. Stewart, *Phil. Trans.* A, 1953, **246**, 215.

‡ H. M. James, *J. Chem. Phys.*, 1935, **3**, 9.

Our final comment is that just as we obtained the lowest two
m.o.'s by using the LCAO forms $\psi_A \pm \psi_B$ and taking ψ_A and ψ_B
to be $1s$ a.o.'s of atoms A and B, so we could get other molecular
orbitals by taking ψ_A and ψ_B to be $2s$, $2p_x$,... orbitals. These are
excited levels, some of which are stable, and others unstable,
dissociating into a proton and an excited hydrogen atom in state
$2s$, $2p_x$,... rather than an unexcited one in state $1s$. Each choice
of ψ_A leads to two m.o.'s one of which is symmetrical and the
other antisymmetrical with respect to the centre of the molecule.

4.6. Hydrogen molecule

We must now consider homonuclear diatomics in general. We
shall find that much of what we have said about H_2^+ may be
carried over to these heavier molecules. The case of H_2 is particularly simple. It differs from H_2^+ solely in that there are two
valence electrons instead of one. Presumably these will both
occupy a m.o. similar to the H_2^+ orbital $\psi_A + \psi_B$, and in the ground
state of H_2 this m.o. will therefore be doubly occupied, the electrons
having opposed spins. The chief differences between the two
molecules are that there are now two electrons contributing binding energy, but that this is somewhat offset by the energy of their
mutual repulsion.[†] It turns out that the energy curve of H_2 is
similar in general appearance to that of H_2^+ but shifted so that
the minimum lies at an internuclear separation $1 \cdot 40 a_0 = 0 \cdot 74$ A.
This is less than the value $2 \cdot 00 a_0$ for H_2^+, but, by accident, the
binding energy of H_2 ($4 \cdot 75$ eV) is about twice that for H_2^+
($2 \cdot 79$ eV).[‡] We have said that this is 'by accident', because when
comparing H_2^+ and H_2 we must remember that there is a large
mutual electron repulsion in H_2 not found in H_2^+, and there is also
a considerable change in the nuclear Coulomb repulsion, $13 \cdot 6$ eV
in H_2^+ and $19 \cdot 3$ eV in H_2. There is no reason why a similar 'accident' should occur with other molecules, and indeed it seldom

---

† This electronic repulsion has the effect of expanding the orbitals somewhat,
as compared with H_2^+, so that the exponent c in (20) is reduced from $1 \cdot 24$ for H_2^+
to $1 \cdot 20$ for H_2. If we compared the appropriate values of c when the internuclear
distance in both cases was the same as in the equilibrium state of H_2, the drop
would be from $1 \cdot 40$ to $1 \cdot 20$. We could say that each electron partially screens
the nuclei from the other electron, and consequently reduces their effective charge.

‡ D. R. Bates, K. Ledsham, and A. L. Stewart, *Phil. Trans.* A, 1953, **246**, 215.

does. It would not even be the case for H_2^+ and H_2 if we calculated the energies of both at the same internuclear distance, and not at their respective equilibrium values. These facts become clear when we consider Table 4† which shows the calculated values of the separate energy terms for H_2. The calculated dissociation energy is about 1·1 eV too small; which is about the best that can be done by the Hartree self-consistent-field approximation for molecules. This error is a little larger than, though of the same order of magnitude as, for the corresponding atomic problem, the ground state of helium.

TABLE 4. *Calculated energy values for* H_2 *at equilibrium distance*

Energy of each separate molecular orbital . . .	16·2 eV
Electronic repulsion between orbitals	17·8 eV
Nuclear Coulomb repulsion	19·3 eV
Energy of two H atoms	27·2 eV
Calculated dissociation energy D_e	
$(2 \times 16·2 + 17·8 - 19·3 - 27·2)$	3·6 eV

In the last line of Table 4 the electronic repulsion 17·8 eV has to be added and not subtracted because, as stated on p. 34, this repulsion has already been counted twice, in the energy of each separate m.o. This table emphasizes once again how much smaller the dissociation energy is than most of the other energy terms.‡

4.7. Homonuclear diatomics

Calculations as detailed as these have not yet been made for other homonuclear molecules, but nevertheless a satisfactory qualitative discussion can be given, chiefly due to Lennard-Jones.§ Thus, when we bring two similar atoms together, each a.o. ψ_A (or ψ_B) splits into two whose LCAO forms are $\psi_A \pm \psi_B$; one of these will usually be bonding, the other anti-bonding, the difference in energy between the two being determined by the appropriate resonance integral β. At large distances the energies of both

† Taken from the 'best possible' m.o. calculations of C. A. Coulson, *Proc. Camb. Phil. Soc.*, 1938, **34**, 204.

‡ It has laughingly been said that calculating the dissociation energy of a heavy molecule is like weighing the captain of a ship by determining the difference in displacement of his ship when he is, or is not, on board!

§ J. E. Lennard-Jones, *Trans. Faraday Soc.*, 1929, **25**, 668.

m.o.'s tend to the energy of the a.o. ψ_A. Thus an atomic $2s$ orbital splits into two molecular levels which could be written

$$\psi_A(2s) \pm \psi_B(2s).$$

A similar situation applies to two atomic p_x orbitals, where the x-axis lies along AB. In each case we find m.o.'s which have symmetry around the axis of the molecule. For the s-type orbitals the boundary contours are shown approximately in Fig. 8 (a).

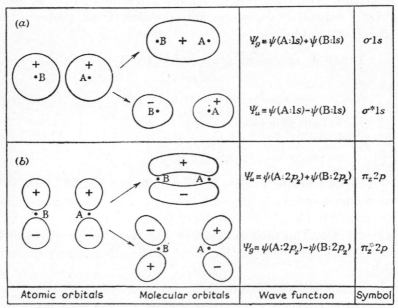

Atomic orbitals	Molecular orbitals	Wave function	Symbol
		$\Psi_g \equiv \psi(A{:}1s) + \psi(B{:}1s)$	$\sigma 1s$
		$\Psi_u \equiv \psi(A{:}1s) - \psi(B{:}1s)$	$\sigma^* 1s$
		$\Psi_u \equiv \psi(A{:}2p_z) + \psi(B{:}2p_z)$	$\pi_z 2p$
		$\Psi_g \equiv \psi(A{:}2p_z) - \psi(B{:}2p_z)$	$\pi_z^* 2p$

Fig. 4.8. Attractive and repulsive σ, σ^* and π, π^* molecular orbitals and their formation from atomic orbitals.

But a new feature comes in if we combine a pair of p_y or p_z a.o.'s. The general shape of a p_z orbital—the dumb-bells of Figs. 2.3 and 2.4—makes it easy to see that the corresponding m.o.'s shown in Fig. 8 (b) are of a quite different appearance. Of the two m.o.'s the top one is $\psi_A + \psi_B$ and is bonding: it consists of two ribbon- or streamer-type regions, in which ψ has different signs, and the original nodal plane remains a nodal plane for the m.o. It is important to realize that the two parts of this 'double streamer' go together; they are one pattern and quite inseparable; together they represent the m.o. But there is no longer symmetry around the bond direction. The visualizing of these streamer orbitals is very important, because m.o.'s similar to them play a dominant role in benzene and other aromatic systems. For that reason we have shown the whole effect in perspective in Fig. 9 for the case of the bonding m.o. If we combine together two p_y a.o.'s instead of p_z, we get precisely the same m.o.'s as before except that they are turned through 90° around the axis. The superposition of

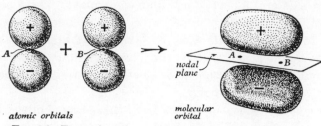

FIG. 4.9. Formation of a π-type bonding molecular orbital.

charge densities corresponding to these two m.o.'s is symmetrical around the bond axis.

This axial symmetry follows from the fact that since a p_y a.o. has the analytical form (2.10)

$$\psi(p_y) = yf(r),$$

where $f(r)$ is some function of the radial distance, therefore the m.o. $\psi_A(p_y) + \psi_B(p_y)$ has the form

$$y_a f(r_a) + y_b f(r_b) = y\{f(r_a) + f(r_b)\}.$$

The density function is therefore

$$y^2\{f(r_a) + f(r_b)\}^2.$$

For the p_z m.o. the density is

$$z^2\{f(r_a) + f(r_b)\}^2.$$

The sum of the two densities is

$$(y^2 + z^2)\{f(r_a) + f(r_b)\}^2,$$

which is obviously symmetrical around the x-axis.

At this stage we must introduce a proper notation for these m.o.'s. They may be classified according to

(1) their symmetry around the molecular axis,

(2) their bonding or anti-bonding character,

(3) The atomic orbitals into which they separate at large distances.

Orbitals which are symmetrical about the axis are called σ orbitals.[†] Those which are formed from p_y or p_z a.o.'s are called π orbitals, and are written π_y or π_z. The mathematical distinction between σ and π (cf. paragraph in small type in § 2.9) is that a σ-type m.o. has zero component of angular momentum around the bond axis and a π-type has unit component. There are also δ-type orbitals with two units. σ, π, δ,... therefore correspond exactly to the subscripts 0, ± 1, ± 2,... used in a.o.'s. σ-type m.o.'s are non-degenerate, the others are each doubly-degenerate, corresponding to a component of electronic current in a positive or negative sense around AB.

The second classification arises from the $\pm$ signs in the LCAO form $\psi_A \pm \psi_B$. One of these is anti-bonding and is designated by an asterisk, e.g. σ^*, π^*: the other has no asterisk. This classification is closely related to the symmetrical and antisymmetrical character of the m.o.'s referred to on p. 85. The suffix g is used in the wave function of an orbital which is symmetrical with respect to its centre: the suffix u for one which is antisymmetrical. Thus, as Fig. 8[‡] shows,

$$\psi_A(1s) + \psi_B(1s) \quad \text{is } g,$$

but $$\psi_A(2p_z) + \psi_B(2p_z) \quad \text{is } u.$$

The opposite holds for the two m.o.'s with minus signs. An important property of the quantum characters σ, π,..., g, u,... is not only that they are valid for individual electrons: they also describe (see later) the totality of electrons in a molecule, and form a basis with which to discuss the selection rules for the allowed transitions. Thus a g state must go to a u state and u to g. Transitions $u \to u$ or $g \to g$ are forbidden.

The third classification of m.o.'s is in terms of the a.o.'s ψ_A, ψ_B out of which the LCAO form is composed, and into which the m.o.

[†] Colloquially, on account of the shape of the boundary surface at the top of Fig. 8 (a) bonding σ-type orbitals are sometimes called 'sausage' m.o.'s.

[‡] Some other schematic diagrams are given by G. Herzberg, *Molecular Spectra and Molecular Structure*, Prentice-Hall, 1939, p. 348, from drawings due to Weizel. But care is needed in using these because the naming of the states is somewhat different from the more modern system described in this chapter.

degenerates when the internuclear distance is increased. Thus the top orbital in Fig. 8 would be written $\sigma 1s$ (or sometimes $1s\sigma$), and the corresponding anti-bonding orbital is σ^*1s. The lower orbitals are $\pi_z 2p$ (or $2p\pi_z$, or sometimes just $p\pi$), and $\pi_z^* 2p$.

The *aufbau* principle may now be used for homonuclear diatomics just as in § 2.8 for atoms: all that we require is to know the relative order of the various m.o. energies. Unfortunately these cannot be calculated *ab initio* with sufficient accuracy, though in fact such calculations as can be made do agree with the observed sequence. But the order can be determined from a study of molecular spectra.† For atoms in the first row of the Periodic Table, this sequence of energies is found to be:

Full notation:
$$\sigma 1s < \sigma^* 1s < \sigma 2s < \sigma^* 2s < \sigma 2p < \pi_y 2p = \pi_z 2p < \pi_y^* 2p = \pi_z^* 2p < \sigma^* 2p$$

abbreviated
notation: $z\sigma$ $y\sigma$ $x\sigma$ $w\pi$ $v\pi$ $u\sigma$

alternative
scheme:
1σ 2σ 3σ 4σ 5σ $1\pi_y$ $1\pi_z$ $2\pi_y$ $2\pi_z$ 6σ

(23)

The $\sigma 2p$ and $\pi 2p$ orbitals have rather similar energies, and occasionally change places in the table. In this list the degeneracy in the π orbitals will be noticed. These are all the m.o.'s that arise from atomic 2-quantum orbitals. There is, of course, a similar scheme for the m.o. from 3-quantum orbitals. However, the ordering of the energies is now rather obscure because, as will be seen in Chapter VIII, the binding is seldom between pure $s, p, d,...$ type a.o.'s, but usually between various combinations of them. In (23) above, we have shown two other notations. The first, due to Mulliken,‡ has the advantage of being applicable to heteronuclear molecules where any particular m.o. may be compounded from a.o.'s of different electronic shells (e.g. $H(1s)$ and $Cl(3p_x)$ of HCl), and for which the former notation is not adequate. It also enables us to discard the assumption that, for example, the $\sigma 2s$ m.o. is entirely composed of atomic $2s$ orbitals. Thus the notation $z\sigma$ means the lowest m.o. of σ-type, which will, in fact, normally be compounded almost entirely, but not completely, of

---

† See, e.g., R. S. Mulliken, *Rev. Mod. Phys.*, 1932, **4**, 1.   ‡ Loc. cit.

$2s$ a.o.'s. The most serious disadvantages of this abbreviated notation are that the x, y, z,... introduced in it have no relation whatever to the Cartesian xyz coordinates used in the top row of the table, and the new notation disguises the simple pictorial relationship between the m.o. and the two a.o.'s into which, as a rule, it reverts on separating the atoms to infinite distance. For that reason we shall more frequently use the older notation; but both should be learnt The abbreviated notation is extended to 3-quantum, or M-shell, orbits by inserting (m) in brackets before the corresponding molecular symbol: e.g. $(m)z\sigma$ would be the abbreviated form of $3s\sigma$. Either notation, of course, brings out the fact that there are molecular shells, whose essential character is very similar to that of the well-known atomic shells. Both notations define molecular configurations, entirely analogous to the atomic configurations described in § 2.8.

The second alternative notation in (23) is exceedingly simple in concept. Thus it recognizes that m.o.'s may be classified into σ, π,... types, and it simply enumerates these in order. Thus the lowest σ orbital is 1σ, the next one is 2σ, and so on. The greatest advantage of this scheme is that it is simple, and covers both homonuclear and heteronuclear diatomics without the need to specify just which a.o.'s are being used. It can also be extended to polyatomic molecules where the σ, π,... classification is replaced by a new classification (e.g. a, b, c...) appropriate to the symmetry of the molecule, and where this notation is now universally used. Its disadvantage is that it says very little about the composition of the molecular orbital, and gives very little clue to the energy. Thus the fact that $1\pi_y$ has a higher energy than 5σ suggests that we have moved a long way from the usual atomic classification, where the principal quantum number n (e.g. in ns or np) does largely determine the energy and the electronic shell. Sometimes, to avoid this difficulty, the inner shells are omitted from the scheme, and then 1σ and 1π, etc., are the lowest σ and π m.o.'s in the valence shell. In this book we shall make most use of the original full notation, but the reader should try to become familiar with the others.

A complete understanding of the mutual relationship of the

m.o.'s in (23) requires us to recognize not only the a.o.'s into which they revert at large internuclear distances, but also those into which they turn when the internuclear distance is reduced to zero, and the two nuclei coalesce. This is called the united-atom viewpoint,† which, together with the separated-atom view-

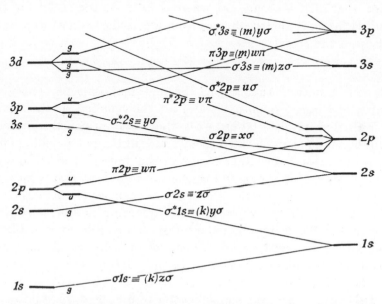

FIG. 4.10. Correlation diagram in homonuclear diatomic molecules. On the left there are the states of the united atom, and on the right those of the separated atoms. The clue to the construction of this diagram is the Pauli Exclusion Principle and the non-intersection of levels which have the same symmetry (e.g. σ or π; and oddness or evenness in the centre of the molecule). The energy scale is purely diagrammatic.

point, enables us to draw a correlation diagram showing the complete behaviour of these m.o.'s at all distances. A copy of this correlation diagram‡ is shown in Fig. 10. This diagram is most important. It has been said of it§ that 'it might well be on the walls of chemistry buildings, being almost worthy to occupy a position beside the Mendeléeff periodic table so frequently found

† The united-atom viewpoint was used as the basis of most of the early nomenclatures for molecules. It is suitable for small molecules, but not for large ones.
‡ Adapted from R. S. Mulliken, *Rev. Mod. Phys.*, 1932, **4**, 1.
§ J. H. Van Vleck and A. Sherman, ibid., 1935, **7**, 167.

thereon. Just as the latter affords an understanding of the structure of atoms so does the former afford an understanding of the
structure of molecules.' In building up this diagram use is made
of the non-crossing rule of § 3.10 which states that levels of the
same symmetry type, e.g. σ, π,..., g, u,... can never cross.† The
fact that $\sigma 1s \to$ atomic $1s$, whereas $\sigma^* 1s \to$ atomic $2p$ for the
united atom, is almost obvious from a consideration of Fig. 8: so
also are the correlations

$$\pi_z 2p \to 2p_z, \quad \pi_z^* 2p \to 3d_{xz}.$$

It will be noticed that among the m.o.'s whose separated-atom
parentage is a 2-quantum state, all the bonding orbitals have
a united-atom correlation with the same principal quantum
number as in the separated atoms, and all the anti-bonding ones
show an increase of either 1 or 2 in the united atom. The only
exception to this is $\sigma 2p$ and this is precisely that m.o. which, as
we said on p. 95, sometimes breaks the sequence of energies there
drawn up. Orbitals whose principal quantum numbers are thus
increased are called promoted orbitals; as would be expected from
our knowledge of the relative energies of the various a.o.'s, the
presence of promoted orbitals in a molecule is usually a hindrance
to their binding.

It is now a relatively simple matter to use the *aufbau* principle
to describe simple homonuclear diatomics. We have seen that H_2
is $(\sigma 1s)^2$. He_2^+ would have a ground state $(\sigma 1s)^2(\sigma^* 1s)$, and He_2
would be $(\sigma 1s)^2(\sigma^* 1s)^2$. Now we have seen (Fig. 3) that $\sigma^* 1s$ is
anti-bonding, so that there are two bonding and two anti-bonding
orbitals. Also, as we saw in the paragraph following (12), the
anti-bonding orbital is more relaxing than the bonding one is
binding. The net result is an unstable molecule, as is well known.
It is only when one of the electrons is excited to an upper level
that a stable system can exist. Such stable excited He_2 molecules
do exist, and have been studied spectroscopically. It is a fairly
general result that the superposition of a starred and corresponding unstarred m.o. leads either to no bonding or to a small degree
of anti-bonding.

† The one-electron molecule H_2^+ is an exception to this rule.

The combination $(\sigma 1s)^2(\sigma^*1s)^2$ will occur in all heavier molecules of this kind. It is interesting to discuss the associated charge distribution. According to (1) and (2) this is

$$2 \times \frac{(\psi_A+\psi_B)^2}{2(1+S)} + 2 \times \frac{(\psi_A-\psi_B)^2}{2(1-S)},$$

which may be written

$$\frac{2}{1-S^2}\{\psi_A^2+\psi_B^2-2S\psi_A\psi_B\}. \tag{24}$$

Now $S = \int \psi_A\psi_B \, d\tau$ and measures the overlap of ψ_A and ψ_B. For H_2 it has the value 0·68, but for heavier molecules it rapidly becomes very small. Thus for Li_2, $S = 0·01$, and for two carbon atoms at the distance appropriate to diamond, S is of the order of 10^{-5}. With these small values (24) reduces to $2(\psi_A^2+\psi_B^2)$, which is just the same as if the two K-shells had remained as they were in the isolated atoms, entirely unaffected by chemical combination. This is the wave-mechanical justification for saying that the inner shells of atoms play no effective part in molecular binding. We have given the argument for the special case of the K-shell, but it applies to every inner shell; and indeed it shows that the superposition of any unstarred m.o. and its associated starred m.o. is practically the same as a simple superposition of the atomic densities. This might have been expected on energy grounds. It means that when giving the electron configuration for a heavier molecule than H_2, we can replace the $(\sigma 1s)^2(\sigma^*1s)^2$ by KK, meaning that both K-shells are fully occupied: and similarly for the L-shells, so that Na_2 would be described as

$$Na_2, \quad KKLL(\sigma 3s)^2. \tag{25}$$

Alternatively, this could be written Na_2, $KKLL(1\sigma)^2$.

Other molecular configurations can be written down at once. Thus Li_2 has two valence electrons outside the inner shells and they occupy the $\sigma 2s$ (or $z\sigma$) m.o., allowing us to write

$$Li[1s^22s]+Li[1s^22s] \rightarrow Li_2[KK(\sigma 2s)^2]. \tag{26}$$

Similarly F_2 is, in the abbreviated notation:

$$F[1s^22s^22p^5]+F[1s^22s^22p^5] \rightarrow F_2[KK(z\sigma)^2(y\sigma)^2(x\sigma)^2(w\pi)^4(v\pi)^4]. \tag{27}$$

The right-hand side of this could equally be written

$$F_2[KK(1\sigma)^2(2\sigma)^2(3\sigma)^2(1\pi)^4(2\pi)^4].$$

Here the $(z\sigma)^2$ and $(y\sigma)^2$ practically cancel one another's bonding, being almost entirely $\sigma 2s$ and σ^*2s: and so do the $(w\pi)^4$ and $(v\pi)^4$. This implies that although all fourteen valence electrons take part, the bond is effectively due to the $(x\sigma)^2$, or $(\sigma 2p)^2$, pair. As two electrons are primarily responsible, it may reasonably be called a single bond; and as these electrons are p_x electrons it is referred to as p-binding. On account of its symmetry it is a σ-type bond.

Molecular nitrogen N_2 is interesting because of the question about how many electrons take part in the bonding, and what kind of a bond it really is. Our present description is

$$N[1s^2 2s^2 2p^3]+N[1s^2 2s^2 2p^3] \rightarrow N_2[KK(z\sigma)^2(y\sigma)^2(w\pi)^4(x\sigma)^2]. \quad (28)$$

The binding is effectively due to $(w\pi)^4(x\sigma)^2$, all six of which electrons are of the bonding type. We may reasonably call it a triple bond. But such a bond is very different from a superposition of three normal single bonds. It is obviously formed by one pair of electrons in σ-type (or sausage) orbitals and two pairs in π-type (or double-streamer) orbitals: and it is axially symmetrical about the bond direction.

In this way we can draw up a table of electron configurations for the simpler molecules entirely analogous to that which is so useful for atoms (see Table 5). This table gives the number of bonding and anti-bonding orbitals in the valence shells of the two atoms. One half of the excess of bonding orbitals could be regarded as a measure of bond multiplicity, which is also shown. This table explains at once why bond orders in excess of 3 do not occur: there are not sufficient bonding orbitals. It also shows a rough proportionality between the bond order and the dissociation energy.

The last column of Table 5 shows the spectroscopic notation for the various states. These involve (a) a raised prefix numeral 1, 2, 3,... in small type, (b) a capital Greek† symbol Σ, Π, Δ,..., and (c) a final subscript u or g in small type. The first of these

† Σ, Π, Δ,... are the Greek capitals corresponding to σ, π, δ,... .

tells us the spin multiplicity. Each pair of electrons which completely fills a m.o. contributes nothing because, by the Pauli Principle, their spins must necessarily be opposed. If there is no resultant spin, the multiplicity is one. However, if there is one unpaired electron, its spin may be α or β (§ 2.5) and the state is a doublet. If there are two unpaired electrons, their spins may be parallel, giving a triplet (e.g. O_2), or they may be anti-parallel, giving a singlet.† The question whether the singlet or triplet is lower, is usually settled by an appeal (p. 35) to Hund's rules. In general the multiplicity is $2S+1$ where S is the resultant spin (counting $\pm\frac{1}{2}$ for each unpaired electron).

The main symbol in the spectroscopic notation denotes the resultant symmetry character, and is again the sum of contributions from each electron. It measures the component of angular momentum around the nuclear axis, as in p. 94. If the total value is 0, the state is a Σ state: if it is 1, the state is Π, etc.

Finally the subscript u or g describes the behaviour of the totality of electrons with references to reflection (inversion) in the mid-point of the nuclei. Since a u-type orbital is multiplied by -1 on reflection, while a g-type orbital is unchanged, the totality of electrons will necessarily be g unless there is an odd number of u orbitals occupied, in which case it must be u. Reference to the last column of Table 5 will show all these rules in operation.

It may be stated that precisely similar descriptions apply to heteronuclear diatomics, with the single exception of the u and g character. On account of the lack of any centre of symmetry in such a molecule, the u and g classification disappears.

At this stage we can see a little more clearly what is meant by a single, double, or triple bond. In the first place it refers to the number of electrons which effectively contribute to the bond, two for a single bond, four for a double bond, and six for a triple bond. This does not mean that the other electrons play no part at all, but merely that they are less significant for bonding. Now two electrons in a σ-type m.o. are called a σ-bond: two in a π-type

† Singlets and triplets are more fully discussed in § 5.9.

TABLE 5. *Electron configurations in ground states of homonuclear diatomic molecules*

There is some uncertainty in the cases of B_2, C_2, N_2^+ for which several assignments of levels have almost identical energies

	$\sigma 1s$	σ^*1s	$\sigma 2s$ $z\sigma_g$	σ^*2s $y\sigma_u$	$\sigma 2p$ $x\sigma_g$	$\pi 2p,\ \pi_u 2p$ $w\pi_u$	$w\pi_n$	$\pi^*2p,\ \pi_g^*2p$ $v\pi_u$	$v\pi_g$	σ^*2p $u\sigma_u$	Bonding	Anti-bonding	Bond order	D_0 (eV)†	Spectroscopic notation
H_2^+	1										1		$\tfrac{1}{2}$	2·65	$^2\Sigma_g$
H_2	2										2		1	4·48	$^1\Sigma_g$
He_2^+	2	1									2	1	$\tfrac{1}{2}$	2·6±0·5	$^2\Sigma_u$
He_2	2	2									2	2	0	0	$^1\Sigma_g$
$He+He = KK$															
Li_2	KK		2								2		1	1·14	$^1\Sigma_g$
Be_2	KK		2	2							2	2	0		$^1\Sigma_g$
B_2	KK		2	2		1	1				4	2	1		$^3\Sigma_g$
C_2	KK		2	2	1	2	1				6	2	2		$^3\Pi_u$
N_2^+	KK		2	2	1	2	2				7	2	$2\tfrac{1}{2}$	6·35	$^2\Sigma_g$
N_2	KK		2	2	2	2	2				8	2	3	7·38	$^1\Sigma_g$
O_2^+	KK		2	2	2	2	2	1			8	3	$2\tfrac{1}{2}$	6·48	$^2\Pi_g$
O_2	KK		2	2	2	2	2	1	1		8	4	2	5·08	$^3\Sigma_g$
F_2^+	KK		2	2	2	2	2	2	1		8	5	$1\tfrac{1}{2}$		$^2\Pi_g$
F_2	KK		2	2	2	2	2	2	2		8	6	1	1·66	$^1\Sigma_g$
Ne_2	KK		2	2	2	2	2	2	2	2	8	8	0	0	$^1\Sigma_g$
$Ne+Ne = KK$															

† From G. Herzberg, *Molecular Spectra and Molecular Structure I, Diatomic Molecules*, Prentice-Hall, 1939, p. 368.

m.o. are called a π-bond. It follows from this and the sequence (23) of m.o. energies that

$$\text{a single bond is of pattern} \quad \sigma^2,$$
$$\text{a double bond is of pattern} \quad \sigma^2\pi^2, \qquad (29)$$
$$\text{a triple bond is of pattern} \quad \sigma^2\pi^4.$$

Incidentally, as is a reasonable deduction from Fig. 8 (a) and (b), the overlap of the component a.o.'s in a π-type m.o. is less than in a σ-type m.o. In carbon, at the distance appropriate to ethane, the overlap integrals for $p\sigma$ and $p\pi$ are in the ratio of about 2 : 1. According to the criterion of maximum overlapping (condition (b) of p. 76) this suggests that a π-bond is weaker than a σ-bond,† and it gives us therefore a theoretical explanation of the high reactivity of a double bond. For it is easier to disengage the π electrons from each other and link them up with other approaching atoms. Some further comments on the double bond, particularly as it occurs in ethylene, are given in § 8.7.

The case of O_2 is interesting. In a formal way, we can-write

$$O[1s^2 2s^2 2p^4] + O[1s^2 2s^2 2p^4] \rightarrow O_2[KK(z\sigma)^2(y\sigma)^2(x\sigma)^2(w\pi)^4(v\pi)^2]. \qquad (30)$$

There are four net bonding electrons, $(x\sigma)^2(v\pi)^2$, giving a double bond O—O. Now the $v\pi$ level is degenerate, since it contains both $\pi_y^* 2p$ and $\pi_z^* 2p$. It will therefore accommodate four electrons. But in (30) it is assigned only two. So we appeal to Hund's rule (§ 2.8), indicating that these two electrons will go one each in $\pi_y^* 2p$ and $\pi_z^* 2p$, and will have parallel spins. In this way we see that the ground state of O_2 should be one with total spin one unit (a triplet whose spectroscopic symbol is $^3\Sigma_g$) and should show paramagnetism. It was one of the earliest triumphs of the m.o. theory‡ that it accounted for this somewhat unusual situation so very neatly. A similar situation occurs in S_2. It will help us to understand the 'feel' of m.o.'s if we illustrate the case of O_2 by introducing the same kind of cell notation as we used in Fig. 2.7 for atoms. On the left and right of Fig. 11 are shown the various

† But at shorter distances the π-bond becomes stronger. In N_2, for example, the π-bonds are stronger than the σ-bonds (Mulliken, *J. Phys. Chem.*, 1952, 56, 295). Hence the order in which the m.o.'s are listed in equation (28).

‡ J. E. Lennard-Jones, *Trans. Faraday Soc.*, 1929, 25, 668.

L-shell levels of the separate atoms, and in the centre are the allowed molecular levels. Lines are drawn connecting the m.o.'s to the a.o.'s from which they are compounded. This figure reveals at once how in the O_2 molecule all the levels up to $w\pi$ are com-

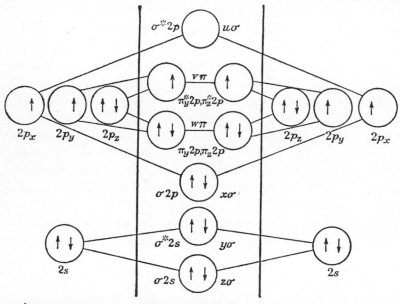

Atomic orbitals   Molecular orbitals   Atomic orbitals

FIG. 4.11. Moleeular orbitals for O_2, showing the triplet nature of the ground state.

pletely filled, and why the two parallel spins in the degenerate $v\pi$ level lead to a triplet ground state. Similar diagrams to this can, of course, be drawn for all molecules.

4.8. Heteronuclear diatomics

The case that we have just been considering, in which the atoms A and B are identical, represents homopolar binding. Such cases are less common than those of heteropolar binding, in which atoms A and B are different. However, the greater part of our previous discussion will still apply. Thus, in heteronuclear diatomics we can still apply the LCAO approximation (§ 4.3) writing for the m.o. an expression

$$\psi = \psi_A + \lambda\psi_B, \tag{31}$$

as in (3): but λ is no longer equal to ± 1. Nor is the energy given by the simple values (6) and (7), but we are obliged to solve the quadratic secular equations (4). The conditions (a)–(c) of § 3, viz. nearly equal energies, maximum overlapping, and the same symmetry around the bond axis, generally allow us to infer quite easily which a.o.'s ψ_A and ψ_B may be compounded together. It is still true that m.o.'s are of σ, π,... type, and the total number of

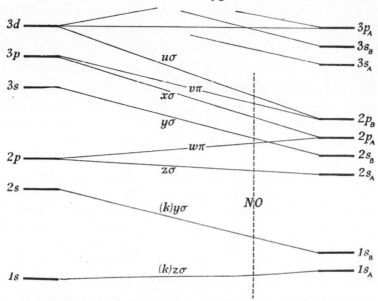

FIG. 4.12. Correlation diagram in heteronuclear diatomic molecules. On the left there are the states of the united atom and on the right those of the separated atoms. The energy scale is purely diagrammatic. The dotted line represents approximately what happens in NO, except that $w\pi$ probably lies above $y\sigma$ at about the same level as $x\sigma$.

such orbitals, i.e. their degeneracy, is the same as in the homonuclear case. The non-crossing rule of p. 69 is still operative to keep the energies of m.o.'s with the same symmetry apart, and to correlate the united-atom and separated-atom parentages of given molecular levels. The corresponding diagram, similar to that of Fig. 10 for homonuclear molecules, is shown in Fig. 12.† It is clear that the chief differences between the two diagrams are (a) the lack of the u-, g-property (p. 94) which follows from the absence

† Adapted from R. S. Mulliken, loc. cit.

of a centre of symmetry in all these molecules; and (b) the fact
that in the separated atoms the energies of similar orbitals are
different. For example, in NO, the $\sigma 2s$ m.o. correlates with the
oxygen $2s$, and the $\sigma^* 2s$ with the nitrogen $2s$: on account of its
greater nuclear charge the oxygen level is lower than the nitrogen
level. But in O_2 both $\sigma 2s$ and $\sigma^* 2s$ correlate with the same atomic
energy at infinite separation of the nuclei.

An example will show the use of this diagram. The process of
formation of NO from N and O would be described in the following
terms:

$$N[1s^2 2s^2 2p^3] + O[1s^2 2s^2 2p^4] \rightarrow NO[KK(z\sigma)^2(y\sigma)^2(x\sigma)^2(w\pi)^4(v\pi)].$$

On account of its single $v\pi$ electron this molecule possesses an
unpaired electron, whose spin will give rise to paramagnetism.
The dotted guide-line in Fig. 12 indicates the approximate position of this molecule on the diagram.

Although the correlation diagram is very useful, we must not
press it too far. It will generally give a correct account of the
change in an orbital as the atoms separate, provided that there
is only one electron in this orbital. But if there are two, their
mutual repulsion may lead to behaviour different from that predicted by a naïve use of the diagram. Consider, for example, the
four-electron molecule LiH. The m.o. description of the mole-
cule is $\{(k)z\sigma\}^2\{(k)y\sigma\}^2$, as suggested by Fig. 12. According to
this diagram, as we separate the nuclei, the lowest energy orbital
should go over into the $1s$ orbital of the lithium atom, and the
second orbital should go over into the $1s$ orbital of hydrogen.
This would correspond to LiH $\rightarrow$ Li$^+$+H$^-$, a situation only found
in solution, where solvation energies favour charged species rather
than neutral ones. The true situation with LiH is that the mutual
repulsion of the two electrons in the $y\sigma$ orbital is sufficiently great
to force them on to different nuclei, leading to

$$LiH \rightarrow Li(1s)^2(2s) + H(1s).$$

But we should have had no similar difficulty with the dissociation
of the three-electron system LiH$^+$. Similarly, in the two-electron
ion HeH$^+$ both electrons ($1s\sigma$) do go to the He atom on dissociation, since the total energy of He+H$^+$ is $-79{\cdot}01$ eV and of He$^+$+H

is $-68\cdot5$ eV. These examples emphasize the need for caution when using the correlation diagram at large internuclear distances.

4.9. Polarity of orbitals†

It should be clear from the foregoing that the chief novelty in heteropolar m.o.'s resides in the value of λ in $\psi_A + \lambda\psi_B$. If $|\lambda| > 1$, we can say that ψ_B plays a larger part in the final m.o. than does ψ_A. The electronic density is greater near B than near A. In more accurate terms,

FIG. 4.13.

the electron is more likely to be near B than near A. If we use the colloquial language referred to in the footnote to p. 94 we should say that a σ-type, or 'sausage' orbital of this kind, was 'fatter' at the end B than at A.

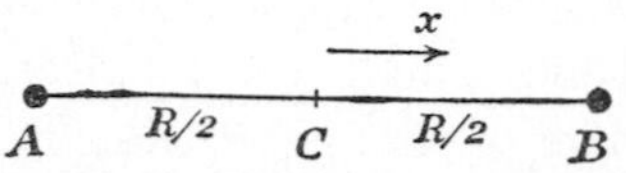

It is clear that λ describes the polarity of the orbital, and is consequently related to the dipole moment of the molecule. If we could calculate λ theoretically, we should have a theoretical calculation of this dipole moment. Unfortunately such calculations are unreliable, so that more frequently we proceed the other way round and use the observed moment to infer the value of λ. The relation between λ and the dipole moment is easily obtained if we think of an electron in an orbital (31) as being spread out in the form of a charge-cloud whose density ρ at any point is proportional to $(\psi_A + \lambda\psi_B)^2$, and, indeed, equal to

$$N^2(\psi_A + \lambda\psi_B)^2,$$

measured in electrons, where N is a normalizing constant such that (equation (2))

$$N^{-2} = 1 + \lambda^2 + 2\lambda S_{AB}.$$

Let us use the notation of Fig. 13 and calculate the coordinate $\bar{x}$ of the centroid of this charge-cloud. If x and $\bar{x}$ are measured from the mid-point C of the line AB, then the usual formula of moments tells us that

$$\bar{x} = \int x\rho\, d\tau$$
$$= N^2 \int x(\psi_A^2 + 2\lambda\psi_A\psi_B + \lambda^2\psi_B^2)\, d\tau$$
$$= N^2\{\bar{x}_A + 2\lambda\bar{x}_{AB} + \lambda^2\bar{x}_B\}, \quad \text{say.} \tag{32}$$

† See R. S. Mulliken, *J. Chem. Phys.*, 1935, **3**, 573.

Now $\bar{x}_A$ is the mean position of the charge-cloud for the a.o. ψ_A, and if ψ_A is any of the a.o.'s of Chapter II, e.g. s-, p-, d-type, all of which possess a centre of symmetry, this centroid is at A, so that $\bar{x}_A = -\tfrac{1}{2}R$. Consequently

$$\bar{x} = N^2\{\tfrac{1}{2}R(\lambda^2-1)+2\lambda\bar{x}_{AB}\}. \qquad (33)$$

The term $\bar{x}_{AB}$, which must be calculated mathematically,† is some-times small and is often neglected. Then the two electrons in a m.o. (31) have their centroid at a distance $N^2(\lambda^2-1)R/2$ from the mid-point of the nuclei. The centre of positive charge ($+e$ at each nucleus) lies at C, so that the combination of positive and negative charge provides a dipole moment

$$\mu \equiv 2e\bar{x} = (\lambda^2-1)N^2eR = (\lambda^2-1)eR/(1+\lambda^2+2\lambda S). \qquad (34)$$

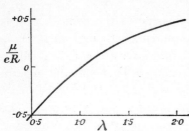

FIG. 4.14. Graph showing relation between μ/eR and λ as expressed in equation (34).

If these are the only two bonding electrons and the polarization of other non-bonding electrons may be neglected (or suitably allowed for), this equation may be used to relate μ and λ. Knowing one of them, we may infer the other.

Fig. 14 shows the relative varia-tions of μ and λ according to (34), giving S the rounded value of $\tfrac{1}{3}$.

Table 6 shows experimental data for a series of molecules‡ from which, by the use of Fig. 14, corresponding values of λ may be deduced. Small deviations of S from the assumed value would scarcely affect the last column in the table, or the appearance of the curve. The values of λ are such that in each case $\lambda > 1$ for the halogen atom orbital. It will be seen from this table that except for very polar molecules, such as HF or KCl, λ does not differ greatly from unity.

There is another simple, though less strictly accurate, interpre-tation of (31). It is to say that the a.o.'s ψ_A and ψ_B occur with

† Tables of integrals prepared by the writer are to be found in *Proc. Camb. Phil. Soc.*, 1942, **38**, 210. See also R. S. Mulliken, C. A. Rieke, D. Orloff, H. Orloff, *J. Chem. Phys.*, 1949, **17**, 1248.

‡ Taking the bonding orbital of the halogen atom to be a pure p orbital. But see Chapter VIII for comments.

TABLE 6. *Values of λ in the m.o. $\psi_A + \lambda\psi_B$, calculated from observed dipole moments using equation (34) with S given the rounded value of $\frac{1}{3}$.*

Molecule	μ/eR expt.	$R \times 10^8$ cm	$\mu \times 10^{18}$ e.s.u.†	λ calculated from (34)
HF	0·43	0·92	1·91	1·88
HCl	0·17	1·27	1·03	1·28
HBr	0·11	1·41	0·78	1·19
HI	0·05	1·61	0·38	1·06
KCl	0·47	2·79	6·3	2·0

† The unit 10^{-18} e.s.u. for dipole moments is called the Debye. Dipole moments lie in the range 0–10 D.

relative weights $1 : \lambda^2$, so that a fraction $1/(1+\lambda^2)$ of the electronic charge may be associated with nucleus A, and $\lambda^2/(1+\lambda^2)$ with B. This is sometimes called the formal charge distribution in the m.o. ψ. If the charges may be supposed to have their centres of mean position at A and B, the dipole moment due to two electrons with this charge distribution, and the positive nuclear charges, is

$$\mu = (\lambda^2-1)eR/(1+\lambda^2). \qquad (35)$$

The analogy with (34) is quite close.

There are two comments to be made on (34) and (35). In the first place the centres of mean position will only lie at A and B if the a.o.'s ψ_A and ψ_B are unpolarized orbitals. This would not be the case, for example, if we used (21) for ψ_A. One condition for this is that there is no hybridization, or mixing, of orbitals such as that discussed in § 8.10, where a refinement of this formula is given. Unfortunately it now seems probable that some measure of hybridization occurs almost always. Our second comment is that the charge distribution $1/(1+\lambda^2)$ and $\lambda^2/(1+\lambda^2)$ is only correct if the overlap integral S_{AB} is zero. A more correct distribution is

$$(1+\lambda S)/(1+\lambda^2+2\lambda S) \quad \text{and} \quad (\lambda S+\lambda^2)/(1+\lambda^2+2\lambda S).$$

These expressions have the same denominator as (34), and reduce to the simpler distribution if $S = 0$. They lead to the same dipole moment as (34), but they are still unsatisfactory from a theoretical standpoint because they effectively neglect the term $\bar{x}_{AB}$ that occurs in (33). Indeed, a charge-cloud whose density varies from place to place cannot possibly be represented adequately by effective charges on the two nuclei.

Complete *a priori* calculations of λ are impracticable since they involve knowledge of E_A, E_B, and β_{AB}. Now E_A is defined by the integral $\int \psi_A H \psi_A \, d\tau$, where H is the Hamiltonian operator *for the molecule.* It is true that in the neighbourhood of atom A, H will resemble the operator for an isolated A atom: this means that E_A is not quite the same as the energy of an isolated a.o., but depends slightly on the rest of the molecule to which A is attached (cf. equation (16)). It is even more true that β_{AB} is a molecular quantity (cf. equation (17)), and at the moment no satisfactory methods exist for its determination. We must fall back therefore on the use of other properties such as the dipole moment or electronegativity.† Consequently our conclusions have more of a qualitative than quantitative character.

4.10. Types of molecular orbital

It follows from our previous discussion that in heteropolar diatomics, electrons may be regarded as occupying four types of orbital. These are (*a*) inner-shell, (*b*) valence-shell non-bonding, (*c*) valence-shell bonding, (*d*) valence-shell anti-bonding. It will be convenient to illustrate these four groups in terms of two particular examples, HCl and O_2.

In HCl all the chlorine K- and L-shell electrons are of type (*a*), quite localized around the chlorine nucleus. The same is true of the two $3s$ electrons.‡ If the x-direction is from Cl towards H, then the valence-shell bonding orbital is compounded from $Cl(3p_x)$ and $H(1s)$, both being of σ character. However, the $Cl(3p_y)$ and $Cl(3p_z)$ orbitals cannot form any LCAO with hydrogen, for the lowest a.o. in hydrogen which possesses π character is the $H(2p)$ whose energy is so much greater than that of $Cl(3p_y)$ that no effective combination occurs. As a result even though they are in the valence shell the electrons in these a.o.'s remain centred round their original nucleus, and merely suffer a small polarization: they are the valence-shell non-bonding electrons. Two electrons with opposed spins in orbits of this kind are called *lone-pair* electrons. This accounts for all the electrons in HCl.

---

† See § 5.8. More complete discussions of electronegativity and its relation to dipole moments and energy, are given by R. S. Mulliken, *J. Chem. Phys.*, 1934, **2**, 782, and loc. cit.; and by L. Pauling, *Nature of the Chemical Bond.*

‡ If hybridization occurs, of the type described in § 8.10, then these electrons are not pure $3s$, but have an orbital which is a mixture of $3s$ and $3p_x$. But of course they are still localized around the Cl nucleus.

In the same way most of the electrons in O_2 can be allotted without difficulty to their proper type, by simple reference to Fig. 11 and Table 5; we must remember that if there are two low-lying orbitals such as $\sigma 2s$ and $\sigma^* 2s$, it is immaterial whether or not we replace them by the a.o.'s $2s_A$ and $2s_B$ from which both were composed (p. 99). Chemical language usually favours the latter description. The only new point about O_2 is the top degenerate level $\pi_y^* 2p$, $\pi_z^* 2p$ (i.e. $v\pi$). This would be expected to be anti-bonding. If it were, the bond energy of O_2^+, in which there is only one of these electrons, should be greater than that of O_2 in which there are two. Such is indeed the case, the appropriate values being 6·48 and 5·08 eV. We may contrast this with the situation in N_2, whose configuration (see Table 5 and equation 28) is similar to Fig. 11 except for the omission of the anti-bonding $v\pi$ electrons, and for which the dissociation of the neutral molecule is greater than that of the positive ion (7·38 eV for N_2, 6·35 eV for N_2^+).

4.11. Isoelectronic principle

Although the diagrams in Figs. 10 and 12 for homonuclear and heteronuclear molecules look so very different, there is in fact one important link between them. This is the so-called *isoelectronic principle*. Historically this principle is important because a comparison of certain isoelectronic molecules provided the first clues to the sequence of orbitals such as we have described earlier. Two molecules with the same number of valence electrons are isoelectronic; and the principle states that such systems will have similar molecular orbitals.

Let us consider a particular example, N_2 and CO. We could imagine ourselves converting N_2 into CO by gradually withdrawing unit positive charge from the first nitrogen nucleus and adding it to the second. If this is done gradually, there will be a gradual change of the m.o.'s and we may expect the N_2 orbitals to be converted by this means, without any discontinuous changes, to CO orbitals. (Such transformations are sometimes called 'adiabatic', but the description is not a happy one.) This implies that the appropriate orbitals in Fig. 12 should be related to those of

Fig. 10 in a manner represented by a decrease in the electro-negative character of one atom and an increase in that of the other.

The isoelectronic principle is not now greatly used except in atomic spectra, and with heterocyclic aromatic molecules (Chapter IX). There are, indeed, sometimes difficulties in its application. The particular case of CO is dealt with in a later chapter (Chapter VIII).

V

DIATOMIC MOLECULES
VALENCE-BOND THEORY

5.1. The valence-bond method

AT the beginning of Chapter IV we said that there were two main approaches to the theory of valence: and we proceeded to develop in some detail the method of m.o.'s. We must now turn to the alternative method, historically the earlier to be developed. This is known as the valence-bond (abbreviated to v.b.) method. Its most characteristic feature is that it considers the combining atoms as a whole. The formation of a molecule is thought of as arising from the bringing together of complete atoms, which are then allowed to interact. In this it differs from the m.o. method, in which only the nuclei (or nuclei+inner shells) are first brought into position, and afterwards the valence electrons are allotted to polycentric molecular orbits. Quite evidently, the v.b. description corresponds more closely with the conventional chemical picture; this, of course, explains its development by Heitler and London,[†] as early as 1927, only one year after Schrödinger's first introduction of the wave equation.

It will be best, in our discussion of the v.b. method, to follow the sequence of Chapter IV and begin with the hydrogen molecule. Not only was this the first molecule to be dealt with by wave mechanics, but it still remains one of the few for which anything like complete extended calculations are practicable. The analysis falls quite distinctly into five stages, each stage corresponding to some new mathematical operation. But we shall see that these operations are not merely mathematical; each one represents the introduction of some aspect of chemical intuition and experience. It is not unfair to say that in this, as in practically the whole of theoretical chemistry, the form in which the mathematics is cast is suggested, almost inevitably, by experimental results. This is not surprising when we recognize how impossible is any exact

† H. Heitler and F. London, *Z. Phys.*, 1927, **44**, 455.

solution of the wave equation for a molecule. Our approximations to an exact solution ought to reflect the ideas, intuitions, and conclusions of the experimental chemist.

Only one new theorem is required, and this is quite simple. It is that if we have two completely distinct, unconnected systems, separately described by wave functions ψ_1 and ψ_2, then the wave function for the two together is the product $\psi_1\psi_2$. For if H_1 and H_2 are the two separate Hamiltonians, and E_1, E_2 the separate energies, the separate wave equations are

$$H_1\psi_1 = E_1\psi_1, \qquad H_2\psi_2 = E_2\psi_2.$$

If there is no interaction between the systems, the complete Hamiltonian is obviously $H = H_1 + H_2$. This follows (§ 3.3) from the manner in which the Hamiltonian operator is written down. It also follows that because H_1 and H_2 involve the coordinates of entirely distinct particles, in the operation $H_1(\psi_1\psi_2)$ we may regard ψ_2 as a constant. Thus $H_1(\psi_1\psi_2) = \psi_2 \times H_1(\psi_1) = E_1\psi_1\psi_2$. This means that the joint wave equation

$$H\psi = E\psi$$

is satisfied by $\qquad \psi = \psi_1\psi_2, \qquad E = E_1 + E_2. \qquad (1)$

This is a useful theorem, which may be extended to any number of isolated, or unconnected, systems.

5.2. The hydrogen molecule H_2

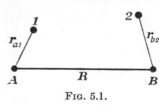

FIG. 5.1.

Stage (a). If the two atoms A and B (Fig. 1) are a long way apart, each being in its ground state, we may say that electron 1 is near nucleus A, electron 2 near nucleus B. The separate wave functions (equation (2.17)) are

$$\psi_A(1) = Ne^{-r_{a1}}, \qquad \psi_B(2) = Ne^{-r_{b2}} \qquad (2)$$

where N is a normalizing factor equal to $\pi^{-\frac{1}{2}}$. We have measured distances in terms of the Bohr radius a_0. The separate energies are each E_h where (3.25) E_h is the energy of a hydrogen atom

$$E_h = -e^2/2a_0 = -13.60 \text{ eV}. \qquad (3)$$

If the internuclear distance R is so great that no appreciable interaction takes place between A and B, then according to the theorem at the end of § 1, the wave function for the molecule is simply

$$\psi = \psi_A(1)\psi_B(2), \tag{4}$$

with energy $\qquad E = 2E_h.$

Now suppose that the atoms are brought closer. A plausible guess would be to suppose that the wave function (4) was still reasonably close to the truth. We could therefore use it in the energy equation (3.33),

$$E = \int \psi H \psi \, d\tau \Big/ \int \psi^2 \, d\tau, \dagger \tag{5}$$

and hope to obtain a reasonable value for the energy. According to the Variation Method (§ 3.6) the energy thus calculated may

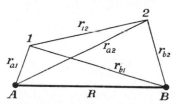

Fig. 5.2. Coordinates for H_2.

be expected to be closer to the truth than the wave function itself. We have already seen in (3.17) that the Hamiltonian operator has the form (notation of Fig. 2)

$$H = -\frac{h^2}{8\pi^2 m}(\nabla_1^2 + \nabla_2^2) - e^2\left(\frac{1}{r_{a1}} + \frac{1}{r_{b1}} + \frac{1}{r_{a2}} + \frac{1}{r_{b2}} - \frac{1}{r_{12}} - \frac{1}{R}\right). \tag{6}$$

Provided, therefore, that we can do the integrations involved in (5) it is a straightforward problem to determine the energy $E(R)$ for any internuclear distance R. Some of these integrals are quite difficult, but they can all be evaluated in closed form,‡ and the analysis completed. A considerable simplification results from the fact that since $\psi_A(1)$ is the wave function for the atomic Hamiltonian

$$H_A \equiv -\frac{h^2}{8\pi^2 m}\nabla_1^2 - \frac{e^2}{r_{a1}}, \tag{7}$$

---

† Our convention is always that $\int \ldots d\tau$ implies integration over all the coordinates represented in the integrand.

‡ H. Heitler and F. London, loc. cit.; Y. Sugiura, *Z. Phys.*, 1927, **45**, 484.

it follows without much trouble that

$$E = 2E_h + \frac{e^2}{R} + \int \int \frac{e^2}{r_{12}} \psi_A^2(1)\psi_B^2(2) \, d\tau_1 \, d\tau_2 - 2 \int \frac{e^2}{r_{a2}} \psi_B^2(2) \, d\tau_2 \quad (8 \, a)$$

$$= 2E_h + Q, \quad \text{say.} \quad (8 \, b)$$

It is interesting to interpret the right-hand side of (8 a). $2E_h$ is the energy of two separate H atoms; e^2/R is the Coulomb repulsion between the two nuclei; the third term is the Coulomb repulsion between two charge-clouds of density $e\psi_A^2(1)$ and $e\psi_B^2(2)$, i.e. the charge-clouds of the distinct hydrogen atoms; the last term represents the attraction between the charge-cloud around B and the positive nucleus A. There is a factor 2 on account of the equal

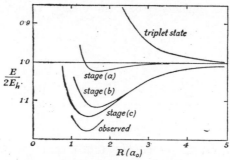

FIG. 5.3. Energy curves for H_2, various stages of approximation.

attraction between the charge-cloud around A and nucleus B. This term arises because the electrons in the molecule are under attraction not to one nucleus only, but to two. According to (8) it is only if this last term is sufficiently large to compensate the other Coulomb terms, that any binding will occur. The actual energy calculated in this way is shown as stage (a) in Fig. 3. The energy curve does have a minimum, at about

$$R = 1 \cdot 7a_0 = 0 \cdot 9 \, \text{A},$$

so that two hydrogen atoms must indeed form a molecule. The observed R agrees fairly closely with the calculated one, but the binding energy, represented by the depth of the minimum below the asymptotic value, is much too small, being about $\frac{1}{4}$ eV instead of $4\frac{3}{4}$ eV. Although we are on the right lines, one essential step must have been omitted.

Stage (b). The introduction of this step is due to Heitler and London.† In the preceding argument we said that electron 1 was to be around nucleus A and electron 2 around B. But how do we know which electron is 1 and which is 2? Electrons are all identical: they carry no labels with which we can identify them. Even if we knew which was electron 1 at one given moment we could not tell subsequently, for, as we showed in Chapter II, there is no hope of being able to follow an electron in any orbit. All this means that the wave function $\psi_B(1)\psi_A(2)$ is as much acceptable as $\psi_A(1)\psi_B(2)$. Presumably the true wave function should have characteristics of both, which are rather like components. We must try the combination

$$\psi = c_1\psi_1 + c_2\psi_2 \qquad (9)$$

where $\psi_1 = \psi_A(1)\psi_B(2)$, $\psi_2 = \psi_B(1)\psi_A(2)$, and c_1, c_2 are constants to be determined from the secular equations, as in (3.41). Since, in these equations, $H_{11} = H_{22}$, $S_{11} = S_{22}$, it follows at once that

$$c_1^2 = c_2^2. \qquad (10)$$

This condition could have been written down without reference to the secular equations, for, on symmetry grounds, the weights of ψ_1 and ψ_2 must be equal. Since the weight is proportional to the square of the coefficient, we have an immediate proof of (10).

There are two roots of (10), $c_1 = \pm c_2$. If we substitute these values in the secular equations we find the corresponding wave functions and energies:

$$\psi_+ = \psi_A(1)\psi_B(2) + \psi_B(1)\psi_A(2), \qquad E_+ = \frac{H_{11} + H_{12}}{S_{11} + S_{12}}, \qquad (11\,a)$$

$$\psi_- = \psi_A(1)\psi_B(2) - \psi_B(1)\psi_A(2), \qquad E_- = \frac{H_{11} - H_{12}}{S_{11} - S_{12}}. \qquad (11\,b)$$

Since H_{11} and H_{12} are found to have the same sign (both are negative) the lowest energy arises from $(11\,a)$ in which $c_1 = c_2$. We must now study this in a little more detail. All the integrals involved may be evaluated, just as in stage (a): and we obtain an energy curve $E(R)$ shown in Fig. 3 as (b). This curve is much more satisfactory: it gives a minimum energy at about the same

† Loc. cit.

internuclear distance as before, but the binding energy is increased to 3·14 eV. This compares very favourably with the observed value 4·75 eV, being obviously a great improvement on the previous value of $\frac{1}{4}$ eV.

It is quite clear that we have now got the basis of the description right. Thus the familiar potential energy curve of a molecule arises because we have to use the wave function (11 a) rather than (4): and this is necessary because we do not know which electron is which. Some people refer to the phenomenon as the 'exchange phenomenon', and in fact it is possible to regard the term H_{12}, which is the most significant new term and is largely responsible for the binding, as representing a new kind of energy which arises when the electrons change places under the influence of the Hamiltonian. The precise form of H_{12} is

$$H_{12} = \int \psi_A(1)\psi_B(2).H.\psi_B(1)\psi_A(2)\, d\tau_1\, d\tau_2, \tag{12}$$

and does show the idea of an exchange. People sometimes say that the electrons exchange, or 'trade', places with one another.

Such language is full of dangers. If we do not know which electron is which, it means nothing to say that they change places. Sometimes, too, a numerical value is assigned to the frequency of exchange. Thus, if we may for the moment neglect S_{12} in (11 a) —a limitation that is of no fundamental significance—then the additional energy of (11 a) compared with (8) is simply H_{12}. It is usually called the *exchange energy*. If we use Planck's relation $E = h\nu$, we may associate with this exchange a frequency H_{12}/h. Numerically this is about 7×10^{14} per second. But it is quite incorrect to think of this as any actual frequency of exchange. The fact that a similar total energy for the molecule is found using the m.o. method, in which no such term appears in this way, should put us on our guard. There is no such thing as an 'exchange phenomenon'. But there *is* a wave function ψ, which in greater or less degree resembles (11 a), and by allowing either electron to be near either nucleus, gives rise to a lowering of the energy. This is because (i) the two electrons are under simultaneous attraction to two positive nuclei instead of one, and (ii) the identical character of the electrons compels us to choose (11 a) and allow greater freedom to the electrons. Such greater freedom is generally followed by a lowering of energy.

We can go a little further in comparing (11 a, b) with (8). But we must first normalize the function ψ_+ of (11 a). Thus

$$\int \psi_+^2 \, d\tau = \int \psi_A^2(1)\psi_B^2(2) \, d\tau + 2 \int \psi_A(1)\psi_B(1)\psi_A(2)\psi_B(2) \, d\tau +$$

$$+ \int \psi_A^2(2)\psi_B^2(1) \, d\tau.$$

We may put $d\tau = d\tau_1 \, d\tau_2$, where $d\tau_1$ and $d\tau_2$ represent integration over the coordinates of electrons 1 and 2 respectively. Then each term of the right-hand side splits up into the product of two separate integrals, since

$$\int \psi_A^2(1)\psi_B^2(2)d\tau_1 d\tau_2 = \int \psi_A^2(1) \, d\tau_1 \times \int \psi_B^2(2) \, d\tau_2 = 1$$

on account of the normalization of ψ_A and ψ_B. And

$$\int \psi_A(1)\psi_B(1)\psi_A(2)\psi_B(2) \, d\tau_1 \, d\tau_2 = \int \psi_A(1)\psi_B(1) \, d\tau_1 \times$$

$$\times \int \psi_A(2)\psi_B(2) \, d\tau_2 = S^2,$$

where S is the overlap integral for the atomic orbitals ψ_A and ψ_B, just as in (4.2). Hence

$$\int \psi_+^2 \, d\tau = 2(1+S^2).$$

In exactly the same way it follows that

$$S_{11} = 1, \qquad S_{12} = S^2,$$

so that we can now evaluate E_+ and E_-. It is not difficult to show, in the same way that we were able to get (8), that

$$E_\pm = 2E_h + \frac{Q \pm J}{1 \pm S^2}, \tag{13}$$

where $\quad Q = \iint \psi_A(1)\psi_B(2)\{H - 2E_h\}\psi_A(1)\psi_B(2) \, d\tau_1 \, d\tau_2, \tag{14}$

and is identical with the Q in equation (8),

$$J = \int\int \psi_A(1)\psi_B(2)\{H-2E_h\}\psi_B(1)\psi_A(2)\,d\tau_1\,d\tau_2$$

$$= \frac{e^2S^2}{R} - 2S\int \frac{e^2}{r_{b1}}\psi_A(1)\psi_B(1)\,d\tau_1 +$$

$$+ \int\int \frac{\psi_A(1)\psi_B(2)\psi_B(1)\psi_A(2)}{r_{12}}\,d\tau_1\,d\tau_2, \qquad (15)$$

$$S = \int \psi_A(1)\psi_B(1)\,d\tau_1. \qquad (16)$$

We have already seen that S is the ordinary overlap integral introduced in Chapter IV: Q is generally called the Coulomb integral, and J the exchange integral.[†]

If we choose the minus sign in (13) we are dealing with the wave function (11 b) corresponding to $c_1 = -c_2$ in (9). The energy curve which results is shown in Fig. 3 where (see § 9) it is described as a triplet level. There is no minimum,[‡] so that this is not a stable state. It is, however, of some interest because the continuous spectrum of H_2 arises from a transition in which an electron falls from some still more excited level to this one, and then dissociates into two separate atoms, with gain in kinetic energy. We have already been led to consider the existence of such repulsive states from our earlier study of m.o.'s.

Stage (c). This brings us to the third stage: and physical evidence is again used to suggest the next improvement.[§] When one atom comes up to the other, it must partially screen it. The electrons are attracted to two centres, so that their orbits are contracted into a smaller region. This would be shown by a change in the exponent of the a.o.'s ψ_A, ψ_B on account of the contraction. We should expect an increased exponent compared with that for an isolated H atom. This suggests that in (11 a) instead of

$$\psi_A = e^{-r_a},$$

we should try $\qquad \psi_A = e^{-cr_a}, \qquad (17)$

[†] In some accounts the exchange integral is called α, and the Coulomb integral K.

[‡] Except at very large R, and of very small magnitude, quite insignificant for chemical purposes. It arises, not from (13), but from the van der Waals forces of attraction.

[§] S. C. Wang, *Phys. Rev.*, 1928, **31**, 579.

where c is some parameter, possibly having a different value for each internuclear distance, and chosen so that the energy function in § 3.6 is minimized. We know what to expect of this constant c. For at large distances the screening will be small so that $c \to 1$ as $R \to \infty$. But at small distances, as we squeeze the two nuclei together to form the united-atom He, c becomes 1·625.† Fig. 4 shows how c varies for other values of R: and in Fig. 3 we have

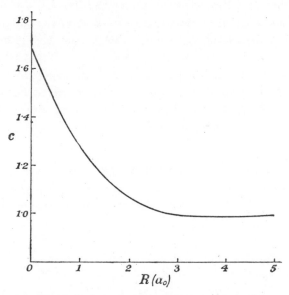

FIG. 5.4. The variation of screening constant with internuclear distance for the Wang function for H_2.

drawn the corresponding energy curve. Since all additional flexibilities in the wave function must lead to a lowering of the energy, curve (c) must lie below both (a) and (b). At the equilibrium distance $c \simeq 1$·166, and the binding energy is 3·76 eV, a considerable improvement on the previous 3·14 eV.

This wave function lends itself quite easily to numerical calculation, and density curves can be drawn entirely analogous to those using the m.o. method in Figs. 4.4 and 4.5. We shall not reproduce these curves, however, because their shape is extremely similar to

† This value is a little more accurate than the value 1·70 suggested by the Slater rules outlined in § 2.8 in small type.

Figs. 4.4 and 4.5, and in § 6.2 we shall have occasion to compare the densities analytically.

Stage (*d*). Chemical evidence provides the next clue for further improvement. Evidently, the presence of one atom near another will polarize it, so that, for example, its charge-cloud is no longer spherically symmetrical about the nucleus. This is a kind of Stark effect, and it is interesting to recollect that some of the earliest views of chemical binding were along the lines of a Stark effect, involving the mutual polarization of both atoms: and that certain loose molecular complexes such as $(O_2)_2$ and $(NO)_2$ are almost certainly largely held together in this way. We shall find that such an effect exists, but is not extremely important. We may allow for it in a similar manner to that used earlier (equation 4.21) for the H_2^+ ion, by replacing the spherically symmetrical a.o.'s (17) by the polarized one †

$$\psi_A = \lambda_1 e^{-cr_a} + \lambda_2 x e^{-cr_a}, \tag{18}$$

where the x-axis is directed from A towards B. A similar change is made in ψ_B and λ_1, λ_2, as well as c, are varied to give minimum energy. This leads to a binding energy 4·02 eV instead of 3·76 eV. The gain is significant, though not large.

Stage (*e*). Once more we use chemical ideas. For not only is the charge-cloud contracted and polarized: there is also the chance, however small, that both electrons should simultaneously be near the same nucleus. This is not at all unreasonable when we remember that the negative ion H^- exists and is quite stable. Now if both electrons are on A, they would have a wave function

$$\phi_A(1)\phi_A(2),$$

where, at least approximately,

$$\phi_A = e^{-c'r_a}. \tag{19}$$

Since we must allow equal weights to the chances of both being on A or both on B, we introduce‡ what may be called an ionic wave function

$$\psi_{\text{ion}} = \phi_A(1)\phi_A(2) + \phi_B(1)\phi_B(2). \tag{20}$$

If we call the previous wave function ψ_{cov}, in which the suffix

† N. Rosen, *Phys. Rev.*, 1931, **38**, 2099.
‡ S. Weinbaum, *J. Chem. Phys.*, 1933, **1**, 593.

implies a purely covalent character for the wave function, then the complete molecular wave function is taken to be

$$\psi = \psi_{\text{cov}} + \lambda_3 \psi_{\text{ion}}, \tag{21}$$

The energy of this wave function depends on λ_1, λ_2, λ_3, c, c', and R. A lot of tedious calculation is required to show which values for these quantities lead to the lowest energy. In the end it appears that the binding energy increases to 4·10 eV, and $\lambda_3 \simeq \frac{1}{4}$, showing

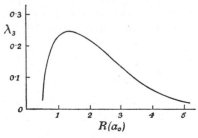

Fig. 5.5. Variation of λ_3 with R for the covalent-ionic resonance in H_2.

that at the equilibrium distance the ionic character of the bond is nothing like so pronounced as the covalent character. At large distances, the ionic character would be expected to be much smaller than $\frac{1}{4}$. Fig. 5† shows how λ_3 varies, when it is defined in such a way that ψ_{cov} and ψ_{ion} are both normalized.

One interpretation of (21) is often given, and is worth mentioning. It is that there is resonance between the 'purely covalent' structure H—H, with a wave function ψ_{cov}, or $\psi(\text{H—H})$: and the two 'ionic' structures H^+H^-, H^-H^+ with wave functions $\psi(H^+H^-)$, $\psi(H^-H^+)$. Provided that we are not tempted thereby to suppose that the purely covalent and purely ionic structures exist, there is no harm in this description, and indeed the fact that λ_3 has its greatest value near the equilibrium value of R adds to its justification. There is a certain advantage in the description, because, as we shall see later in §§ 7 and 8 when discussing polar molecules, we may relate the polarity of the molecule to the importance of certain of these ionic structures. But it is only in a formal sense

† C. A. Coulson and Miss I. Fischer, *Phil. Mag.*, 1949, **40**, 386. These calculations were actually made neglecting the polarization effect (d). This neglect would not be very likely to change the curve significantly.

that we describe this as covalent-ionic resonance. The most accurate way of interpreting our final wave function is to say that ψ must have characteristics which, at the same time, though in differing degrees, resemble those of covalent, polar, and ionic models, and so may be regarded as a composite of them all. However, as the m.o. account shows very clearly, there are alternative ways of dissecting ψ into contributions with chemical significance.

This is as far as we shall want to go. But there is nothing, beyond the labour, to prevent us going farther, and introducing as much flexibility as we wish. James and Coolidge,[†] for example, recognized that all the wave functions described above lacked any specific reference to the inter-electron distance r_{12}. Without explicit inclusion of r_{12} the best energy which they obtained was 4·27 eV: but when they introduced it, using a trial wave function with no less than thirteen terms, they were able to get within 0·05 eV of the true value. More recently[‡] Kolos and Roothaan, with a similar fifty-term function, obtained an energy $D_e = 4·7467$ eV, to be compared with the experimental value $4·7466 \pm 0·0007$ eV. This truly remarkable work shows that for sufficiently small molecules, modern electronic computers have brought us to a situation where calculation may give a more accurate result than experiment! (See Table 7.) It is not unreasonable to claim that these highly laborious calculations, yielding such an excellent final result, represent one of the most satisfactory 'proofs' of the validity of the original wave equation when applied to problems with more than one electron. For if the original equation was not correct, it is hard to see how the numerical answer could be so good.

The actual function used by James and Coolidge is of some interest. It is expressed in terms of the spheroidal coordinates of the two electrons. These are λ, μ, ϕ, where $\lambda = (r_a + r_b)/R$, $\mu = (r_a - r_b)/R$, $\phi = $ azimuthal angle round AB. The actual function was a linear combination of terms such as $\lambda_1^m \lambda_2^n \mu_1^j \mu_2^k r_{12}^p e^{-\alpha(\lambda_1 + \lambda_2)}$, where m, n, j, k, p are integers, α is some constant, and the suffixes 1 and 2 relate to the two electrons. The secular determinant is found as in § 3.8, and thus the energy is obtained. One significant fact about a wave function such as this is that no mention

† J. Chem. Phys., 1933, 1, 825.
‡ W. Kolos and C. C. J. Roothaan, Rev. Mod. Phys., 1960, 32, 219.

occurs of the exchange integral. This confirms our previous view that the 'exchange phenomenon' is no phenomenon at all, but merely an apparent one resulting from the way in which we choose to build up our complete wave function.

. TABLE 7. *Energy values for ground state of* H_2 *using various approximate wave functions*†

Type of wave function	Maximum binding energy	Equilibrium separation
'Heitler–London'	3·14 eV	0·869 A.
'Heitler–London' with screening (Wang) . .	3·78	0·743
'Wang'+polarization (Rosen)	4·04	0·74
'Wang'+ionic (Weinbaum‡)	4·02	0·749
'Wang'+ionic+polarization (Weinbaum) . .	4·12	(0·749)
Molecular orbital $\{\psi_A(1)+\psi_B(1)\}\{\psi_A(2)+\psi_B(2)\}$§ .	2·70	0·85
Molecular orbital, plus screening‡ . . .	3·49	0·732
Correlated m.o. $\{\psi_A(1)+\psi_B(1)\}\{\psi_A(2)+\psi_B(2)\}(1+pr_{12})$†† .	4·11	0·71
Best possible molecular orbitals (self-consistent field)‖	3·62	(0·74)
Coolidge–James, without r_{12} terms . . .	4·29	(0·740)
Coolidge–James, with r_{12} terms (13-term function)	4·72	0·740
Coolidge–James, with r_{12} terms (50-term function)‡‡	4·747	0·741
Observed values	4·747	0·741

† A complete bibliography of hydrogen molecule calculations is provided by A. D. McLean, A. Weiss, and M. Yoshimine, *Rev. Mod. Phys.*, 1960, **32**, 211.
‡ Loc. cit.
§ C. A. Coulson, *Trans. Faraday Soc.*, 1937, **33**, 1479.
‖ C. A. Coulson, *Proc. Cambridge Phil. Soc.*, 1938, **34**, 204.
†† A. A. Frost and J. Braunstein, *J. Chem. Phys.*, 1951, **19**, 1133.
‡‡ W. Kolos and C. C. J. Roothaan, *Rev. Mod. Phys.*, 1960, **32**, 219.

5.3. Other homonuclear diatomics

The essential feature in the v.b. description of H_2 was the selecting of two electrons in a.o.'s ψ_A, ψ_B around A and B, and the forming of a joint wave function $\psi_A(1)\psi_B(2)+\psi_B(1)\psi_A(2)$. This process is referred to as pairing the electrons, and the method is sometimes called the method of electron-pairs. We shall see later in § 9 that bonding results only if the spins of the electrons are anti-parallel; we may therefore speak of them as coupled. Indeed, only if the electron in ψ_A is free to be coupled with ψ_B is this whole process possible. We can only form a bond by using electrons not already paired in the original atoms. There is, however, no reason why, if there are two—or three, or more—unpaired electrons in one atom, we should not pair these with corresponding electrons in another atom. In this way we shall get multiple bonds. If we are not sure which electrons to pair with which, we can make use once more of the criterion of maximum overlapping (§ 4.3). This criterion still applies because, as follows from (13)–(15), the greatest binding occurs when J is numerically greatest, and the explicit form of J in (15) shows us that the integrand is large only if there are regions where the product $\psi_A \psi_B$ is large. This can occur only if the boundary surfaces of ψ_A and ψ_B (§ 2.3) overlap to a considerable extent. The pairing of ψ_A and ψ_B will therefore yield a strong bond if ψ_A and ψ_B have considerable overlap. A rough measure of the strength of a bond† is the overlap integral $\int \psi_A \psi_B \, d\tau$. Numerically J is negative for hydrogen, and is assumed to be negative for all but the ferromagnetic atoms. Here the ferromagnetism arises from the fact that if $J > 0$, the lower energy in (13) is E_-, and this (§ 9) involves parallel spins for the electrons.

A few examples will show at once the way in which we apply all this.

(i) The Li—Li bond is a single bond, since an isolated Li atom is described in terms $(1s)^2(2s)$: the bond arises from the pairing together of the two previously unpaired $2s$ electrons of the separate atoms.

(ii) The N≡N bond is a triple bond since a N atom is

$$(1s)^2(2s)^2(2p_x)(2p_y)(2p_z).$$

We may therefore pair together the two $2p_x$ a.o.'s in which the x-direction is along the nuclear axis to form a σ-bond, and the $2p_y$ and $2p_z$ a.o.'s to form two π-bonds, just as in § 4.7. Nothing can be done with the $2s$ electrons because they are already paired internally in the separate atoms.

(iii) The bonds in F_2, Cl_2,... are single. In the case of Cl_2, for example, the only unpaired atomic electrons are the $3p_x$ ones. If we suppose the x-direction to lie along the bond,

† Comments on the inadequacy of this and of the examples (i)–(iii), without qualifications, are reserved for Chapter VIII.

then the mutual pairing of these two a.o.'s leads to a σ-bond.

(iv) Two normal He atoms, on approaching each other, will not form a bond at all, since there are no unpaired electrons available in either atom. If any sort of bond is to be formed, it can be only after one atom has been excited. This is in complete agreement with a good deal of spectroscopic evidence concerning He_2.

In this way much of the information obtained from the m.o. method in Table 5 (page 102) may be verified again in the v.b. theory. But there are certain difficulties, one at least of which must be mentioned. Since an oxygen atom has the configuration

$$(1s)^2(2s)^2(2p_x)^2(2p_y)(2p_z)$$

we should have expected that mutual coupling of the two sets of unpaired electrons would lead to a double bond. Further, the criterion of maximum overlapping would suggest that one of these should be a σ-type bond and the other a π-type. Now the bond is generally regarded as double, but this description does not show us that such a state has to be a triplet, with a pair of parallel spins, rather than the expected singlet. A lengthy discussion[†] shows that the explanation lies in the fact that even if we take one of the electron pairs to be $\sigma 2p_x$, there is still uncertainty as to whether the other pair should be $\pi 2p_y$ or $\pi 2p_z$. If it is $\pi 2p_y$, then each oxygen atom has $(2p_z)$ as a lone-pair. Otherwise it has $(2p_y)$. Both possibilities have to be considered, and a more complicated wave function results.

It is evident from the above that the v.b. method can give a pretty good qualitative account of normal homonuclear diatomics. But relatively few quantitative calculations have been made. The reason for this is threefold.

(a) To be satisfactory, the wave functions used would have to include most of the refinements elaborated in § 2 for the H_2 molecule. In view of the large number of electrons involved, this would lead to serious computational difficulties.

† G. W. Wheland, *Trans. Faraday Soc.*, 1937, **33**, 1499.

(b) The electrons in the inner-shells, and the electrons in the valence-shells which are internally paired, ought all to be included, since they exert appreciable forces.

(c) We have to include other possible modes of electron-pairing as well as that one which is suggested as the most natural one by the criterion of maximum overlapping. Indeed, in principle we ought to consider all possible pairing combinations, and represent our wave function as a suitable linear sum. This implies that no one single pairing scheme is completely satisfactory. The case of O_2 emphasizes this trouble very clearly.

All this means that unless we have access to a large electronic computer we must be content with a qualitative account, and abandon any hope of complete *ab initio* determinations of the energy. But the general principles which we have described are a very useful guide to our understanding of the nature of a covalent bond.

5.4. Heteronuclear diatomics

It is a natural extension of the arguments we have just been using, to describe heteronuclear diatomics in a similar way. But one new feature occurs, similar in many respects to the new feature which we introduced in § 4.8 in the m.o. theory. This feature is the polarity of the molecule. In m.o. language this was expressed by a m.o. $\psi_A + \lambda \psi_B$, which was no longer symmetrical in the nuclei. In v.b. language, it must be expressed by saying that one or other of the ionic structures A^+B^-, A^-B^+ will be much more important than the other, and more important in relation to the covalent structure, than with homonuclear molecules. Let us suppose that atom A is the more electronegative. Then we must consider the three structures $A—B$, A^-B^+, A^+B^-, with wave functions

$$\psi_A(1)\psi_B(2) + \psi_B(1)\psi_A(2), \qquad \psi_A(1)\psi_A(2), \qquad \psi_B(1)\psi_B(2). \qquad (22)$$

Stage (c) of our earlier work—the screening effect—may be considered to be already included in the definitions of ψ_A and ψ_B. Stage (d)—the polarization effect—is omitted because it does not appear to play a tremendously important part, and is very clumsy to deal with. This means that we replace the wave function (21) by the new one:

$$\psi = c_1\{\psi_A(1)\psi_B(2)+\psi_B(1)\psi_A(2)\}+c_2\psi_A(1)\psi_A(2)+c_3\psi_B(1)\psi_B(2). \quad (23)$$

When writing the ionic terms we have supposed that the a.o.'s involved are the same as those in the covalent term. This has been shown to be nearly true. Its assumption is a simplification that introduces no appreciable error.

From here the matter is quite simple, at least in principle. We have to choose the three constants c_1, c_2, c_3 so that the energy function (3.33) is stationary. In practice, however, one further approximation is almost always permissible. If A is the more electronegative atom, we can neglect the chance of both electrons being on B, and omit the c_3-term in (23). If ψ_{cov} and ψ_{ion} now represent the normalized wave functions for the covalent and ionic structures, this becomes

$$\psi = \psi_{cov}+\lambda\psi_{ion}, \quad (24)$$

where λ is a constant† whose value determines the asymmetry of charge, i.e. the polar character of the bond, sometimes called the degree of ionicity. We may say that the weights of the covalent and ionic parts‡ are in the ratio $1 : \lambda^2$. The percentage ionic character (see § 6) is then defined to be $100\lambda^2/(1+\lambda^2)$.

It would be nice if we could calculate the value of λ by direct methods. However, except for very small molecules, this is too difficult because of the large number of electronic interactions, including those from inner-shell electrons, which ought to be included. We are obliged to proceed somewhat empirically. Thus we can either

(a) use the observed dipole moment to determine λ in a manner similar to that of § 4.9;

(b) set up some sort of scale of electronegativity for the elements from which λ can be estimated; or

† Not of course to be confused with λ in the m.o. $\psi_A+\lambda\psi_B$.

‡ It has been suggested (Y. K. Syrkin and M. E. Dyatkina, *Structure of Molecules*, Butterworths, 1950, 205) that when we square ψ in (24) to obtain the probability function, we ought to include a transitional structure as well as covalent and ionic. The weights of the three types would be in the ratio $1:\lambda^2:2\lambda$. Although (see p. 65) this is strictly more accurate, it is far less pictorial, and there does not seem to be any great advantage in using it for general descriptive purposes.

(c) try to develop rules whereby approximate values are found for all the matrix elements (see p. 62) that occur in the secular equations resulting from (24), and thereby deduce both the energy and the corresponding λ.

All three methods have been used, and will be described shortly. None of them is really satisfactory. But before describing them an example will show more clearly the significance of (24). Let us consider HCl. The electrons to be paired together to form the bond are the hydrogen $1s$ electron and the chlorine $3p_x$. If, for the moment, we leave out of account all the other electrons of chlorine, the unnormalized covalent wave function is

$$\psi(\text{H} : 1)\psi(\text{Cl} : 2) + \psi(\text{H} : 2)\psi(\text{Cl} : 1), \tag{25}$$

and the ionic wave function is

$$\psi(\text{Cl} : 1)\psi(\text{Cl} : 2). \tag{26}$$

We can see immediately why the other possible ionic function $\psi(\text{H} : 1)\psi(\text{H} : 2)$ need not be considered. The energy required to remove (ionize) an electron from H is 13·60 eV, and from Cl it is 13·01 eV. The energy gained when an electron is added to H to form H^- (electron affinity) is 0·72 eV, and for Cl it is 4·0 eV. Thus it requires $13.60 - 4.0 = 9.6$ eV to take an electron from H and give it to Cl, and it requires $13.01 - 0.72 = 12.3$ eV to take an electron from Cl and give it to H. Since the Coulomb forces between H^+ and Cl^-, and between H^- and Cl^+ will be very similar at equal separations of the nuclei, we conclude that the structure H^+Cl^- is nearly 3 eV more stable than H^-Cl^+. The criterion of nearly equal energies (cf. page 74) for effective combination in a linear variation function is not satisfied, so that the weight of H^-Cl^+ will be expected to be less than that of H^+Cl^-. Unless we are trying to make exceedingly detailed calculations the function for H^-Cl^+ may therefore be neglected. With more polar molecules this situation is even more definite.

5.5. Quantum-mechanical structures and the meaning of resonance

From time to time we have used the word 'structure' in describing the composition of our various wave functions. The idea of a quantum-mechanical structure has played a most important part in the development of the theory of valence, and deserves a separate discussion.

When we speak of a structure, we mean a certain way of pairing electronic orbitals together,† using for this purpose certain component a.o.'s. For example, we have just been discussing the so-called covalent structure obtained by pairing ψ_A and ψ_B: and the ionic structures in which both electrons are on A, or on B. The various wave functions are the ones involved in (23). Now the first thing to say about these structures is that they do not exist in themselves: they have no objective reality, and it is quite inaccurate to speak of any kind of resonance between two or more structures as implying that each structure exists for a fraction of the time given by its weight in the compound wave function. There is no such thing as an independent ionic or covalent structure, for the simple reason that their wave functions are not eigenfunctions for the allowed stationary states. But the genius of the v.b. method is that it selects as component structures wave functions which do carry a pictorial connotation. Thus if we could allow two atoms to approach, keeping the various electron orbits entirely unaffected, except that one electron in one atom is paired with one electron in the other (this, see § 9, is really a statement about the alinement of their spins) then we should have a covalent structure, and by analogy with the conventional chemist's picture of a non-polar bond, we could think of it as represented by the symbol A—B. Similarly we can say that the ionic structures are represented by the conventional chemical symbols A^-B^+ and A^+B^-.

It is possible to associate an energy with any structure. For if the wave function for the structure is ψ, this energy is simply

$$E = \int \psi H \psi \, d\tau \Big/ \int \psi^2 \, d\tau. \tag{27}$$

Thus we can speak of the energy of a pure covalent structure A—B, or of a pure ionic structure A^-B^+, etc. Like the structures themselves, these energies are fictitious. The only energy that does

---

† With this definition we should not, therefore, call (4) a structure; but we should do so with (25) and (26).

possess a real objective character is the energy associated with the complete wave function. From the very nature of the variation method this energy will lie below any of the components E_{cov} or E_{ion}. With the usual care about the meaning of our words, we could say that the superposition of structures corresponds to a species of resonance, as a result of which the energy is lowered. The amount of lowering below that of the least component energy is termed the resonance energy. This resonance energy, of course, has no absolute meaning but is necessarily relative to the basic structures we have chosen. If we vary the structures we vary the resonance energy. For that reason the covalent-ionic resonance which we have stressed in § 4 is essentially only a convenient language.

For many purposes it is desirable to have some rough estimate of the energies E_{cov}, E_{ion} of the covalent and ionic structures. On account of the complicated character of the Hamiltonian operator these cannot be calculated by using relations such as

$$E_{cov} = \int \psi_{cov} H \psi_{cov} \, d\tau \Big/ \int \psi_{cov}^2 \, d\tau.$$

We are compelled to have recourse to other, more empirical, arguments. Consider the ionic structure A^-B^+ first. If B is a hydrogen atom, as in the hydrogen halides, then B^+ is a proton, and E_{ion} is simply the energy of interaction between a proton and the atomic ion A^-, whose wave function may be written down following the rules in § 2.8. Calculations of this kind may be made quite accurate. They are also simple if we do not attempt to allow for polarization of the charge-cloud round A. If B is a heavier atom such as an alkali atom, e.g. Na, and A is a halogen, e.g. Cl, we require the energy of Na^+Cl^-. Now (see Chapter XI) in the crystal of NaCl, the sodium atoms are almost completely stripped of their outer electrons and the chlorine atoms have received them. It is known from the work of Born[†] that a good description of such ionic crystals is obtained if we treat the charge transfer as almost complete, so that there is an attractive potential

[†] See, for example, J. Sherman, *Chem. Rev.*, 1932, **11**, 93; M. Born, *Atomic Physics*, Blackie, 1944; or R. H. Fowler, *Statistical Mechanics*, Cambridge Univ. Press, 1936.

e^2/R due to the Coulomb force between the ions: and if we introduce a repulsive potential b/R^9 between every pair of neighbours, where b is a constant chosen so that the interatomic spacing in the crystal is the one for which the total energy is least. In this way values of b are found for any given pair of atoms. We may now calculate E_{ion} for the molecular structure A^-B^+ as the sum of the same Coulomb attraction and the same b/R^9 repulsion. More accurate values in which we allow for polarization and use a different index n in the repulsive potential b/R^n for each pair of ions, are not justified in this connexion.

There is really no satisfactory way of estimating E_{cov}: for there is no parallel to the ionic crystal from which we can obtain suitable numerical data. As a rule, therefore, one of two postulates is adopted. It is supposed that the energy of a covalent structure $A—B$ is either the arithmetic mean, or else the geometric mean, of the observed energies of the bonds $A—A$ and $B—B$.† There is no proof for either of these postulates, although a rough m.o. treatment suggests the arithmetic mean as the more reasonable. Some purely numerical calculations‡ by Pauling and Sherman, however, favour the geometric mean. Fortunately, the two means are quite similar unless the energies of $A—A$ and $B—B$ differ very greatly. Thus the A.M. and G.M. of 40 and 60 are 50 and 49 respectively. As a result it makes little difference which we use, though in some cases (e.g. LiH, NaH), the G.M. seems definitely the better.

The value of E_{cov} thus obtained is merely the value appropriate to the minimum on the potential curve for this structure. This minimum is taken to lie at an internuclear distance equal to the sum of the covalent radii of the two atoms (which are usually obtained spectroscopically). To get the value of E_{cov} for other internuclear distances, we suppose that the shape of the $E_{cov}(R)$ curve is the same as that found experimentally for most molecules, and adequately represented by a Morse§ curve (see § 1.4)

$$E(R) = D\{e^{-2a(R-R_e)} - 2e^{-a(R-R_e)}\},$$

† The small amounts of ionic structures A^+A^-, A^-A^+, etc., are included, for convenience, in the values assigned to $A—A$ and $B—B$.

‡ L. Pauling and J. Sherman, *J. Amer. Chem. Soc.*, 1937, **59**, 1450.

§ P. M. Morse, *Phys. Rev.*, 1929, **34**, 57.

where D is the bond strength, R_e is the equilibrium distance, and a is a constant. If a cannot be determined experimentally, some empirical relation between R_e and a has to be used. The one most commonly used is due to Badger.†

It may well be asked, after all this, whether much reliability can be assigned to the final numerical values. The answer seems to be, no. But the procedure is completely systematic, so that we may expect general trends to be correctly reproduced. In

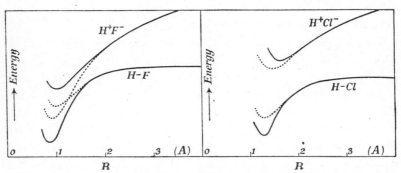

FIG. 5.6. Energy curves for HF and HCl (after Pauling). The covalent and ionic energies are shown separately as dotted curves, and also their resonance hybrids as solid lines.

view of the unreality of the structures themselves, perhaps this is as much as we have any right to expect.

The E_{cov} and E_{ion} curves for HF and HCl, calculated according to this scheme, are shown in Fig. 6 as dotted lines. In the case of HF the curves cross, showing that for this highly polar molecule, the ionic structure is actually the more stable at small internuclear distances. This is not true for the less polar HCl. The thick curves in Fig. 6 show the result of covalent-ionic resonance, and so represent our best approximations to the ground state, and to one of the excited states. But now, on account of the non-crossing rule (§ 3.10), the curves cannot intersect.

The chief use of these component energy curves is in estimating the ionic character of a bond, a matter to which we must now turn.

5.6. Dipole moments

The most elementary way of estimating the ionic character of

† R. M. Badger, *J. Chem. Phys.*, 1934, **2**, 128.

a bond is by its dipole moment. Thus in HCl the dipole moment is $1{\cdot}03 \times 10^{-18}$ e.s.u. corresponding to charges $\pm 0{\cdot}17e$ on the nuclei. Now if we adopt the wave function (24), viz.

$$\psi = \psi_{\text{cov}} + \lambda\psi_{\text{ion}},$$

we should expect zero charges with ψ_{cov}, and charges $\pm 1{\cdot}0e$ with ψ_{ion}.† We may say that the percentage ionic character is 17. Using Table 6 (p. 109) we can draw up the following set of values (Table 8).

TABLE 8. *Percentage ionic character in hydrogen halides*

Molecule	HF	HCl	HBr	HI
Percentage ionic character .	40	17	11	5
λ	0·77	0·45	0·36	0·23

According to this view, λ is related to the percentage ionic character by the equation

$$\frac{100\lambda^2}{1+\lambda^2} = \text{percentage ionic character.} \qquad (28)$$

The curve relating λ and ionic character is shown in Fig. 7.

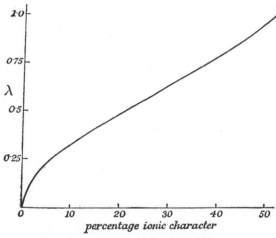

FIG. 5.7. Variation of parameter λ in $\psi = \psi_{\text{cov}} + \lambda\psi_{\text{ion}}$ with percentage ionic character, according to equation (28).

Appropriate values of λ for the hydrogen halides are shown in Table 8, when ψ_{cov} and ψ_{ion} are each separately normalized.

† This neglects possible hybridization of orbits, as in § 4.9 also.

The objection to this is that it does not take a sufficiently detailed account of the charge distribution. An argument entirely similar to that used in § 4.9 shows that the centre of position of the charge-cloud of electron 1 lies at a distance $\bar{x}$ from the mid-point of AB, where

$$\bar{x} = \int\int x(1)\psi^2 \, d\tau_1 \, d\tau_2 \Big/ \int\int \psi^2 \, d\tau_1 \, d\tau_2. \qquad (29)$$

When the expression (24) is used for ψ and the appropriate normalized forms of ψ_{cov} and ψ_{ion} are used, the integrations may be made, and a rather clumsy result is obtained. Now both electrons have the same mean position, so that, just as in (4.34), the dipole moment may be written down. If we make the usual hypothesis that the a.o.'s ψ_A and ψ_B have no separate dipole moment, and that $\bar{x}_{ab} = 0$ (see § 4.9), we find that

$$\mu = 2e\bar{x} = eR\left\{\frac{\lambda^2 + 2\lambda S/(2+2S^2)^{\frac{1}{2}}}{1+\lambda^2+4\lambda S/(2+2S^2)^{\frac{1}{2}}}\right\}, \qquad (30)$$

where S = overlap integral = $\int \psi_A \psi_B \, d\tau$. The percentage ionic character is now 100 times the expression in brackets in (30). Only if S is zero is this the same as the simple form (28). However, for most purposes the contributions from other electrons not included in (30) make it superfluous to attempt a better estimate of λ than follows from (28).

5.7. Ionic-covalent resonance energy

The second measure of the ionic character of a bond is the difference between the actual dissociation energy $D(A\text{—}B)$ and the energy of the covalent structure $E_{\text{cov}}(A\text{—}B)$ determined according to the prescription of § 5. If the bond $A\text{—}B$ is purely covalent, this difference, usually called Δ (or Δ', if the geometric mean is used instead of the arithmetic mean), is zero. Large values of Δ imply large ionic contributions, and in fact Δ (or Δ') may be called the ionic-covalent resonance energy. According to our definition of $E_{\text{cov}}(A\text{—}B)$, it follows that Δ is the heat liberated in the reaction $\frac{1}{2}A_2 + \frac{1}{2}B_2 \to AB$, the substances all being in the gaseous phase. Since resonance between covalent and ionic structures must necessarily lower the energy, our definition of $E_{cov}(A—B)$ is only sensible if Δ is positive. For the hydrogen halides and halogen halides this is universally the case, values of Δ being found between 64·0 kcal/mole for HF and 0·7 kcal/mole for BrCl. The trend of Δ-values is similar to that of the λ-values in § 6; which justifies us in using Δ as a measure of ionic character. However, the situation is entirely different for the alkali hydrides. Here the Δ-values are negative, showing that our estimate of $E_{cov}(A—B)$ is wrong. But the Δ'-values are satisfactory. Values of Δ and Δ' for a series of molecules are shown in Table 9.†

TABLE 9. *Ionic-covalent resonance energies*

These tables are based on the bond energies (dissociation energies) shown in brackets: H_2 (103·4), Li_2 (27·2), Na_2 (18.5), F_2 (37·7), Cl_2 (57·8), all in kcal/mole.

Bond	HF	HCl	ClF	LiH	NaH
Bond energy . .	135·1	102·7	86·4	57·7	52·3
E_{cov} arithmetic mean	70·6	60·6	47·8	65·3	61·0
Δ	64·5	22·1	38·6	−7·6	−8·7
E_{cov} geometric mean	62·4	77·3	46·7	53·0	43·6
Δ'	72·7	25·4	39·7	4·7	8·7

As a result of the ionic-covalent resonance the final ground state energy always lies below the lower of the two separate energies E_{ion} and E_{cov}. But unless these two components have approximately equal energies, the degree of mixing is small and the final energy curve is almost indistinguishable from that of the lower component. Now there is also a second energy which is derived from E_{ion} and E_{cov}, and this (§ 3.10) always lies above the higher of the two energies. This upper state is important because electronic transitions from the lower state to the upper are responsible for one of the characteristic absorption bands. On account of the fact that, as a rule, one of the states is largely covalent and the

† Numerical data largely drawn from G. Herzberg, *Molecular Spectra and Molecular Structure*, vol. i, *Diatomic Molecules*, Prentice-Hall, 1939, pp. 483–94, and from L. Pauling, *Nature of the Chemical Bond*. But a much lower value has been used for the dissociation energy of F_2, as shown by J. G. Stamper and R. F. Barrow, *Trans. Faraday Soc.*, 1958, **54**, 1592.

other largely ionic, we have a wave-mechanical parallel to the classical picture of an electron oscillating from one end of the molecule to the other, so that such absorption may be expected to be intense.

Before leaving this section there are three further comments to be made. The first is that we need expect no sudden transition from a covalent to an ionic type of bond: all intermediate gradations are allowed. The second comment is that in no circumstances is any bond either completely ionic or completely covalent:

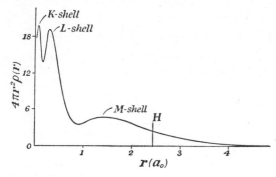

Fig. 5.8. Electronic density curve for Cl⁻. H denotes the position of the hydrogen atom in the molecule HCl. This shows the penetration of the proton into the valence shell of the heavy atom.

even CsF, the most polar of all molecules, is only 91 per cent. ionic. And the third is that we must be careful not to use the numerical results of this section without safeguarding ourselves. The complete neglect of polarization effects, to name but one deficiency, may be quite serious. This may be seen from Fig. 8† in which the charge density $\rho(r)$ in Cl⁻ is plotted against r, and a mark is made at H corresponding to the position of the proton in HCl. This diagram shows that the proton lies well inside the outer (i.e. valence, or M-) shell of Cl⁻, so that even if it only carries a fractional positive charge it will polarize considerably the chlorine charge-cloud.

† Taken from K. Fajans and N. Bauer, *J. Chem. Phys.*, 1942, **10**, 410, who used self-consistent-field calculations. Use of the Slater a.o.'s (§ 2.8) for Cl would yield a substantially similar result, with just a little less overlapping between the H and Cl charge-clouds.

5.8. Electronegativity scale

We have discussed both the dipole moment and the ionic-covalent-resonance methods of estimating the ionic character of a bond. There still remains a third method, whose application involves us in an account of the electronegativity scale for the elements. Our present discussion supplements the references already made to this topic in Chapter IV.

We know that in a polar molecule HCl, charge flows from H on to Cl. We could describe this by saying that chlorine was more electronegative (i.e. electron-attracting) than hydrogen. Indeed, if we can associate a number x_A with any atom A, to be called its electronegativity, and if this number is characteristic of all atoms A irrespective of the other atom or atoms to which A is bonded, then a measure of the ionic character of a bond AB is the absolute magnitude $|x_A - x_B|$ of the difference between the electronegativities of A and B. Our object, therefore, is to use some type of experimental measurement as a basis for these x-values. The most natural quantity to choose is the ionic-covalent resonance energy Δ of § 7, since by definition this is zero for a purely covalent bond (in which, of course, $x_A = x_B$), and increases with increase of polarity in the bond. Pauling,[†] on purely empirical grounds, first suggested that $\sqrt{\Delta_{AB}}$ was a satisfactory measure of $|x_A - x_B|$. It was left to Mulliken[‡] to show that a better measure of x_A is $\frac{1}{2}(I_A + E_A)$, where I_A is the ionization potential, and E_A the electron affinity, of A. Fortunately $\sqrt{\Delta_{AB}}$ seems to be almost proportional to the difference between $\frac{1}{2}(I + E)$ for atoms A and B; and it also satisfies an approximately additive relation

$$\sqrt{\Delta_{AB}} + \sqrt{\Delta_{BC}} = \sqrt{\Delta_{AC}},$$

where A, B, and C are in ascending order of electronegativity. This latter condition is necessary if $\sqrt{\Delta_{AB}} \propto |x_A - x_B|$. In this way we may say that the electronegativity scale possesses both an experimental and a theoretical basis. Table 10 (p. 140) gives the electronegativity values for some of the more common atoms. These numbers are chosen, to the first decimal, to give the best

[†] *J. Amer. Chem. Soc.*, 1932, **54**, 3570.
[‡] *J. Chem. Phys.*, 1934, **2**, 782; 1935, **3**, 573. See also W. E. Moffitt, *Proc. Roy. Soc.* A, 1949, **196**, 510, for a more sophisticated justification.

agreement with Δ-values: indeed, if Δ_{AB} is measured in eV then the scale is such that

$$\sqrt{\Delta_{AB}} \simeq |x_A - x_B|. \tag{31}$$

This means that the covalent-ionic resonance energy is approximately equal to

$$(x_A - x_B)^2, \quad \text{in eV}.$$

The relation between this x scale and the Mulliken scale

$$M_A = \tfrac{1}{2}(I_A + E_A)$$

is that $\qquad M_A - M_B = 2 \cdot 78(x_A - x_B). \tag{32}$

Table 10 shows the expected increase in electronegativity from left to right along any row of the periodic table, and a decrease down any column.

TABLE 10. *Electronegativity values*

H 2·1						
Li 1·0	Be 1·5	B 2·0	C 2·5	N 3·0	O 3·5	F 4·0
Na 0·9	Mg 1·2	Al 1·5	Si 1·8	P 2·1	S 2·5	Cl 3·0
K 0·8			Ge 1·8	As 2·0	Se 2·4	Br 2·8
Rb 0·8						I 2·5
Cs 0·7						

An important property of these electronegativity values is that the dipole moment μ_{AB} (in Debyes) of the bond AB is almost equal to the difference $x_A - x_B$. Table 11 shows the agreement for the hydrogen halides.

TABLE 11. *Dipole moments and electronegativity differences*

	HF	HCl	HBr	HI
$x_A - x_B$ . . .	1·9	0·9	0·7	0·4
μ (Debyes) . .	1·74†	1·03	0·78	0·38

† D. W. Magnuson, quoted by G. A. Kuipers, *J. Molec. Spec.*, 1958, **2**, 75.

Now there must be some relation between the percentage ionic character (28) and the electronegativity difference $x_A - x_B$. It is of the very essence of the idea of an electronegativity scale that this should be so. The most satisfactory relation† is

$$\text{percentage ionic character} = 16|x_A - x_B| + 3 \cdot 5|x_A - x_B|^2.$$

$$(33)$$

The graph of this expression is shown in Fig. 9.

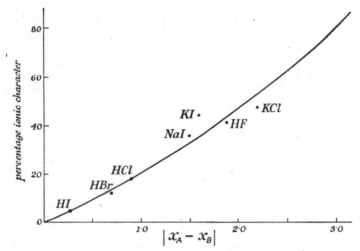

Fig. 5.9. Percentage ionic character in terms of electronegativity difference $|x_A - x_B|$, according to Hannay and Smyth's formula in equation (33). Experimental values shown by dots.

The following simple argument‡ will show the connexion between electronegativity and $\frac{1}{2}(I+E)$. A covalent bond is defined in terms of the wave function (23) by the condition that $c_2 = c_3$. It is clear that in general this will involve $H_{22} = H_{33}$, approximately where

$$H_{22} = \int\int \psi_A(1)\psi_A(2)H\psi_A(1)\psi_A(2)\,d\tau_1 d\tau_2 = \text{energy of structure } A^-B^+,$$

and H_{33} is the energy of A^+B^-. If we may neglect polarization and certain small differences in repulsive energies, this implies that, starting with two

† N. B. Hannay and C. P. Smyth, *J. Amer. Chem. Soc.*, 1946, **68**, 171. We have discounted an earlier formula of Pauling's, viz. $100[1 - \exp\{-(x_A - x_B)^2/4\}]$, which does not fit well for large $x_A - x_B$. But it is only fair to add that there are 'rival' curves to that in Fig. 9, using observed nuclear quadrupole coupling constants as measures of ionicity. A good review is by W. Gordy, *Faraday Soc. Discussions*, 1955, **19**, 14.

‡ R. S. Mulliken, loc. cit.

neutral atoms A and B, the same amount of energy is needed to create A^+B^- as A^-B^+, i.e.

$$I_A - E_B = I_B - E_A.$$

In other words, for a covalent bond

$$I_A + E_A = I_B + E_B.$$

For a polar bond we should expect that

$$(I_A - E_B) - (I_B - E_A) \propto x_A - x_B.$$

This implies that $\qquad x_A \propto (I_A + E_A),$

as required in Mulliken's theory.

It should be added in this connexion that Mulliken's estimates of electro-negativity are fundamentally much more precise than are Pauling's, since they are based entirely on observable quantities. Mulliken has extended his theory to deal with atoms in different stages of hybridization (§ 8.9), and is able thereby to account for such details as the undoubted increase in electronegativity between a carbon atom in methane and in acetylene. This difference is shown by the greater acidity of acetylene.

5.9. Singlets and triplets: the Pauli Exclusion Principle

We must now return to complete a discussion previously left incomplete. In (11 a) and (11 b) we introduced the Heitler–London wave functions

$$\psi_{\pm} = \psi_A(1)\psi_B(2) \pm \psi_B(1)\psi_A(2). \tag{34}$$

The $+$ sign gave rise to the lower energy level: the $-$ sign to a higher one. In addition we can show that the $+$ sign leads to a singlet and the $-$ sign to a triplet energy level, a matter to which reference has already been made in § 3. The distinction arises because of the electron spin. We know (§ 2.5) that the spin appears in the wave function for a single electron either as α or β. This does not, however, settle the matter if there are two or more electrons. Let us consider the specific case of two. Then, if we omit all mention of spin, the wave functions are as in (34). A study of atomic spectra shows that there is very little direct interaction between the spin of an electron and the orbits of other electrons—i.e. except for heavy atoms the spin–orbit interaction is negligible—so we may use the theorem at the end of § 1 to infer that we can incorporate the spins of the two electrons if we multiply the functions (34) by some appropriate spin wave function.

If both electrons have spin α, their combined spin wave function is simply $\alpha(1)\alpha(2)$. Similarly if they have spin β, it is $\beta(1)\beta(2)$.

Difficulty only arises if one of them has spin α and the other spin β.

Let us imagine that electron 1 has spin α, and electron 2 spin β. The wave function is then $\alpha(1)\beta(2)$. But precisely the same point arises as arose in § 2 when discussing the space wave functions. We cannot tell which electron is which, so that we are forced to consider also the spin function $\beta(1)\alpha(2)$.

An identical argument to that which led from (4) to (11) leads us to the allowed combinations for this case. They are

$$\alpha(1)\beta(2) \pm \beta(1)\alpha(2). \tag{35}$$

Combining the allowed spin functions with the allowed space functions leads to the various possibilities listed below

Space factor	*Spin factor*	
	(i)	(ii)
$\psi_A(1)\psi_B(2)+\psi_B(1)\psi_A(2)$ $\times$	$\alpha(1)\beta(2)-\beta(1)\alpha(2)$	$\alpha(1)\alpha(2)$
		$\beta(1)\beta(2)$
		$\alpha(1)\beta(2)+\beta(1)\alpha(2)$
$\psi_A(1)\psi_B(2)-\psi_B(1)\psi_A(2)$ $\times$	$\alpha(1)\alpha(2)$	$\alpha(1)\beta(2)-\beta(1)\alpha(2)$
	$\beta(1)\beta(2)$	
	$\alpha(1)\beta(2)+\beta(1)\alpha(2)$	

The product functions associated with column (i) spin factors are essentially different from those associated with column (ii). This difference is one of symmetry. If we interchange 1 and 2 in every part of the function, we find that the four product functions involving column (i) are all multiplied by -1, those in column (ii) being unchanged. We say that the first are antisymmetrical with respect to interchange of the electrons, the second are symmetrical. Now it may be shown from the general principles of quantum theory that a symmetry property of this kind is unchanged (is 'a constant of the motion'), so that symmetrical wave functions remain symmetrical, etc. There is no way of deciding *a priori* whether nature requires symmetrical or antisymmetrical functions. But experiment shows† very clearly that for electrons, protons, neutrons, and all particles with an odd spin $((n+\frac{1}{2})h/2\pi$ in the usual units) only antisymmetrical wave functions occur: and for alpha particles, photons, certain types of meson, and all particles with an even spin $(nh/2\pi$, where n is integral or zero), only symmetrical ones are found. We must therefore reject column (ii) of the wave functions in the table above, and accept only column (i). This shows us that the ground state wave function $\psi_A(1)\psi_B(2)+\psi_B(1)\psi_A(2)$ can have only one possible spin factor, but that the excited state function can have three. If we include spin–orbit interaction the three energies are slightly separated, leading us to the statement that the ground state (11 a) is a singlet, the upper state (11 b) is a triplet. As electrons cannot change their spin (except very slowly due to spin–spin and spin–orbit interactions) no direct transitions between the states (11 a) and (11 b) are allowed.

The statement that every final wave function for an atom or a molecule must be antisymmetrical in every pair of electrons is one of the most fundamental statements of the Pauli Exclusion Principle. It follows from the fact, which may be proved without difficulty, that if two electrons had entirely equivalent orbitals, including spin, and we accepted the principle of indistinguishability of all electrons, then any conceivable wave function that might represent them would necessarily be unchanged if we interchanged the numbering of the electrons. This conflicts with the principle of antisymmetry.

This may be put more generally. Suppose that it is known that the orbitals A, B,..., K are occupied by electrons 1, 2,..., k. In this notation the spin factor is included in the functions A,.... . Then the argument that led us from (4) to (11) leads us to replace the initial product wave function

$$\psi = A(1)B(2) \ldots K(k),$$

which implies that the electrons are distinct, since we are told which electron is in which orbital, by the determinant

$$\psi = \begin{vmatrix} A(1) & A(2) & . & . & A(k) \\ B(1) & B(2) & . & . & B(k) \\ . & . & . & . & . & . \\ K(1) & K(2) & . & . & K(k) \end{vmatrix}, \tag{36}$$

† Discovered first in this form by W. Heisenberg, *Z. Phys.*, 1926, **39**, 499, to distinguish between *ortho*- and *para*-helium.

which takes account of their identity. It follows at once from (36) that no two electrons can have completely identical orbitals, including spin, for if any two of A, B,... are equal, two rows of the determinant are identical, the determinant vanishes identically, and there is no acceptable wave function.

When we use the spin function $\alpha(1)\alpha(2)$ it is clear that the spins are parallel, having equal components along any chosen direction: and similarly for $\beta(1)\beta(2)$. The total electron spin is thus 2 units, i.e. $2 \times \frac{1}{2}\frac{h}{2\pi} = h/2\pi$. It may also be shown that in $\alpha(1)\beta(2)+\beta(1)\alpha(2)$ the total spin is again 2 units. The distinction between the three spin functions $\alpha(1)\alpha(2)$, $\beta(1)\beta(2)$, $\alpha(1)\beta(2)+\beta(1)\alpha(2)$ is that although all three correspond to the same total spin, they are such that the component of this spin in the chosen direction is $+\frac{h}{2\pi}$, $-\frac{h}{2\pi}$, 0, respectively. However, in the singlet series, for which the spin function is $\alpha(1)\beta(2)-\beta(1)\alpha(2)$, the total spin is zero, as well as its component. So the two electron spins really are anti-parallel. It is this fact which justifies us in saying that the condition for a firm bond is the pairing together of electrons in orbitals ψ_A and ψ_B with opposed (i.e. anti-parallel) spins.

Similar arguments about spin apply equally in the molecular-orbital theory of Chapter IV. It should now be clear why (§ 4.7 and Fig. 4.11) the O_2 molecular configuration

$$KK(z\sigma)^2(y\sigma)^2(x\sigma)^2(w\pi)^4(v\pi_y)(v\pi_z)$$

leads to a triplet or singlet, according as the spins of the electrons in the two $v\pi$ m.o.'s are parallel or anti-parallel. Without actual calculation, however, such arguments do not tell us which possibility leads to the lower total energy for the molecule. It is not necessary in the above that the two m.o.'s $(v\pi_y)$ and $(v\pi_z)$ should have equal energy. Indeed, it follows at once that whenever we have all m.o. levels doubly-filled, except two, which contain one electron each, the resulting configuration must be either a singlet or a triplet, according to the spins of the two electrons in these orbitals. With three 'odd-electrons' (cf. the N atom) we find a doublet or a quartet level; and with four unpaired electrons (cf. the important case of an excited C atom) we have a singlet, triplet, or quintet level.

PRELIMINARY COMPARISON OF MOLECULAR-ORBITAL AND VALENCE-BOND THEORIES

6.1. Significance of pairing

A PRELIMINARY comparison of the m.o. and v.b. theories is now possible. In the first place it is necessary to stress that both theories are in the nature of approximations—and that, even as approximations, their use is prohibitively complicated without the introduction of certain empirical constants or the use of electronic computers. It is, for example, an approximation to suppose that the pairing together of any two electrons in atoms A and B is sufficiently unique to render all other possible pairings irrelevant —and that is what the simple v.b. theory does suppose. It is equally an approximation to suppose, as in the m.o. theory, that there are m.o.'s at all, so that the same kind of technique which works well for atoms may be applied to molecules. Even if, after accepting these theoretical approximations, we do the best we can with our subsequent calculation, we know that errors in the absolute value of the energy of the order of 1–2 eV† per bond will inevitably occur in both methods. In practice, of course, there are limitations to the amount of calculation that is worth while, so that an additional source of error, up to 1 eV, is introduced. Such large errors ought by this time to have convinced us that it is in the field of qualitative understanding, and not quantitative calculation, that the value of the theories must be sought.

In this qualitative understanding, the two theories have much in common. Thus they both assert that the bonding electrons 'belong' to both nuclei, though they put this in different terms. The m.o. description $\psi_A + \lambda\psi_B$ immediately stresses this 'common belonging': so also the v.b. wave function $\psi_A(1)\psi_B(2) + \psi_B(1)\psi_A(2)$ implies that electron 1 may be found around either A or B.

In a similar way both theories introduce the mutual pairing of

† 1 eV = 23·06 kcal/mole.

orbitals and of spins, but again they put this in characteristically different ways. This is sufficiently important to be worth describing a little more fully. If we consider the m.o. theory first, we determine certain allowed m.o. energy levels—the cells of Fig. 4.11 for example—and then we feed the electrons into these levels. What happens is that each electron tries to get into the lowest possible m.o., and they would therefore all go into the very lowest if it were not for the Pauli Exclusion Principle. By allowing only two electrons to have the same space wave function, and then with opposed spins, this automatically tells us that the electrons must be thought of in pairs, with anti-parallel spin. But in certain circumstances, as, for example, when there is degeneracy such as occurs in O_2 (Fig. 4.11 again), two or more of the electrons are able to avoid pairing (which in fact, they would always like to do on account of a greater Coulomb repulsion between electrons in the same space-orbit) and we have a triplet, or higher multiplet level. In a single sentence, the pairing arises solely because of the Exclusion Principle and the desire to have as low an energy as possible.

All this is a little less obvious in the case of the Heitler–London theory. The pairing of orbits is clear enough, but the pairing of spins needs a separate explanation. Consider a bond (e.g. H_2 or LiH) which involves just two electrons. Then the Pauli Principle requires that the complete wave function, including spin, shall be antisymmetric. This may be achieved by having spin antisymmetric and space symmetric, or vice versa. Now if the space part is symmetric, of form $\psi_A(1)\psi_B(2)+\psi_B(1)\psi_A(2)$, there is (see § 2) a piling-up of charge between the nuclei, and a tendency to bond. If the space part is antisymmetric, of form $\psi_A(1)\psi_B(2)-\psi_B(1)\psi_A(2)$, there is no piling-up and no tendency to bond. Bonding, therefore, requires the spin part to be antisymmetric, a condition only possible of fulfilment if the spins are opposed. All this means that spin-pairing is not forced upon us as a direct fundamental principle; it is forced upon us by a combination of the symmetry requirements of the Pauli Principle and the need for a certain choice of possible space functions in order to give bonding. Contrary to what is sometimes said, in this theory it is the space part which determines the spin alinements; and not primarily the other way round.

This pairing of electrons is, of course, the wave-mechanical justification for the original idea of G. N. Lewis (§ 1.2). It goes on farther and justifies the octet rule of Langmuir and Kossel. Again the explanations are a little different in the two theories, though the conclusion is the same. In the v.b. theory we can only form a two-electron bond by pairing an orbit on atom A with one on B: and only one electron is allowed to be in each of these orbits before the pairing. The number of unpaired electrons is the valence number of an atom. If we agree to interpret a wave function $\psi_A(1)\psi_B(2)+\psi_B(1)\psi_A(2)$ as meaning that both electrons are associated with both nuclei ('shared-electrons' in the original sense of Lewis), then the formation of a bond fills up the a.o.'s ψ_A and ψ_B by putting two electrons in each with opposed spins. With atoms in the first two short rows of the periodic table, this filling-up process may go on as long as there are unpaired electrons, that is, until the octets around each atom are complete. Since, in general, the use of an unpaired electron in the formation of a bond adds to the total binding energy, we should expect, where possible, that atoms would try to surround themselves with such octets. With heavier atoms, including those in the long periods, on account of d electrons, the rule does not hold. This octet formation explains at once the stabilities of many molecules (e.g. HCl, HF, F_2) and the willingness of other radicals with an odd number of electrons either to give or receive an extra one (e.g. OH^-, SO_4^{--}). The matter is so familiar that it does not need further elaboration.

In the m.o. theory each bonding electron goes into an orbital $\psi_A+\lambda\psi_B$, and in general there are two electrons with this space wave function. If we associate these electrons with both A and B, and if we use the results on pages 98–99 to deal with electrons in anti-bonding m.o.'s, the conclusion about the octet rule follows at once.

There is one further point in the m.o. theory which arises at this stage. Since we regard the electron orbitals as polycentric, we can speak of molecular shells, just as we speak of atomic shells.

For example, in a homonuclear diatomic molecule such as F_2, we could speak of all the m.o.'s which arise from the atomic L-shell orbitals as forming a molecular shell. Sub-shells exist in the same way, and are sometimes convenient for rapid description of the electronic structure. Thus $\sigma^2\sigma^{*2}$ is one possible sub-shell, and $\pi^4\pi^{*4}$ is another (the π-shell).

This continual reference to m.o.'s for individual electrons has certain other advantages. It enables us to speak of bonding and anti-bonding electrons, and to introduce (Table 5, p. 102) a definition of bond order which involves the numbers of both types. In case any confusion may arise, it must be stressed that the description of an orbital as bonding or anti-bonding refers only to its effect on the dissociation energy D of the bond. If removal of the electron increases D, the electron is anti-bonding, and vice versa. This effect must be distinguished from the changes that occur in the total energy E of the system. Removal of any electron in the molecule must necessarily decrease the heat of formation out of nuclei+electrons. For example, the $1s$ electrons in Cl_2 are non-bonding since, although considerable energy is required to remove one of them by ionization (i.e. E is much altered), this removal makes no effective difference to the dissociation energy of the bond D (Cl_2).

Both theories preserve the important σ, π,... character of separate bonds, but bond order, in the v.b. theory, is simply the number of pairs of electrons whose spins are coupled together: the notion of anti-bonding only arises because there is a repulsion between all electrons whose spins are not paired, so that, e.g. in F_2, the bond would arise from pairing the $2p_x$ (σ-type) orbits and there would be repulsion between the four atomic pairs of $2p_y$ and $2p_z$ electrons. This repulsion corresponds to the m.o. conclusion that a bonding and anti-bonding orbital of the same kind, such as $\sigma\sigma^*$, or $\pi\pi^*$, are together equivalent to a slight repulsion.

The fact that we discuss the behaviour of individual electrons is a great advantage when dealing with electronic excitation, and makes the m.o. method conceptually much the simpler for this purpose. The following examples will make this clear. In H_2 two of the many possible electronic transitions could be represented on the m.o. theory by

$$(a) \quad (\sigma 1s)^2 \rightarrow (\sigma 1s)(\sigma^* 1s),$$

$$(b) \quad (\sigma 1s)^2 \rightarrow (\sigma 1s)(\pi 2p).$$

In the first, an electron is excited from $\sigma 1s$ to $\sigma^* 1s$, and in the second to $\pi 2p$. In v.b. theory the first would be represented by a transition from the conventional ground state to a purely ionic-type wave function $\psi_A(1)\psi_A(2) - \psi_B(1)\psi_B(2)$; and in the second to a wave function involving no less than four terms of the type $s_A(1)\pi_B(2)$, on account of the fact that we do not know whether the π orbital is to be associated with A or B, and correspondingly the s orbital with B or A. But for both transitions, in v.b. language we are obliged to consider wave functions intimately involving both electrons: in m.o. language we need only consider the one electron which is excited, leaving the unexcited ($\sigma 1s$) orbital more or less unchanged. This is the great advantage which results from the idea (§§ 2.8 and 4.7) of a molecular configuration.

6.2. Charge-density

An important fact about the two theories is that they both predict a piling-up of charge between the nuclei. This may be seen easily enough in Figs. 4.4 and 4.5 in the m.o. theory, but it follows quite simply from the electronic density function. The ground state of H_2 will serve as an example.

In the m.o. theory there are two electrons, and according to § 4.6 each of them has an orbital.

$$(\psi_A + \psi_B)/\{2(1+S)\}^{\frac{1}{2}}, \tag{1}$$

where S is the overlap integral $\int \psi_A \psi_B \, d\tau$. Each separate electron contributes to the density of the charge-cloud an amount

$$\frac{(\psi_A + \psi_B)^2}{2(1+S)} = \frac{\psi_A^2 + \psi_B^2 + 2\psi_A\psi_B}{2(1+S)}. \tag{2}$$

So the total electronic density is

$$\frac{\psi_A^2 + \psi_B^2 + 2\psi_A\psi_B}{1+S} = \psi_A^2 + \psi_B^2 + \frac{2\psi_A\psi_B - S(\psi_A^2 + \psi_B^2)}{1+S}. \tag{3}$$

This shows that the actual density in the molecule exceeds the sum of the two isolated-atom densities $\psi_A^2 + \psi_B^2$ in those regions where $\psi_A \psi_B$ is large; in other regions it is less. Now the product $\psi_A \psi_B$ can be large only if neither ψ_A nor ψ_B is small. This will occur in the region between the nuclei, since, as Fig. 4.5 shows, at least one of ψ_A and ψ_B is extremely small outside this overlapping region. A similar argument shows that except in this central region the molecular charge-density is less than the sum of the two atomic densities. Thus the formation of the bond is accompanied by a flow of charge-cloud into the central part between the nuclei. This explains why the size of the molecule is usually less than the sum of the sizes of the two atoms. But of course with the σ^*1s m.o. $\psi_A - \psi_B$, exactly the opposite holds. The last term in (3) which measures the migration of charge in bond formation could be called the bond charge.

The v.b. theory gives a similar result. We have to start with the joint probability function $\{\psi_A(1)\psi_B(2) + \psi_B(1)\psi_A(2)\}^2/2(1+S^2)$, which measures the probability that electron 1 is in unit volume around one point, and electron 2 is in unit volume around some other point. If we are only interested in the density distribution of electron 1, we must sum this probability function for all positions of electron 2. Thus, instead of (2), we have a density function for electron 1 given by

$$\rho(1) = \int \frac{\psi_A^2(1)\psi_B^2(2) + \psi_B^2(1)\psi_A^2(2) + 2\psi_A(1)\psi_B(1)\psi_A(2)\psi_B(2)}{2(1+S^2)} \, d\tau_2$$

$$= \frac{\psi_A^2 + \psi_B^2 + 2S\psi_A\psi_B}{2(1+S^2)}. \quad (4)$$

The similarity between (2) and (4) is very close, though since $S < 1$, (2) gives a slightly greater piling-up of charge than (4). The truth almost certainly lies close to these two values.

This conclusion about the charge-cloud holds quite generally, so that we may describe a single bond as due to the pairing of two electrons resulting in a greater probability that both are to be found in the region between the nuclei, and a smaller probability that they are outside this region. The total amount of bond charge between the nuclei is not large, being usually of the order of $\frac{1}{10}$ to $\frac{1}{4}$ of an electron. But it is largely due to the lowering of potential energy as a result of the fact that this charge is near to two positive nuclei instead of one, that the molecule is formed and is stable.

6.3. Polarity

There are two distinct definitions of a covalent bond. In the m.o. method, a covalent bond is defined to be one in which the bonding m.o. is of the form $\psi_A + \lambda\psi_B$ with $\lambda = 1$. In the v.b.

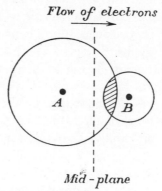

Flow of electrons

A B

Mid-plane

FIG. 6.1. The build-up of charge in the bond occurs in the overlap region shown shaded. This contributes a dipole moment in the direction of the arrow.

theory it is one for which the coefficients c_2, c_3 of the ionic structures in the resonance hybrid

$$c_1\psi_{\text{cov}}(A-B)+c_2\psi_{\text{ion}}(A^+B^-)+c_3\psi_{\text{ion}}(A^-B^+)$$

are equal. In both cases we can say that, on the average, there is equal negative charge to be associated with the two nuclei, though in fact, as (4.33) shows, this does not necessarily mean that there is no dipole moment. This may be described by saying that in addition to any polarity due to ionic structures, there may be a *homopolar dipole*.

There is a simple physical explanation of the origin of this homopolar dipole. Thus consider (Fig. 1) the case of a covalent bond between two orbitals of different size. The figure shows their boundary surfaces (p. 20) and the region of overlapping. It is obvious that this overlap region lies on the side of the midplane towards the smaller atom. But we have seen in § 2 that this is the region where the build-up of charge occurs. Hence the bond-charge is not central, and gives rise to a dipole moment, whose negative end is towards the smaller atomic orbital involved in the bond.

This homopolar dipole is often neglected: but a simple calculation shows that this neglect is not valid. For consider the homopolar dipole associated with a covalent m.o. $\psi_A + \psi_B$, where ψ_A and ψ_B are the $1s$ a.o.'s of two

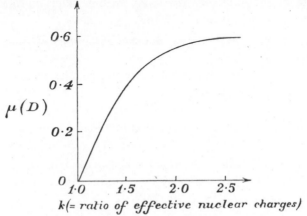

$\mu(D)$

$k(=$ *ratio of effective nuclear charges*$)$

Fig. 6.2. Homopolar dipole term for molecule $A-B$.

nuclear charges e and ke. If we measure distances in a_0, then these wave functions are

$$\psi_A = \pi^{-\frac{1}{2}}e^{-r_a}, \qquad \psi_B = (k^3/\pi)^{\frac{1}{2}}e^{-kr_b}.$$

It follows, from (4.32), that

$$\bar{x}_{AB} = \frac{k^{\frac{3}{2}}}{\pi}\int xe^{-r_a-kr_b}d\tau,$$

and that the homopolar dipole $= 2e\bar{x}_{AB}$

$$= \frac{5\cdot12\bar{x}_{AB}}{1+S_{AB}} \text{ Debyes.} \qquad (5)$$

Fig. 2 shows how this dipole moment depends on k for the particular case of a bond length $R_{AB} = 2a_0$. When $k = 1$, so that the molecule is homonuclear, $\mu = 0$, but even a small asymmetry leads to a contribution of the order of $0\cdot3$ D. The more dissimilar the two atoms are in size, the larger is this homopolar dipole term. For atoms as distinct as H and Cl, the homopolar dipole is approximately equal to $1\cdot0$ Debye. The calculation shows how dangerous it was, on page 108, to neglect $\bar{x}_{AB}$ completely.

With a bond that is not covalent, the polarity is expressed in different ways in the two theories. In the v.b. theory polarity is shown by the relative weight of the chief ionic structure, and in the m.o. theory by the coefficient λ in the orbital $\psi_A + \lambda \psi_B$. This latter method appears the more natural and conceptually the simpler, but the structures used in the v.b. description do correspond to pictures long familiar, in classical form, to experimental chemistry, and this link with the older and more conventional language is of considerable value. Both methods predict dipole moments in substantially the same terms. This moment is the sum of four contributions, of which

(a) one is due to the asymmetry of charge in the bonding electrons;

(b) a second is the homopolar dipole, arising from inequality of size in the atoms;

(c) a third is due to the possible asymmetry (e.g. hybridization, see Chapter VIII) of the a.o.'s involved in the bond;

(d) the fourth is the polarization of any non-bonding electrons.

Accurate calculation of any of these contributions presents serious difficulties, but reasonable estimates may be made without too much trouble.

6.4. Equivalence of the two methods

We have seen that the v.b. and m.o. methods are both approximations. We must now show that if we carry the approximations a little farther than the first stages, the methods converge and become completely equivalent. We can see this most easily in terms of a homonuclear molecule, such as H_2. According to the Heitler–London treatment, the wave function, neglecting spin, is

$$\psi_A(1)\psi_B(2) + \psi_B(1)\psi_A(2). \tag{6}$$

Let us abbreviate this to $ab + ba$, in each case regarding the first factor of each product as a function of the position of electron 1, and the second of electron 2. The corresponding m.o. wave function is

$$\{\psi_A(1) + \psi_B(1)\}\{\psi_A(2) + \psi_B(2)\}, \quad \text{i.e.} \quad (a+b)(a+b). \tag{7}$$

Neither of these is a perfect solution of the wave equation; they may both be improved by adding other functions with the same symmetry properties. Thus (6) is improved by writing

$$(ab+ba)+\lambda(aa+bb),\tag{8}$$

and (7) by writing

$$(a+b)(a+b)+k(a-b)(a-b).\tag{9}$$

Equation (8) represents the interaction of the purely covalent function with the appropriate ionic function, and equation (9) represents the interaction of a configuration in which both electrons are in the bonding orbital $a+b$ and a configuration in which both are in the anti-bonding orbital $a-b$. It is not difficult to show that there is no interaction with a configuration $(a+b)(a-b)$ on account of unequal symmetry. A simple expansion of (8) and (9) shows that, apart from a normalizing factor (which is of no significance), they are entirely equivalent, provided that

$$\lambda = -\frac{1+k}{1-k}.\tag{10}$$

Now in each case we choose k and λ (§ 3.8) so as to make the energy function stationary: consequently we shall get precisely the same wave function by either method. In this way, therefore, both the m.o. and v.b. methods become equivalent if we carry them beyond the simplest forms. This is quite generally true[†] however complicated the molecule may be.

We have already seen (Fig. 5.5) how the coefficient λ, which measures the importance of the ionic structure, varies with R for the H_2 molecule. Its maximum value is about $\frac{1}{4}$ and occurs near the equilibrium distance. Equation (10) allows us to infer the value of k. But more significance attaches to this coefficient if we normalize the component configurational wave functions in (9), writing it in the form

$$\frac{(a+b)(a+b)}{2\{1+S\}}-\kappa\frac{(a-b)(a-b)}{2\{1-S\}},\tag{11}$$

where

$$\kappa = \frac{1-S}{1+S}k.\tag{12}$$

κ now measures the weight of the excited configuration $(a-b)(a-b)$

† H. C. Longuet-Higgins, *Proc. Phys. Soc.*, 1948, **60**, 270.

which interacts with the basic configuration $(a+b)(a+b)$. The graph of κ against R is shown in Fig. 3.† At the equilibrium distance κ is rather less than λ, showing that the deficiencies in the two simple treatments are about equal in magnitude (incidentally the energy given by the v.b. method is a little better than that by the m.o. method, but other properties are almost the same). As the internuclear distance increases, however, the ionic

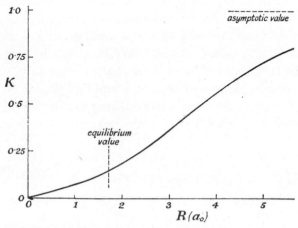

Fig. 6.3. Configuration interaction in H_2. (See equation (11).)

contribution, measured by λ, decreases to zero, but the configurational interaction, measured by κ, increases up to unity. This is a serious situation, warning us that at large distances the simple m.o. method is quite unreliable. For example, if we wished to follow the whole course of a chemical reaction by calculating the energy of the compound system at all stages of the reaction,‡ we should have to choose the v.b. method rather than the m.o. if we wanted anything like reliable results.

This failure of the m.o. description at large internuclear distances illustrates one big distinction between the two theories. In a single sentence, we can say that the m.o. method under-estimates

† C. A. Coulson and Miss I. Fischer, *Phil. Mag.*, 1949, **40**, 386. But the first attempt at such a comparison is due to J. C. Slater, *Phys. Rev.*, 1930, **35**, 509.

‡ See, for example, H. Eyring, J. Walter, and G. E. Kimball, *Quantum Chemistry*, John Wiley, 1944, or S. Glasstone, K. J. Laidler, and H. Eyring, *Theory of Rate Processes*, McGraw-Hill, 1941, for a description of this very important part of chemical kinetics, developed largely by Eyring and Polanyi.

electron-correlation, and the v.b. method over-estimates it. By this we mean that the presence of the Coulomb repulsion e^2/r_{12} between the two electrons of a bond must actually tend to keep them apart. There is, for example, only a small chance that both electrons should be simultaneously in exactly the same small region, and if the first electron is momentarily in the neighbourhood of one nucleus, there is a greater chance of the second electron being away from this nucleus, and in the neighbourhood of the other. We say that their positions are correlated, the one with the other. Such correlation is completely absent from the simple m.o. wave function $(a+b)(a+b)$, since the distribution of electron 2 is entirely independent of the instantaneous position of electron 1. When electron 1 is near A, electron 2 has an appreciable possibility of being there also. Indeed, if we expand the m.o. and write it as

$$ab+ba+aa+bb,$$

we can interpret it to mean that there is an equal probability of $\frac{1}{4}$ for the four components ab, ba, aa, and bb. These ratios are independent of the nuclear separation so that we should be led to infer that when the molecule dissociated there was a chance of 2 in 4 that it separated as two H atoms, and 1 in 4 each that it separated as A^-B^+ or A^+B^-. It is precisely the omission of any reference to electron-correlation that allows the possibility of A^-B^+ and A^+B^-. Electron-correlation has the effect of diminishing the weight of the component $aa+bb$. On the other hand, the simple v.b. wave function $ab+ba$, although it correctly describes the dissociation, over-emphasizes electron-correlation; for it insists that, at all internuclear distances, if one electron is near A, the other must be near B.

This unsatisfactory character of the m.o. theory at large distances has one other important corollary. It implies that the correlation diagrams for heteronuclear diatomics, such as Fig. 4.12 in which we follow the behaviour of individual m.o.'s as we change from the united-atom through the actual molecule to the separated atoms, must be treated with suspicion, since they may lead us into quite false conclusions. This is because, as was stated at the end of § 4.8, they imply that both electrons of the bond (which naturally occupy the same m.o.) will behave in the same way on dissociation. Most frequently this will not be the case since electron repulsion, and the saturation of electronegativity of the more electronegative atom, will force them on to different nuclei. This difficulty on dissociation disappears if we use a m.o. wave function with configuration interaction.

It seems probable that the general situation we have just described for certain simple molecules holds for other molecules too: and then the truth will lie somewhere intermediate between the v.b. and m.o. theories. For that reason, in cases where both theories predict similar conclusions, there is considerable ground for believing that these conclusions are correct. Fortunately this is usually the case. But there are occasions where it is not, and then we cannot tell, without further inquiry, which is the more valid approximation.

6.5. One-electron and three-electron bonds

Our discussion has so far dealt almost exclusively with two-electron bonds. But there are quite interesting stable molecules in which an odd number of electrons participate, and which we may call one-electron and three-electron bonds. The simplest of all one-electron bonds is the hydrogen molecule ion H_2^+, already dealt with quite fully in Chapter IV. Indeed there is no difficulty at all in the m.o. description of these bonds. The only difference between a one- and two-electron bond is that one of the allowed orbitals is only half-filled. In H_2^+ the ground state is simply $(\sigma 1s)$, and in Li_2^+ it is $KK(\sigma 2s)$, etc. It is not surprising that the strength of such bonds is about one-half the strength of the corresponding two-electron bonds in H_2 and Li_2. It is true that the matter is not quite so simple† as might be suggested by the naïve argument that there is only one instead of two bonding electrons; for on passing from H_2 to H_2^+, or Li_2 to Li_2^+, an important repulsion energy between the two electrons is lost, and is balanced by an increased internuclear separation.

The three-electron bond is treated similarly, and in fact does not appear as a separate problem in m.o. theory. In He_2^+, for

† See § 4.6 for a discussion of this point.

example, which is known† to be stable, the m.o. description (Table 5, p. 102) is simply $(\sigma 1s)^2(\sigma^*1s)$; its stability is to be attributed to the removal of an anti-bonding orbital σ^*1s, leaving an excess of bonding over anti-bonding m.o.'s. Such bonds are called three-electron bonds because the three electrons involved all arise from similar a.o.'s (here $1s$) in the isolated atoms.

By far the most interesting three-electron bond is the case of nitric oxide NO (see Fig. 12 in § 4.8). If we take the x-axis along the line of centres, we can describe the separated atoms‡ as

$$ \text{N} \quad (1s)^2(2s)^2(2p_x)(2p_y)(2p_z), $$
$$ \text{O} \quad (1s)^2(2s)^2(2p_x)(2p_y)(2p_z)^2. $$

The m.o. description of the molecule is then

$$ \text{NO} \quad KK(2s_O)^2(2s_N)^2(\sigma 2p_x)^2(\pi 2p_y)^2(\pi 2p_z)^2(\pi^*2p_z). \tag{13} $$

The groups $(\sigma 2p_x)^2(\pi 2p_y)^2$ provide a σ- and a π-bond respectively, but the group $(\pi 2p_z)^2(\pi^*2p_z)$ is a three-electron bond. It is a result of the additional stability conferred by this bond, and the mutual repulsion of non-paired electrons discussed in § 7.7, that no firm chemical dimer (ON)—(NO) is actually found. The species $(NO)_2$ which does exist consists of two separate NO molecules, parallel to each other and arranged head-to-tail at a mutual distance large compared to a normal bond length. The two molecules are thus held together by weak forces, partly the electrostatic interaction of their two dipoles, and partly dispersion forces. It is not surprising that the NO^+ ion, in which the antibonding π^*2p has been removed, is actually more strongly bound than the normal molecule; nor that the first excited electronic level,§ in which the π^*2p-electron is excited to an outer, Rydberg-type, relatively non-bonding m.o., behaves just as if a triple bond existed between the N and O atoms. Thus on excitation the bond length drops from $1\cdot 14$ A to $1\cdot 06$ A, the length to be expected for a triple bond.

There is one further point about NO which is of interest because

† Spectroscopically estimated $D = 2\cdot 5$ eV. Calculated $D = 2\cdot 2$ eV by S. Weinbaum, *J. Chem. Phys.*, 1935, **3**, 547.

‡ We could, of course, interchange the y and z directions without affecting our description of NO. An LCAO calculation is due to H. Brion, C. M. Moser, and M. Yamazaki, *J. Chem. Phys.*, 1959, **30**, 673.

§ See W. Jevons, *Report on Band Spectra of Diatomic Molecules*, 1932, Physical Society, 288.

it illustrates a form of argument which is now being increasingly used. This is the numerical value of the dipole moment, which, on the grounds that O is more electronegative than N, would not have been expected to have an experimental value so small that $\mu \leqslant 0\cdot2$ D. In the notation of (13) it is probable that the $(\sigma 2p_x)^2$ electrons are polar with direction $\overset{+\ -}{\text{NO}}$, and that this uses up the excess electronegative character of O, so that the $(\pi 2p_y)^2(\pi 2p_z)^2$ group is practically non-polar. The remaining electron $(\pi^* 2p_z)$ was originally an oxygen electron, but in the m.o. it is probably much more nearly a covalent orbital similar to $(\pi 2p_z)$. In such a case the almost complete cancellation of the moment due to the former electron becomes at least understandable.† This explanation would lead us to believe that three-electron bonds, when they exist at all, are not highly polar. Experiment seems to confirm this view.

In the v.b. theory the explanations of one- and three-electron bonds‡ are as follows. Consider the one-electron case first, choosing H_2^+ as a particular example. We may imagine that the single electron is either on nucleus A or on nucleus B, so that we are presented with two 'structures' (a) and (b) in which the dot denotes the odd electron.

(a) H·   H

(b) H   ·H

Resonance between these structures leads to combinations $(a)\pm(b)$, and the rest of the discussion now follows just as in the m.o. theory. With the three-electron bond, as in He_2^+, the structures are (c) and (d):

(c) He: He·

(d) He·   He:

Resonance between these structures leads us once more to combinations $(c)\pm(d)$. We cannot, with a wave function of this kind, speak of any pairings of electrons between the nuclei A and B. The only pairings that exist are within each separate structure,

---

† Another possible explanation of this lack of dipole moment is suggested in § 8.11.

‡ L. Pauling, *J. Amer. Chem. Soc.*, 1931, **53**, 3225.

and the final wave function can be interpreted to imply that there is one electron (though we do not know which!) that is sometimes paired with an electron on A and sometimes on B. Such bonds are occasionally written in the symbolic form $A \cdots B$. In the case when the atoms A and B are not identical, the energies of the structures (a) and (b), or (c) and (d), will not be the same, and the conditions for strong resonance will not be satisfied. One- and three-electron bonds are not stable therefore, except between atoms of nearly equal electronegativity. This is one reason for their relative rarity and small dipole moment.

On the whole the m.o. description of these odd-electron molecules seems simpler and more convincing than the v.b. description. It is certainly an advantage not to have to invoke any new mechanism for these bonds, and not to have to refer, as in the v.b. explanation, to a 'new type of bond'.

This concludes our preliminary comparison of the two theories. Practically everything that we have hitherto said about diatomic molecules carries over in similar form to polyatomic molecules; and indeed much of its significance will become clearer in the course of the next four chapters.

POLYATOMIC MOLECULES

7.1. Localized and non-localized molecular orbitals: bond properties

WE have now reached the stage when we can discuss polyatomic molecules. By this time the distinctions and parallels between the v.b. and m.o. theories are sufficiently clear for us to be able to discuss both methods in the same chapter without causing confusion. Our next four chapters are concerned with different types of polyatomic molecule: first, the quantum-mechanically simplest; then the whole field of non-conjugated carbon compounds, in which the important concept of hybridization is developed; next come aromatic and conjugated molecules, and finally molecular complexes.

When we attempt to apply m.o. methods to polyatomics, we are met by an immediate difficulty. This can best be illustrated by means of an example. Let us consider the methane molecule CH_4. According to the principles of Chapter IV, which proved so effective for diatomic molecules, we shall argue that the ten electrons of methane are distributed so that two of them complete the K-shell of carbon, and the remaining eight occupy m.o.'s of a polycentric character embracing all five nuclei. Such a description presents more problems than it solves—for it is well known that the C—H bond has characteristic properties, such as its length, force constant, and polarity, which, while not exactly constant, vary only relatively little from molecule to molecule. For example, the existence of a characteristic infra-red CH vibration frequency in the region of $3\,\mu$ is used not only to verify the presence of CH bonds in an unknown molecule, but also to estimate how many such bonds there are. Since all the bond properties which we have listed depend upon the detailed distribution of electric charge, it is hard to see why the CH bond should be so reproducible in character and so relatively insensitive to the nature of the other substituents around the carbon atom, when the m.o's themselves must be quite sensitive to them. In simple terms:

bond properties seem to imply localized distributions of charge, but the m.o. method seems to require delocalized orbitals. The only satisfactory way out of the dilemma is that a possible alternative description can be found in which, despite the polyatomic nature of the molecule, the m.o.'s are effectively bi-centric. Following F. Hund† we can say that chemical intuition and experience force us to seek a replacement of the anticipated non-localized orbitals by localized ones. In this way the bonds of a polyatomic molecule will each separately resemble a bond such as those discussed in Chapters IV and V.

Energy considerations support this view. The fact that the heat of formation of H_2O (219 kcal/mole) differs by only about 10 per cent. from twice the heat of formation of the OH radical ($2 \times 99 \cdot 4 = 198 \cdot 8$ kcal/mole) leads us immediately to the conclusion that the two OH bonds in H_2O closely resemble the one bond in the OH radical. Precisely the same situation is found in the paraffin series, where the assumptions‡ that the C—C and C—H bond energies are 80 and 98 kcal/mole respectively lead to molecular heats of formation in error by only 1 or 2 kcal/mole. Indeed, the very existence of tables of bond energies§ forces us to the conclusion that in general bonding electrons are localized in the region of one particular bond.

It should be added at this point that completely delocalized m.o.'s can be set up, and their details calculated. We shall return to this matter later (§ 3). But it is important that we should emphasize at once the distinction which we have made between localized and non-localized m.o.'s. Of course, if localized m.o.'s can be used, it is better to do so, for they are vastly easier to imagine and handle than are non-localized m.o.'s, and they preserve the idea of a bond between two of the atoms in a polyatomic molecule, represented in conventional chemical diagrams by the symbol $A—B$, as in the molecule $A—B—C$. If we do not use localized m.o.'s for those simple cases where they can be used,

---

† Z. Phys., 1931, **73**, 1, 565; 1932, **74**, 1, 429.

‡ These are not the only values that would do this.

§ Originally introduced by K. Fajans, Ber., 1920, **53**, 643; 1922, **55**, 2826. For numerical values see Tables 12 (single bonds, p. 185) and 14 (multiple bonds, p. 190).

we do violence to the long chemical tradition dating from G. N. Lewis's famous 1916 paper on electron-pair bonds. However, this language of localized m.o.'s breaks down completely when we come to deal with aromatic and conjugated compounds in Chapter IX: and it is equally necessary to abandon it when discussing the excited states (as opposed to the ground state) of molecules such as H_2O, NH_3, and CH_4, where there is a certain amount of geometrical symmetry.

It is possible to give a plausible justification for the use of localized m.o.'s if we invoke the criterion of maximum overlapping of § 4.3. Let us illustrate it in terms of the water molecule H_2O.

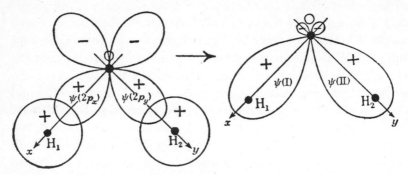

FIG. 7.1. Localized molecular orbitals for water H_2O.

In Fig. 1 the plane of the molecule coincides with the plane of the paper, which is the xy-plane, and the oxygen atom is at the origin. Now the available a.o.'s for our LCAO wave functions are the two $1s$ orbitals of the hydrogens H_1 and H_2, and the $2p_x$ and $2p_y$ orbitals of oxygen. This is because the $2p_z$ electrons are not able to combine with the hydrogen $1s$ a.o.'s on account of their antisymmetry in the xy-plane: and the oxygen $2s$ electrons are too tightly bound† to be of much use by themselves for molecule formation. Let us place the H atoms as shown on the left of Fig. 1, directly along the directions of the $2p_x$ and $2p_y$ orbitals of O. Then there is strong overlap between H_1 and $2p_x$, and between H_2 and $2p_y$, but practically none at all between any other pair. Thus

† Estimated ionization potential 32 eV, as compared with 13 eV for the $2p_z$ oxygen electrons. See, however, p. 221 for hybridization effects.

instead of a linear combination of all four a.o.'s we shall introduce only a small error if we consider just two at a time. Indeed we use H_1 and $2p_x$ to form a localized m.o. of the form

$$I = \psi(H_1) + \lambda\psi(O : 2p_x). \tag{1}$$

In a similar way we form

$$II = \psi(H_2) + \lambda\psi(O : 2p_y). \tag{2}$$

These two m.o.'s are shown—a little schematically—on the right-hand side of the figure. To a first approximation they are quite independent of one another, so that if we replace one hydrogen atom H_2 by some other group, e.g. a methyl group, CH_3, we shall expect to change II, but make little alteration in I.[†] In other words the electrons in an O—H bond have characteristic wave functions. This is the basis of the approximate constancy of the energy, length,..., of this bond.

7.2. Directed valence

The discussion which we have just given provides us with one important clue to a more general situation. In the case of H_2O, the approximate independence of the localized m.o.'s was obtained because we chose $2p_x$ and $2p_y$ a.o.'s of oxygen, which did not overlap at all, i.e.

$$\int \psi(O : 2p_x)\psi(O : 2p_y)\, d\tau = 0.$$

This integral is zero because of the perpendicular directions associated with $2p_x$ and $2p_y$. Now (§ 2.4) the p-type a.o.'s behave like vectors, so that instead of $2p_x$ and $2p_y$ we could have chosen two others, linear combinations of these, which would still be mutually independent, but which would no longer have zero overlap. With these new a.o.'s as basis, we should no longer be able to separate the complete non-localized linear combinations into localized pairs. This argument shows that one essential condition for localized bonds is that the oxygen orbitals, neglecting overlap between H_1 and H_2, are mutually orthogonal. In the next chapter we shall find this condition extremely important.

† But see §§ 10 and 11 for more detailed comment on this statement, and on the calculation of λ.

In the case of H_2O, where (1) and (2) are the m.o.'s, we shall once more expect greatest binding if the overlap of $\psi(H_1)$ and $\psi(O : 2p_x)$ is as great as possible. This has already been achieved in our case by our first decision to place the H atoms along the x- and y-axes. It shows us, however, why the valence angle is expected to be about 90°. It will always be about 90° if the central atom has two unpaired p electrons with which to form bonds. Thus we should expect SH_2 to be approximately right-angled, and indeed it is (92°).

Arguments of this kind provide the basis of a theory of directed valence, and so lead us to the very heart of the theory of stereochemistry. This basis rests on two principles:

(1) the possibility of using localized m.o.'s;
(2) the criterion of maximum overlapping.

We may generalize the argument used above for H_2O. If a central atom has three unpaired p electrons with which it may form bonds, then the bond directions will be approximately at right angles. In fact, all p bonds of this kind are approximately at right angles to each other. Nitrogen, with an atomic configuration

$$(1s)^2(2s)^2(2p_x)(2p_y)(2p_z),$$

provides an example. We satisfy the orthogonality condition at the N atom itself if we use the $2p_x$, $2p_y$, and $2p_z$ a.o.'s: and we get maximum overlapping with the three attached hydrogens in a molecule such as ammonia, if these are placed along the x, y, z directions. The ammonia molecule should therefore be a pyramid whose apical angle is in the region of 90°. The same is true of the trivalent compounds of phosphorus and arsenic.

Each of the p-type a.o.'s we have just been using has symmetry around its axis. This means that the bond which is formed, and which has a m.o. such as (1) or (2), is itself symmetrical around the line of nuclei. It may therefore be called a σ bond, by analogy with the situation (§ 4.7) in diatomic molecules. It must be remembered, of course, that if some of the adjoining bonds are highly polar, their resulting electric field may succeed in partially destroying the σ character of the first bond. There is, however, no evidence to suggest that such distortions are large.† On the other hand, although our argument has suggested 90° as the characteristic valence angle, the observed angles are somewhat greater (104° 31′ for H_2O, 107° for NH_3, 94° for PH_3, 92° for AsH_3, 92° for H_2S).‡ The chief reasons for this are:

(a) Coulomb repulsion between the attached atoms, which carry a net positive or negative charge. Thus in H_2O we obtain the correct dipole moment of 1·51 D for the OH bond if we suppose that the H atoms have a resultant positive charge equal to $0·32e$. The electrostatic interaction between these two like charges on the two hydrogens§ would be expected to open out the angle to about 95°. Although important, this is clearly not sufficient. Furthermore, we shall show later that a good deal of the total molecular dipole moment comes from the lone-pair electrons of the oxygen atom. This reduces the formal charges on the hydrogens and thus decreases their electrostatic interaction.

(b) Coulomb and exchange repulsion (see §§ 4 and 5) between the two O—H bonds. If we compare an isolated O atom with a water molecule, we see that whereas in the former there is just one p electron along the x- and y-axes, in the latter there are two electrons in each. These will repel each other, so that we could speak of a bond-bond repulsion, tending to open out the valence angle.

(c) Intervention of the oxygen lone-pair electrons $(2s)^2$. We shall show in Chapter VIII that if we reject the 'pure-p' type of bond in favour of one in which the oxygen s and p electrons together play a part, we get both a stronger bond and a larger angle.

(d) Configurational attraction of the kind illustrated in § 6.4 for H_2. In v.b. language this corresponds to alternative

† See, for example, E. Gorin, J. Walter, and H. Eyring, *J. Amer. Chem. Soc.*, 1939, **61**, 1876, for a discussion of some of these distortions.

‡ These, and many other, geometrical angles and distances in molecules, are taken from the excellent compilation *Tables of Interatomic Distances and Configuration in Molecules and Ions*, London, 1958, Chemical Society Special Publication No. 11, edited by L. E. Sutton.

§ D. F. Heath and J. W. Linnett, *Trans. Faraday Soc.*, 1948, **44**, 556.

pairing schemes. The magnitude of this effect is not known, though some calculations by Slater† suggest that for H_2O it is not large. It is a combination of (a), (b), (c), and (d) which is responsible for the observed increase in angle above $90°$.

The notation which we used for diatomic molecules will serve almost equally well to describe the electronic structure of poly-atomics. Thus we could describe H_2O as

$$O(1s)^2(2s)^2(2p_z)^2[O(2p)+H(1s), \sigma]^4, \qquad (3)$$

and NH_3 as $$N(1s)^2(2s)^2[N(2p)+H(1s), \sigma]^6, \qquad (4)$$

in which the symbol $[O(2p)+H(1s), \sigma]$ implies a m.o. of type 1, compounded out of $O(2p)$ and $H(1s)$. This notation does not, of course, show how much weight each a.o. has in the LCAO m.o.

7.3. Non-localized orbitals: case of H_2O

At the beginning of this chapter we outlined the distinction between localized and completely non-localized m.o.'s, stressing the desirability of using localized m.o.'s wherever possible. It is not necessary to do this, however, for the whole theory can be developed in terms of non-localized orbitals. When this is done, it turns out that there are some interesting relations between the two types of m.o. It will be sufficient if we illustrate this by a single example. Let us therefore consider non-localized m.o.'s for H_2O,‡ and suppose that the a.o.'s involved in the binding of the molecule are the two oxygen p-type a.o.'s, $2p_x$ and $2p_y$, and the two hydrogens H_1 and H_2. For the moment let us suppose that the HOH angle (Fig. 2) is 2α: one of our objects will be to see for what value of α the total energy is a minimum. If the valence angle is $90°$, then $\alpha = 45°$.

Let us use $p_x,...$ to denote $\psi(O : 2p_x),...$ for convenience. Then we are to form m.o.'s by linear combination of p_x, p_y, H_1, and H_2. But a glance at Fig. 2 shows that if we introduce axes ξ, η bisect-ing H_1OH_2 internally and externally, then the molecule is sym-metrical in $O\xi$. More precisely, it is symmetrical with respect to

† *Phys. Rev.*, 1931, **38**, 1109.
‡ F. Hund, *Z. Phys.*, 1931, **73**, 24; 1932, **74**, 429.

reflection in the plane $zO\xi$. This implies, entirely analogously to § 4.5, that the allowed m.o.'s must be either symmetrical or anti-symmetrical in this plane. So instead of H_1 and H_2 we must choose either (H_1+H_2) or (H_1-H_2). Evidently p_x and p_y are not convenient for this symmetry operation: however, the vector

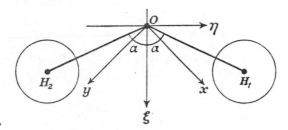

FIG. 7.2. Non-localized molecular orbitals for water .

character of p orbitals shows that instead of a linear combination of p_x and p_y, we could equally well have chosen a linear combination of p_ξ and p_η. This follows because

$$p_\xi = \frac{1}{\sqrt{2}}(p_x+p_y), \qquad p_\eta = \frac{1}{\sqrt{2}}(p_x-p_y), \qquad (5)$$

$$p_x = \frac{1}{\sqrt{2}}(p_\xi+p_\eta), \qquad p_y = \frac{1}{\sqrt{2}}(p_\xi-p_\eta). \qquad (6)$$

Now p_η is antisymmetric in the plane $zO\xi$ and p_ξ is symmetrical. But no combinations are allowed (§ 4.3) between orbitals of differing symmetry. This means that the allowed m.o.'s are combinations of p_ξ with (H_1+H_2), or of p_η with (H_1-H_2). If we call them A and B, then

$$A = p_\xi+\mu(H_1+H_2), \qquad (7)$$
$$B = p_\eta+\nu(H_1-H_2), \qquad (8)$$

where μ and ν are two constants depending on the angle and the electronegativities of H and O.

We are now ready to write down the secular equations (3.41). For simplicity let us neglect all overlap integrals. If we do so, and then eliminate the constants μ and ν (effectively the ratios

$c_1 : c_2$ in the standard form (3.41)), they give us the secular determinants

$$\begin{vmatrix} E_p-E & H_\xi \\ H_\xi & 2(E_H-E) \end{vmatrix} = 0, \quad \text{from the m.o. (7)}$$

$$\begin{vmatrix} E_p-E & H_\eta \\ H_\eta & 2(E_H-E) \end{vmatrix} = 0, \quad \text{from the m.o. (8)} \tag{9}$$

In these equations E_p denotes the energy of a $2p$ orbital of oxygen (either $2p_x$, $2p_y$, $2p_\xi$, or $2p_\eta$); E_H denotes the energy of a hydrogen electron: H_ξ and H_η are defined in terms of the Hamiltonian $\mathbf{H}$ by the relations

$$H_\xi = \int p_\xi.\mathbf{H}.(H_1+H_2)\,d\tau, \quad H_\eta = \int p_\eta.\mathbf{H}.(H_1-H_2)\,d\tau; \tag{10}$$

where, in addition to the overlap integrals S, we have neglected $\int H_1.\mathbf{H}.H_2\,d\tau$. The roots of these two secular determinants are

$$E = E_\xi = \tfrac{1}{2}(E_p+E_H)\pm\tfrac{1}{2}\{(E_p-E_H)^2+2H_\xi^2\}^{\frac{1}{2}},$$

and similarly $E = E_\eta$ with H_η replacing H_ξ. Now we have four electrons to put in the lowest energy values of those two determinants. These are the lowest roots of each separate determinant, and correspond to the choice of negative signs in the formulae for E_ξ and E_η. Consequently the total energy of the four electrons is

$$2E_\xi+2E_\eta = 2(E_p+E_H)-\{(E_p-E_H)^2+2H_\xi^2\}^{\frac{1}{2}}-\{(E_p-E_H)^2+2H_\eta^2\}^{\frac{1}{2}}. \tag{11}$$

What we are now going to show is that (11) has a minimum value when $2\alpha = 90°$. To do this we require to express H_ξ and H_η in terms of the angle α. Now p_ξ can be resolved into $\cos\alpha$ times a p orbital directed along OH_1, together with $\sin\alpha$ times a p orbital perpendicular to OH_1. Consequently

$$\int p_\xi.\mathbf{H}.H_1\,d\tau = \beta_{OH}\cos\alpha, \tag{12}$$

where β_{OH} denotes the resonance integral between a hydrogen orbital and an oxygen $2p$ orbital directed straight towards it. The term in $\sin\alpha$ vanishes on account of symmetry. Similarly

$$\int p_\xi.\mathbf{H}.H_2\,d\tau = \beta_{OH}\cos\alpha$$

so that $\qquad\qquad H_\xi = 2\beta_{OH}\cos\alpha. \tag{13 a}$

Similarly $\qquad H_\eta = 2\beta_{OH}\sin\alpha.$ $\qquad\qquad$ (13 b)

Combining (13 a) and (13 b) with (11) we have for the total energy

$$2(E_p+E_H) - \{(E_p-E_H)^2 + 8\beta_{OH}^2\cos^2\alpha\}^{\frac{1}{2}} - \{(E_p-E_H)^2 + 8\beta_{OH}^2\sin^2\alpha\}^{\frac{1}{2}}.$$
$$(14)$$

It is a matter of straightforward calculus to verify that this has its least value when $\alpha = 45°$. This shows that the right-angled model is the most stable.

Anyone who compares this theory with the earlier account in § 2 cannot fail to recognize how most of the pictorial character has been lost in these non-localized orbitals. Even the justification for a right-angled molecule seems to depend on the introduction of specific quantities, such as E_p, E_H, and β_{OH}, which were not apparently necessary in the localized orbitals. There is also the fact that the whole analysis has proceeded on the basis of complete symmetry in the $zO\xi$ plane, so that if one of the hydrogens was replaced by another atom, the calculation would break down, leaving us no valid ground for the experimental constancy of any separate O—H bond.

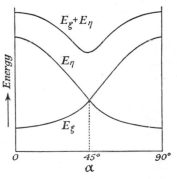

These are fair comments. But on the other hand there are certain advantages to set against the disadvantages. The first of these is that we can follow the way in which the energies of the two bonding orbitals change when the angle α varies from 0° to 90°: and this gives

Fig. 7.3. Variation of energies E_ξ and E_η of non-localized m.o.'s for water with the valence angle 2α (H...H repulsions are neglected.)

us more insight into the nature of the molecule.† Fig. 3 shows this variation of the two energies E_ξ and E_η, and also of their sum $E_\xi+E_\eta$. At the equilibrium position $E_\xi+E_\eta$ is least and the angle $\alpha = 45°$; also $E_\xi = E_\eta$ and the two curves cross. There is, of course, no objection to this crossing since they correspond to wave functions with different symmetries. When $\alpha = 45°$ it follows

† A careful numerical study of H_2O along these lines has been made by F. O. Ellison and H. Shull, *J. Chem. Phys.*, 1955, **23**, 2348.

that $\mu = \nu$ in (7) and (8). We may reasonably suppose that even when some of the refinements which we have omitted are included, this approximate equality of μ and ν will still obtain.†

However, more important than this variation of energy with angle is the introduction of molecular symmetry. In H_2O there is not much symmetry, but there is sufficient to divide the allowed m.o.'s into those which are

(a) symmetrical or antisymmetrical with respect to the plane of the molecule xOy,

(b) symmetrical or antisymmetrical with respect to the mid-plane $zO\xi$.

It was on account of (a) that the two lone-pair oxygen electrons $(2p_z)^2$ could be left out of our discussion: it was on account of (b) that we were able to form the non-combining groups $H_1 \pm H_2$, etc. In more complicated molecules, for example benzene or methane, this symmetry plays a much larger part. Thus, whereas in H_2O there are just two types of symmetry, in methane there are more than twenty. We are able to avail ourselves of the powerful methods of group theory‡ in order to write down the numbers and types of the allowed m.o.'s. This apparatus is mathematical and the analysis is somewhat complicated. For that reason, and because it is possible by simple symmetry arguments to circumvent it in those cases where we shall later require its results, we shall not attempt to develop this very interesting subject here.§ The 'symmetry classes' into which the allowed m.o.'s are gathered, and of which we have seen two examples in the case of H_2O, include both the a.o.'s of the central atom, and of the attached groups. They are the molecular analogues of the atomic division into s, p, d,... orbitals. For deciding what electronic transitions are allowed and what are forbidden, and for studying the way in which vibrations of the molecule, by temporarily breaking the complete symmetry, interfere with these selection rules, it is almost

† A full discussion of the variation of m.o. energies with valence angle has been given by A. D. Walsh, *J. Chem. Soc.*, 1953, pp. 2260–2331.

‡ A careful numerical study of H_2O along these lines has been made by F. O. Ellison and H. Shull, *J. Chem. Phys.*, 1955, **23**, 2348.

§ The introduction of group theory in this connexion is due to R. S. Mulliken, *Phys. Rev.*, 1933, **43**, 279.

imperative to use group theory. We have in fact already met one example, when we were discussing homonuclear diatomics, and introduced (§ 4.7) the g and u classification. We stated that allowed transitions were necessarily $g \to u$ or $u \to g$. This is merely an illustration (actually the simplest possible molecular illustration) of the way in which the geometrical shape of the molecule determines symmetry classes for the allowed m.o.'s. But with this brief introduction to the use of group theory, we must leave it: for though very useful, it is not necessary in the theory of valence.

It can be shown† that there is quite a simple relation between the non-localized m.o.'s such as (7) and (8), and the localized ones such as (1) and (2). The example of H_2O will serve to illustrate the argument. There are four electrons to be considered, and if we adopt the localized description, they have orbitals

$$\text{I } \alpha, \quad \text{II } \alpha, \quad \text{I } \beta, \quad \text{II } \beta,$$

in which the spin part has now been included. According to (5.36) this would lead to a wave function for the complete set of four electrons:

$$\Psi_{\text{loc}} = \begin{vmatrix} \text{I (1) } \alpha \text{ (1)} & \text{II (1) } \alpha \text{ (1)} & \text{I (1) } \beta \text{ (1)} & \text{II (1) } \beta \text{ (1)} \\ \text{I (2) } \alpha \text{ (2)} & \text{II (2) } \alpha \text{ (2)} & \text{I (2) } \beta \text{ (2)} & \text{II (2) } \beta \text{ (2)} \\ \text{I (3) } \alpha \text{ (3)} & \text{II (3) } \alpha \text{ (3)} & \text{I (3) } \beta \text{ (3)} & \text{II (3) } \beta \text{ (3)} \\ \text{I (4) } \alpha \text{ (4)} & \text{II (4) } \alpha \text{ (4)} & \text{I (4) } \beta \text{ (4)} & \text{II (4) } \beta \text{ (4)} \end{vmatrix}. \quad (15)$$

In a similar way, the non-localized orbitals (7) and (8) lead to a wave function:

$$\psi_{\text{non}} = \begin{vmatrix} A \text{ (1) } \alpha \text{ (1)} & B \text{ (1) } \alpha \text{ (1)} & A \text{ (1) } \beta \text{ (1)} & B \text{ (1) } \beta \text{ (1)} \\ A \text{ (2) } \alpha \text{ (2)} & B \text{ (2) } \alpha \text{ (2)} & A \text{ (2) } \beta \text{ (2)} & B \text{ (2) } \beta \text{ (2)} \\ A \text{ (3) } \alpha \text{ (3)} & B \text{ (3) } \alpha \text{ (3)} & A \text{ (3) } \beta \text{ (3)} & B \text{ (3) } \beta \text{ (3)} \\ A \text{ (4) } \alpha \text{ (4)} & B \text{ (4) } \alpha \text{ (4)} & A \text{ (4) } \beta \text{ (4)} & B \text{ (4) } \beta \text{ (4)} \end{vmatrix}. \quad (16)$$

The determinants (15) and (16) look entirely different. But in fact they are very similar. By adding and subtracting columns in (16) we make no difference to ψ. This is exactly the same, therefore, as if we had used linear combinations of $A\alpha$, $B\alpha$, $A\beta$, $B\beta$ when forming the determinant. In particular we could have used the combinations

$$(A+B)\alpha, \quad (A-B)\alpha, \quad (A+B)\beta, \quad (A-B)\beta$$

without changing ψ except by an irrelevant numerical factor. Now on account of the relations (5) and (6) the combinations $A \pm B$ are simply

$$A + B \equiv \sqrt{2}p_x + (\mu+\nu)H_1 + (\mu-\nu)H_2,$$
$$A - B \equiv \sqrt{2}p_y + (\mu+\nu)H_2 + (\mu-\nu)H_1. \quad (17)$$

We have seen that μ is either exactly or very nearly equal to ν. If $\mu = \nu$

† C. A. Coulson, *J. Chim. Phys.*, 1949, **46**, 198.

then (17) reduces to (1) and (2), showing that when they are expanded, ψ_{loc} and ψ_{non} are identical. This would mean that it was entirely arbitrary whether we used localized or non-localized orbitals. However, if $\mu - \nu$ does not exactly vanish, then the correct interpretation of (17) is that the bonding electrons cannot quite be localized; but that there is a certain small probability that an electron involved in the bond OH_1 is found on H_2. In this way we can see that the assumption of localized m.o.'s is an approximation, and we are prepared for the fact that interactions between bonds do occur, so that energies are not exactly additive, etc.

Analysis similar to the above can be applied to all simple molecules which possess symmetry properties.[†] Nor is it necessary, in the particular case of H_2O, that the valence angle should be exactly 90°.[‡]

7.4. The v.b. approximation of perfect pairing

Our previous discussion of localized m.o.'s should have prepared the way for our present application of the v.b. method to polyatomic molecules. Clearly the significance of a localized bond $A-B$ in such a molecule is that one electron on A is paired with an electron on B, and that this pairing is independent of any other pairings that may take place in the rest of the molecule. If we can once agree to this, then the rest of the discussion regarding the p valences in H_2O, NH_3, etc., follows very much as in § 7.2. Our first, and most important, task is therefore to understand and justify this so-called approximation of perfect pairing.

To do this we must return to (5.13), in which it is shown that with a homonuclear diatomic molecule, the energies of the symmetrical and antisymmetrical wave functions

$$\psi_A(1)\psi_B(2) \pm \psi_B(1)\psi_A(2)$$

are
$$E_{\pm} = 2E_0 + \frac{Q \pm J}{1 \pm S^2}. \tag{18}$$

E_0 is the energy of $\psi_A(1)$ alone, Q is the Coulomb term, and J the exchange integral. It may be shown that if A and B are dissimilar atoms, $2E_0$ is replaced by $E_A + E_B$, the other symbols retaining their former significance.

---

† Other relevant group-theoretical discussions are given by J. H. Van Vleck, *J. Chem. Phys.*, 1935, **3**, 803, and J. E. Lennard-Jones, *Proc. Roy. Soc.* A, 1949, **198**, 1, 14.

‡ Somewhat more general discussions for H_2O along these lines have been given by L. Burnelle and C. A. Coulson, *Trans. Faraday Soc.*, 1956, **53**, 403, and W. Hamilton, *J. Chem. Phys.*, 1956, **26**, 345.

We are now going to make three assumptions:

(i) that the overlap integral S^2 may be neglected: this is equivalent to assuming the near orthogonality of all a.o.'s, such as ψ_A and ψ_B;

(ii) that the Coulomb term is so much smaller than the exchange term, that its influence on the binding may be neglected. We shall return to this matter in § 7.9, but for the moment we may content ourselves with the remark that in most polyatomic molecules, this is a much better approximation than might have been expected, since although Q does not vanish, it remains effectively constant when the molecule is deformed, as for example by changes in the bond angles. Numerically Q is often taken to be about 15 per cent. of J (but see § 9);

(iii) that E_A and E_B are independent of the molecular configuration and indeed of the rest of the molecule. This is certainly not a valid approximation if the molecule contains strongly polar groups, but it is not unreasonable for nearly homopolar binding.

With these assumptions, the effective part of (18) is simply

$$E_{\pm} = \pm J. \qquad (19)$$

The discussion in § 5.9 showed that the energy E_+ was associated with opposed spins of the two electrons, and resulted in a singlet energy level; but the energy E_- was associated with parallel spins, and a threefold energy degeneracy. In other words, if we know that the spins are opposed, the interaction between ψ_A and ψ_B is represented by $+J$; if we know they are parallel, by $-J$. But suppose they are quite random: then we must give equal weight to all four possible spin orientations. There are four of these (§ 5.9), of which three correspond to a triplet state and one to a singlet. This would lead to an interaction energy

$$\tfrac{1}{4}(+J)+\tfrac{3}{4}(-J), \quad \text{i.e.} \quad -\tfrac{1}{2}J. \qquad (20)$$

It is interesting to note that this formula was used long ago† by H. Eyring to study the interactions between pairs of non-bonded

---

† *J. Amer. Chem. Soc.*, 1932, **54**, 3191. See also F. J. Adrian, *J. Chem. Phys.*, 1958, **28**, 608.

hydrogen atoms, as, for example, in ethane, and to discuss their effect on the hindered rotation which exists around the $\geq$C—C$\leq$ bond (see § 13.5).

We need to say a few words about the magnitude of J. If the overlap integral $S = 0$, then according to (5.15)

$$J = \int \psi_A(1)\psi_B(2)\psi_B(1)\psi_A(2) \, d\tau_1 \, d\tau_2/r_{12}. \qquad (21)$$

If we write this in the form

$$J = \int \psi_A(1)\psi_B(1).\frac{1}{r_{12}}.\psi_A(2)\psi_B(2) \, d\tau_1 \, d\tau_2,$$

we see that J is only large if there are regions of space where

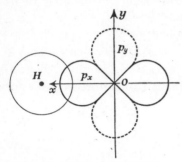

FIG. 7.4. Pairing of orbitals in the OH radical.

$\psi_A(1)\psi_B(1)$ and $\psi_A(2)\psi_B(2)$ are large. This means that the boundary surfaces of ψ_A and ψ_B (§ 2.3) must overlap as much as possible. Large values of J are associated with a.o.'s which satisfy the Criterion of Maximum Overlapping. Thus this criterion plays as important a role in v.b. theory as we have already seen for m.o. theory.

The reader may perhaps have spotted an apparent difficulty here.

If we neglect overlap integrals, by putting $S = 0$, then the formula (5.15) shows that J is necessarily positive (as indeed it always is for atoms). Yet bonding (p. 126) requires that J shall be negative. But a careful investigation into the likely relative magnitudes of the three terms in (5.15) shows that the second term, $-2S\int \frac{e^2}{r_{b1}}\psi_A(1)\psi_B(1) \, d\tau$, is usually larger than the term (21), and so leads to a negative J, as required. But this term itself is only large if ψ_A and ψ_B overlap well, so that our previous conclusion is quite valid.

There is one further result which we require; and this will appear most naturally if we consider the OH molecule. If we make the usual assumption that the inner electrons of O make no contribution to the binding, and that the two $2s$ electrons are internally paired together, and also the two $2p_z$ electrons, we are left with an oxygen atom in which there are two effective orbitals ($2p_x$ and $2p_y$ in Fig. 4) that might be used for valence binding. They each contain one electron, which could be paired with the hydrogen $1s$ electron. Clearly, if we pair the p_x orbital with H($1s$) we shall get maximum overlapping provided that H is placed along the x-axis. The unpaired electron would then be p_y. But suppose we

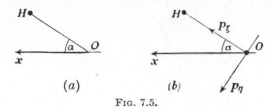

(a)   (b)

Fig. 7.5.

placed H at an angle α with the x-direction, as shown in Fig. 5 a. The exchange integral may be called $J(\alpha)$, where

$$J(\alpha) = \int \psi(\text{H} : 1)\psi(p_x : 2).\frac{1}{r_{12}}.\psi(\text{H} : 2)\psi(p_x : 1)\,d\tau_1\,d\tau_2. \quad (22)$$

Now the vector character of p-type a.o.'s allows $\psi(p_x)$ to be resolved (Fig. 5 b) into

$$\psi(p_x) = \cos\alpha\psi(p_\xi) + \sin\alpha\psi(p_\eta).$$

Substitution of these expansions in (22) shows that

$$J(\alpha) = \cos^2\alpha J(0°) + \sin^2\alpha J(90°), \quad (23)$$

the term in $\sin\alpha\cos\alpha$ vanishing because of symmetry. This is an important relation which we shall have occasion to use later. For the particular case of hydrogen and oxygen, calculation shows that, at least approximately,

$$J(0°) = -2.0 \text{ eV}, \qquad J(90°) = +0.6 \text{ eV},$$

so that the variation of the exchange integral with angle is as shown in Fig. 6.

Now consider the OH radical a little more fully. If we agree to pair O($2p_x$) with H($1s$), then there will be a contribution $J(\alpha)$ to the exchange energy. But there will also be an exchange energy with O($2p_y$). The situation here is that once we have paired $2p_x$

and $1s$, then the relation of either of these with any other electron is completely random. Consequently the exchange energy is $-\frac{1}{2}J(90°-\alpha)$. There is also an exchange between $2p_x$ and $2p_y$, but this, being solely an internal atomic energy, does not affect the binding. So the total effective exchange energy is

$$J(\alpha)-\tfrac{1}{2}J(90°-\alpha). \tag{24}$$

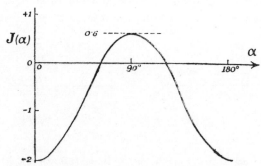

FIG. 7.6. Variation of $J(\alpha)$ with α (equation (23)).

Similar formulae hold for the Coulomb energies, except, of course, that these are always just additive. The total Coulomb energy is therefore

$$Q(\alpha)+Q(90°-\alpha).$$

Reference to (23), which also holds for the Q integrals, shows that this reduces simply to $Q(0°)+Q(90°)$, and is therefore independent of α. This type of argument is quite general, and provides a basis for the comment which we made in (ii) above.

It follows immediately from (24) that the total energy is least when $\alpha = 0°$, which corresponds to maximum overlapping of $H(1s)$ and $O(2p_x)$. This illustrates once more the need to pair together orbitals that overlap as much as possible.

Our discussion of the OH radical leads us to anticipate the following formula, which gives the energy of any system of electrons in a molecule:

$$E = E_{\text{atoms}}+ \sum_{\substack{\text{all } i,\, j}} Q_{ij}+ \sum_{\substack{\text{paired}\\ \text{orbitals}}} J_{ij} - \tfrac{1}{2}\sum_{\substack{\text{non-paired}\\ \text{orbitals}}} J_{ij} - \sum_{\substack{\text{orbitals with}\\ \text{parallel spins}}} J_{ij}. \tag{25}$$

According to (25), in addition to the sum of the atomic energies

E_{atoms}, and the Coulomb energies Q_{ij} for every combination of the orbitals i and j, every pair of electrons involved in a covalent bond contributes $+J_{ij}$; every pair, of which one is in one bond and another in some other bond, so that their spins are entirely independent, contributes $-\frac{1}{2}J_{ij}$, and every pair with coupled parallel spins, contributes $-J_{ij}$. Electrons which are not actively paired together always exert a repulsion on each other. Naturally enough all these J integrals are not equal: those that correspond to greatest overlapping will be numerically larger than the rest. The formula (25), known as the 'Approximation of Perfect Pairing', lies at the heart of nearly all stereochemistry. But before we show how it is used, it is desirable to list the assumptions involved in its derivation. These are

(1) assumption that a.o.'s are linked together in pairs, so that only one pairing scheme need be considered;

(2) neglect of all overlap-integrals S;

(3) neglect of all ionic terms, or polar terms;

(4) inclusion of simple exchange integrals such as (21), but neglect of all higher-order exchanges.

This is a formidable list; nevertheless careful study of one or two particular cases shows that in its qualitative aspects the approximation of perfect pairing is surprisingly accurate. But evidently we must not expect to get detailed numerical results from so rough-and-ready a method.

We have not yet proved (25); but we have at least made it plausible. However, a proof can be given, subject of course to the limitations (1)–(4). This proof is somewhat mathematical,† and so we shall content ourselves with this reference to its existence, relying for our confidence in (25) on the semi-empirical arguments with which we led up to it earlier in this section.

7.5. The water molecule

In order to illustrate the use of the approximation of perfect pairing, let us reconsider the water molecule. In the notation of Fig. 7 we suppose that the hydrogens H_a and H_b are paired with $O(2p_x)$ and $O(2p_y)$, though for the moment we suppose that the

† P. A. M. Dirac, *Proc. Roy. Soc.* A, 1929, **123**, 714.

lines OH_a, OH_b make non-zero angles α and α' with the directions of the p_x and p_y orbitals. According to (25) the exchange energy with this pairing is

$$E_{\text{exch.}} = +J(p_x, H_a) + J(p_y, H_b) - \tfrac{1}{2}J(p_x, H_b) - \tfrac{1}{2}J(p_y, H_a) -$$
$$- \tfrac{1}{2}J(H_a, H_b) - \tfrac{1}{2}J(p_x, p_y). \quad (26)$$

There are two J's with coefficient $+1$, arising from the bonded pairs, and four with coefficient $-\tfrac{1}{2}$, arising from non-bonded orbitals. There are no orbitals whose spins are coupled parallel, so that (as usually occurs) there are no coefficients -1.

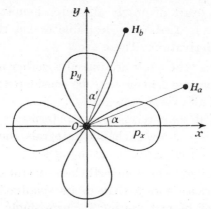

FIG. 7.7. Perfect pairing in the water molecule H_2O.

The term $J(p_x, p_y)$ is merely an internal integral for the oxygen atom, and is independent of α and α': if wanted, its value may be found from a spectroscopic study of the oxygen atom. $J(H_a, H_b)$ measures the universal repulsion between the two H atoms which are not bonded to each other. If we are interested in directional valence at the oxygen atom, we shall therefore omit the last two integrals in (26) and retain only the first four. These may all be expressed in terms of α and α' by use of (23). And now a very simple calculation shows that the energy is least when $\alpha = \alpha' = 0$, so that the angle HOH $= 90°$. Similarly, by using a formula for Q analogous to (26) but with all the coefficients equal to $+1$, we can prove that the Coulomb energy provides no directional effects. The same is true if we include Coulomb terms between the neglected $(2s)^2(2p_z)^2$ electrons and the rest, as may soon be verified. Strictly, of course, we ought to include in (26) exchange energy terms between the non-bonding pairs $(2s)^2(2p_z)^2$ and the electrons of the bonds. These energies would obviously be independent of α and α', so that our previous conclusions would be unaffected. The contribution from the $(2s)^2$ pair, for example, would be

$$2 \times \{ -\tfrac{1}{2}J(2s, p_x) - \tfrac{1}{2}J(2s, p_y) - \tfrac{1}{2}J(2s, H_a) - \tfrac{1}{2}J(2s, H_b) \}.$$

This analysis has revealed the basis of the stereochemistry of two p-bonds. It also provides us with an explanation of the approximate constancy of bond energies. For according to (26), if we neglect H—H repulsions and internal energies of the O atom, we may associate with each O—H bond an exchange energy

$$J(p_x, H_a) - \tfrac{1}{2}J(p_y, H_a) - J(2s, H_a) - J(p_z, H_a) \qquad (27)$$

and a Coulomb energy

$$Q(p_x, H_a) + Q(p_y, H_a) + 2Q(2s, H_a) + 2Q(p_z, H_a). \qquad (28)$$

Needless to say, the arguments here developed for H_2O would apply in a similar manner to NH_3 and other molecules of this kind in which not more than three p electrons are involved. Subject to the restrictions (1)–(4) of § 4, they also apply when the atoms attached to the central atom are not identical, as, for example, in CH_3OH as well as HOH. Furthermore we can use formulae such as (26) to study the change in energy when α or α' varies from the value characteristic of the equilibrium configuration. This enables us to calculate the transverse vibration frequency, generally called ν_2, in which the motion is almost entirely a periodic opening and closing of the HOH angle. By this means, including explicit account of the H—H repulsions, a value 1,660 cm^{-1}, only 4 per cent. different from the experimental value of 1,595 cm^{-1}, is obtained.† This agreement seems almost unnaturally good, in view of the approximations involved in E, and the fact that ν_2 depends on the second derivative of E.

7.6. Summary of valence rules

A comparison of the v.b. and m.o. treatments such as those just given already reveals a considerable measure of agreement

† J. H. Van Vleck and P. C. Cross, *J. Chem. Phys.*, 1934, **1**, 357.

regarding what we may call the simple rules of valence. For example:

(a) atoms with 1, 2, or 3 unpaired p electrons in their valence shell have a natural valence of 1, 2, or 3 respectively, and the bonds, when formed, have a natural angle of 90° between them;

(b) so far as atoms in group V, VI, and VII of the Periodic Table are concerned, this leads to natural valences of 3, 2, and 1, and in each case the saturation of valence completes the octet of electrons;

(c) these bonds involve electrons with paired spin, and with a charge-cloud localized in the region of the bond: such localization is the basis of the approximate constancy of bond properties;

(d) excitation of an electron from one a.o. to another will often result in an increase of two in the number of unpaired electrons, and hence in an increase of two in the possible valence number. It appears, however, that excitation to an a.o. with increased total (or principal) quantum number (i.e. $K \to L$, $L \to M$ shell, etc.) requires so much energy that it does not take place. But excitation from an s to a p, or p to d within the same shell may take place much more easily. This explains, for example, the quadrivalence of carbon ($2s \to 2p$, discussed in more detail in the next chapter), the divalence of mercury ($6s \to 6p$), and the pentavalence of phosphorus ($3p \to 3d$). However, in the first complete row of the Periodic Table (Li–F) there are no d-type orbitals available with the same total quantum number, with the result that although PCl_5 exists as well as PCl_3, there is only NCl_3, and not NCl_5. More than one electron may be excited for this purpose. Thus there are two in $SF_6[(3s)(3p) \to (3d)^2]$ and BrF_5. Nor does it follow that all electrons *must* be paired (e.g. OH and ClO_2). This is particularly true with d-type a.o.'s, a situation related to the great diversity of valences shown by atoms with incomplete d-shells. Thus vanadium, with an atomic ground state configuration $...(3d)^3(4s)^2$, shows apparent valences 2, 3, 4, and 5 (VCl_2, VCl_3, VCl_4, VF_5);

(e) removal of an electron by ionization may so much increase the energy of binding through the possibility of an extra bond, as to make this process quite a frequent one. Hence, for example, the existence of ammonium type compounds such as NH_4^+, in which the removal of a $2s$ electron from nitrogen leaves four unpaired a.o.'s, where there were three before. The converse of this also holds and partly accounts for the stability of ions such as SO_4^{--} and BH_4^-.

These rules follow quite plausibly from the discussion of §§ 1–5. But it is only fair to point out certain apparent exceptions,† not understandable on this theory. The first is that they do not explain the apparent tetravalent character of oxonium compounds

$\left(\text{when written in a form such as } \begin{array}{c} C_2H_5 \\ \diagdown \\ C_2H_5 \end{array} \hspace{-4pt} >\hspace{-4pt} O \hspace{-4pt} <\hspace{-4pt} \begin{array}{c} H \\ \diagup \\ Br \end{array}\right)$; since oxygen has

no d orbitals with the same principal quantum number, 2, as the occupied L-shell a.o.'s, no excitation of the kind envisaged in (d) is permitted. The true explanation here is that such molecules are largely ionic in character. A more proper description would

therefore be $\left(\begin{array}{c} C_2H_5 \\ \diagdown \\ C_2H_5 \end{array} \hspace{-4pt} >\hspace{-4pt} O - H \right)^+ Br^-$. Secondly, certain excitations

of this kind, although theoretically permitted, do not appear to take place. An interesting example is argon, with an outer shell configuration $(3s)^2(3p)^6$. This is a completed shell, indicating no valence at all; but by excitations $3p \to 3d$, we might have expected possible valences of 2, 4, or 6. None of these is known. Perhaps the decisive factor is the energy of excitation. For in argon the lowest transition $(3p)^6 \to (3p)^5(3d)$ requires about 14 eV. It would only be worth while making this excitation if the two valences thereby created contributed at least this much energy

---

† See, e.g., J. H. Van Vleck and A. Sherman, *Rev. Mod. Phys.*, 1935, **7**, 167. These rules were discussed wave-mechanically first by F. London, *Z. Phys.*, 1927, **46**, 455.

in bond formation. But no single bonds are as strong as this: and d electrons are not very effective at overlapping.

Various explanations may be advanced to show why the rules (a)–(e) are not completely firm, with no exceptions such as those just described. Thus we can assert that the approximation of perfect pairing is not applicable, or that ionic structures are very important, or that the often-neglected Coulomb terms play a major role. But explicit calculations are wanting with which to test any of these, or other, possibilities. However, notwithstanding this, it is fair to say that the v.b. and m.o. methods agree surprisingly well in explaining the greater part of the empirical rules of valence, and in relating the number and type of the valences around an atom to the valence angles which are exhibited. Further confirmation of this will appear in the next chapter.

7.7. Significance of the repulsion terms in the energy formula

It is very easy to see the significance of the terms $+\sum J_{ij}$ in (25): for these are the terms that really bind the atoms together. But though the terms $-\frac{1}{2}\sum J_{ij}$, summed over the non-paired orbitals, do not appear to be so fundamentally significant, they are nevertheless of considerable interest. A few examples of the way in which they make their presence felt will show their importance.

Consider first the likely structure of an H_3 group. If (Fig. 8 a) we imagine the three atoms at the corners of an equilateral triangle, we should write down various possible 'structures', one of which, corresponding to the pairing of H_b and H_c, is shown in the figure. Now the energy of this structure is

$$+J_{bc}-\tfrac{1}{2}J_{ab}-\tfrac{1}{2}J_{ac} = 0,$$

if all the distances are equal, and we use the usual spherically-symmetrical $1s$ atomic orbitals. In this case, therefore, the repulsion terms cancel the attractive ones. If, however, as in Fig. 8 b, the molecule is linear, the term J_{ac} is greatly reduced, so that the binding is increased. In both cases it may be shown that there are just two independent ways of pairing to consider, so that even without further calculation, we should expect that the most stable configuration of H_3 would be linear. Accurate work† confirms this.

A second example is the relative weakness of bonds between heavy atoms. This is brought out very clearly in Table 12,‡

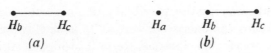

FIG. 7.8. Bond structures for an equilateral (8 *a*) and linear (8 *b*) molecule H_3.

which shows the energy values for bonds between pairs of similar atoms. As one goes down the individual columns of this table, the bonds tend to become weaker (N, O, F represent exceptions to this rule). The interpretation is that with heavier atoms there are usually more electrons in the valence shells to exert both exchange and Coulomb repulsions upon each other. There are

TABLE 12. *Bond energies (kcal/mole) for bonds X—X*

H 104							He 0
Li 26	Be	B 83	C 80§	N 38	O 34	F 38‖	Ne 0
Na 18	Mg	Al	Si 45	P 53	S 63	Cl 57	A 0
K 12			Ge 45	As 35	Se 50	Br 45	Kr 0
Rb 12			Sn 35	Sb 30	Te 49	I 36	Xe 0
Cs 10							

† J. O. Hirschfelder, H. Eyring, and N. Rosen, *J. Chem. Phys.*, 1936, **4**, 121; D. Stevenson and J. O. Hirschfelder, ibid., 1937, **5**, 933; J. O. Hirschfelder, ibid., 1938, **6**, 795.

‡ Chiefly taken from K. S. Pitzer, *J. Amer. Chem. Soc.*, 1948, **70**, 2140, and T. L. Cottrell, *The Strengths of Chemical Bonds*, Butterworths. But other values, differing by as much as 10 kcal/mole, have been proposed by other writers.

§ This value is based on a latent heat of sublimation of graphite to the ³P carbon state equal to 170 kcal/mole. See p. 206.

‖ J. G. Stamper and R. F. Barrow, *Trans. Faraday Soc.*, 1958, **54**, 1592.

also more electrons in inner shells to exert a Coulomb repulsion so that the bond lengths are larger. On the other hand, the positive contribution to the bond energy can only come from one exchange integral in each case.

We can put this repulsion between non-bonded electrons in another way. The Pauli Exclusion Principle effectively limits the number of electrons that can be in the same region of space and have the same spin. So as soon as two charge-clouds begin to overlap, but without the possibility of spin coupling, the Pauli principle forces the energy upwards. It is as if we almost compelled the superfluous electrons to go into higher energy orbitals (cf. the idea of promotion in the correlation diagram discussion of § 4.7). Thus the repulsive energy term usually increases very rapidly when the non-bonded electron clouds approach too closely. It is probable that this rapid increase in the repulsive energy plays a large part in determining the equilibrium lengths of most bonds. For, by analogy with H_2, it seems likely that the binding exchange term $+J_{ij}$ would continue to increase numerically if the orbitals i and j were brought closer together. But if there is a sudden increase in the repulsive energy, due to the proximity of one atom to the inner-shell electrons of the other atom, then at that point there will be a minimum of the total energy of interaction.

These arguments fit in well with the experimental fact that multiple bonds are practically confined to the first two rows of the Periodic Table. For with a multiple bond the increased binding would try to shorten the bond length (e.g. in carbon, from 1·54 A to 1·34 A). But this would introduce all the additional repulsive interactions just described, with the result that such multiple bonds would be inordinately weak compared with an equivalent number of single bonds.

These repulsions between non-bonded electrons provide us with a partial explanation of the relatively low strength of the F—F bond (38 kcal/mole according to Table 12). If, in v.b. language, we think of the bond as due to the pairing of two electrons, one from each F atom, and imagine ourselves bringing the two atoms towards each other from a large distance, then, since the F atom is fairly small, bonding only begins to be effective when the two atoms are brought quite close together. As soon as this happens we shall find repulsions between the six valence-shell electrons of each atom which are not engaged in forming the bond. The number of these inter-electronic repulsions is so large as to reduce considerably the energy of the bonding electrons.† An alternative way of describing this effect is to use the m.o. language of Table 5 (p. 102), from which it will be seen that there are no less than three pairs of related occupied orbitals in the valence shell, such as $\sigma^2\sigma^{*2}$, $\pi^2\pi^{*2}$. All of these related bonding and anti-bonding pairs give a repulsion (cf. §§ 4.5 and 4.7). This repulsion is the analogue of our former repulsion between non-paired electrons. In the same way the crystal of fluorine is molecular, composed of F_2 units, rather than atomic, as, for example, lithium, which, though also monovalent, lacks the non-bonding valence-shell electrons of fluorine; for in the atomic case each atom is closely surrounded by a large number, usually twelve, of neighbours, and these repulsions would be very considerable. In the molecular case, see § 11.2, the number of near neighbours is only one.

Another case where repulsions of non-bonded electrons dominate the shape of the molecule is H_2O_2, where, as Penney and Sutherland‡ showed, a coplanar arrangement of all four atoms would involve much larger repulsions between the parallel pairs of non-bonding $2p$ electrons of the oxygen atoms than would be involved in the observed skew configuration where the mutual angle of twist around the O—O bond is rather more than 90°. A similar situation occurs in gaseous (but not necessarily crystalline) S_2H_2, S_2Cl_2, and N_2H_4.

This last molecule (hydrazine) is interesting because, by progressive addition of protons it is possible to draw away part of the lone-pair charge from near the nitrogen nuclei. In this way

---

† It is also true that, on account of the tighter binding of the non-bonding electrons in F as compared with Cl or Br, there will be a smaller van der Waals dispersion energy tendency to increase the binding energy. This (see K. S. Pitzer, *J. Chem. Phys.*, 1955, **23**, 1735) is less for F_2 than Cl_2. Recently, however, G. L. Caldow and C. A. Coulson (*Trans. Faraday Soc.*, 1961, **57**, in press) have shown the dominating importance of the Coulomb term (§ 9).

‡ *J. Chem. Phys.*, 1934, **2**, 492.

we reduce the lone-pair repulsion. An excellent illustration of this is given by the frequency changes in the N—N bond in H_2N—NH_2 (880 cm^{-1}), H_2N—$\overset{+}{N}H_3$ (965 cm^{-1}), and $H_3\overset{+}{N}$—$\overset{+}{N}H_3$ (1,030 cm^{-1}). In this last case particularly, on account of the repulsion between the two net positive charges, we should have expected a longer and a weaker bond. But in fact its frequency of vibration has increased: and its length has decreased. The corresponding bond lengths are

$$H_2N-NH_2,\ 1\cdot47\pm0\cdot02;\ H_2N-\overset{+}{N}H_3^+,\ 1\cdot45;\ H_3\overset{+}{N}-\overset{+}{N}H_3,\ 1\cdot41\pm0\cdot01,$$

all in A.

7.8. Atomic radii and bond lengths

The fact that in most polyatomic molecules the bonds are effectively localized, provides us with an explanation of the almost constant length for bonds between given atoms. It is certainly true that there are often small, and extremely interesting, differences between the lengths of a particular bond A—B which depend on the rest of the molecule. But these may be neglected for our present purposes. The near constancy of the length A—B suggests that we should try to express it as a sum r_A+r_B, where r_A and r_B are the atomic radii of atoms of types A and B. Table 13† shows the atomic radii for several atoms, including double-bond and triple-bond radii for carbon and nitrogen.

It will be noticed that as we proceed from left to right across this table, the single-bond radii all decrease, in agreement with the electronegativity scale in Table 10 (p. 140). In the same way the radii increase as we go down any column towards heavier atoms. It is interesting to note the fact, which we shall use in Chapter 12, that the shortening from single to double and then to triple bond is practically the same in carbon and nitrogen. This shortening does not appear to depend very much on the nature of the atom.

Table 13 may be used at once to estimate the bond length of most molecular bonds. But it fails when the atoms differ very greatly in their electronegativity, so that the bond is considerably

† Taken largely from L. Pauling, *Nature of the Chemical Bond*, as amended by V. Schomaker and D. P. Stevenson, *J. Amer. Chem. Soc.*, 1941, **63**, 37.

TABLE 13. *Covalent radii for atoms (in A)*

	H 0·30					
	Li	B	C	N	O	F
Single-bond	1·34	0·81	0·77	0·73	0·74	0·72
Double-bond			0·67	0·61	0·57	
Triple-bond			0·60	0·55		
	Na 1·54		Si 1·17	P 1·10	S 1·04	Cl 0·99
	K 1·96		Ge 1·22	As 1·21	Se 1·17	Br 1·14
	Rb 2·11		Sn 1·40	Sb 1·41	Te 1·37	I 1·33
	Cs 2·25					

ionic. Schomaker and Stevenson† have suggested that there is then a shortening expressed by means of the equation

$$r_{A-B} = r_A + r_B - \beta|x_A - x_B|, \tag{29}$$

in which β is a constant with the value $\beta = 0·09$ and x_A, x_B are the two electronegativities. This correction certainly helps to give agreement for polar bonds such as $\geqslant$C—O— and $\geqslant$C—N$\langle$, but there are other occasions where it does not work so well.‡ In the light of the discussion of hybridization which we shall give in the next chapter, it is not surprising that no one simple formula will give all bond lengths in this manner.

We have already given (Table 12) the bond energies for single bonds between like atoms. This may be supplemented by the following comparison (Table 14) of single-, double-, and triple-bond energies. Values for other bonds could be given, but both the lengths and the energies are often so dependent on the nature of their environment in the molecule, that the values are not of great significance. A similar difficulty is experienced with dipole moments, and is frequently to be interpreted as implying either a small delocalization of the bonds, i.e. a failure of the approximation of perfect pairing, or a change of hybridization in one or both atoms.

† Loc. cit. When using this rule the atomic radius for hydrogen is taken to be 0·37 A.

‡ A. F. Wells, *J. Chem. Soc.*, 1949, 55.

TABLE 14. *Multiple-bond energies* (kcal/mole)

	Single bond	Double bond	Triple bond
C—C . .	83	146	201
N—N . .	39	100	225
O—O . .	34	117	..
C—N . .	73	142	210

* Selected from a table due to G. E. Coates and L. E. Sutton, *J. Chem. Soc.*, 1948, 1187, except for O—O and O=O, which are due to K. S. Pitzer, loc. cit. Small differences in C—C, N—N, and C—N between Tables 12 and 14 are due to a small alteration in the assumed latent heat of sublimation of carbon, which, in Table 14, is taken as 170·4 kcal/mole at 0° K (171·6 kcal/mole at 293° K). The value for C=N is an average of values between 137 and 147 kcal/mole.

7.9. Numerical value of the Coulomb term

The physical significance of the Coulomb terms that we have described in § 7 raises the question of their numerical values. The theoretical situation here is not at all satisfactory. Relatively few precise calculations are available, except for H_2; but the following conclusions appear to be valid:

(a) At the equilibrium distance in H_2 the Coulombic energy is about 10 per cent. of the total. At larger distances it increases up to 15 per cent., and then decreases again. Figs. 9† and 10‡ show this effect quite clearly. But in the range of significance, a value between 10 and 15 per cent. of the total binding energy seems reasonable. The value 14 per cent. is often used.

(b) As the principal quantum number n is increased, this ratio increases. For s electrons§ it may rise as high as 0·40 when $n = 4$.

(c) For p-binding‖ the percentage of Coulombic energy may be much larger than for s-binding. The specific calculation by Woods†† for CH_4, where (Ch. VIII) the binding is a

† H. Eyring and M. Polanyi, *Z. phys. Chem.* B, 1931, **12**, 279.
‡ J. O. Hirschfelder and F. Daniels, quoted by S. Glasstone, K. J. Laidler, and H. Eyring, *Theory of Rate Processes*, McGraw-Hill, 1941, 83.
§ N. Rosen and S. Ikehara, *Phys. Rev.*, 1933, **43**, 5.
‖ J. H. Bartlett, ibid., 1931, **37**, 507. See also S. Fraga and R. S. Mulliken, *Rev. Mod. Phys.*, 1960, **32**, 254
†† *Trans. Faraday Soc.*, 1932, **28**, 877.

mixture of s and p, indicate a Coulomb energy greater than 50 per cent. of the whole.

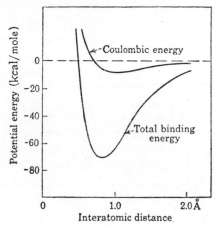

FIG. 7.9. The Coulombic and total binding energies in H_2.

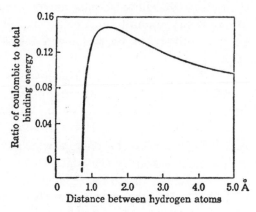

FIG. 7.10. Ratio of Coulombic and total binding energies in H_2.

This is a most unsatisfactory situation. Fortunately, however, the non-directional character of the Coulomb energy in many molecules makes our ignorance of its true value less disastrous than it might at first seem to be. It is now customary to refer to calculations of reaction rates in which the Coulomb energy plays a significant role as 'semi-empirical'. The description is evidently perfectly fair.

7.10. Accuracy of the approximation of perfect pairing

It is clear that unless we are able by some means to calculate the Coulomb terms, we shall not get very reliable measures of the energy. But even if we do make the calculations, there are still several other sources of error. These have already been listed in § 4, but it is instructive to have their numerical values for a particular molecule, H_2O. There are four chief sources of error, as follows:

(1) Failure of perfect pairing. It is not correct to assert, as (25) does, that certain a.o.'s are always paired together. It may be true that, on account of their greater mutual overlapping, certain pairings are much more favoured than others. In the case of H_2O alternative pairings contribute only a small additional energy, of the order of $0 \cdot 1$ eV.

(2) Non-orthogonality. Now average values of S_{ij} are in the range $\frac{1}{4}$ to $\frac{1}{2}$. Consequently the neglect of all such integrals in (25) is liable to be quite serious on an absolute scale. The error may easily amount to $2\frac{1}{2}$ eV. On a relative scale, however, it is unlikely to be serious in terms of stereochemical properties.

(3) Neglect of polar and ionic terms. The formula for perfect pairing completely neglects polarization of the a.o.'s and the possibility that the bonds are partly ionic. We know (Ch. V) that both effects occur, and for H_2O the ionic character is quite large. The error in the energy which results from its neglect has been shown by Coolidge† to be about $2\frac{1}{4}$ eV.

(4) Higher-order exchange integrals. Neglect of overlap integrals leads to neglect of certain of these higher-order exchange integrals, in which permutations of more than two a.o.'s occur. No reliable estimate seems to have been made of the effect of such integrals. Perhaps 2 eV is not an unreasonable value to assign to this neglect.

These are serious errors, which confirm our previous suspicions that it is in qualitative and semi-quantitative understanding of valence theory that these methods will be most convincing. Indeed

† *Phys. Rev.*, 1932, **42**, 189.

the approximation of perfect pairing is now never used except for qualitative purposes. For quantitative study of polyatomic molecules the method of delocalized m.o.'s is nearly always employed. Here, on account of the orthogonality of all the m.o.'s, many of the above difficulties disappear. But the price that we have to pay for better energy values is a more complicated wave function, and a diminished chemical insight!

7.11. Ionic effects

In a diatomic molecule $A—B$ we can represent covalent-ionic resonance by a composite wave function (§ 5.4)

$$\psi = \psi_{\text{cov}} + \lambda\psi_{\text{ion}}. \tag{30}$$

But in polyatomic molecules there may be several ionic structures, and we need to elaborate (30) a little further. Once again consider H_2O. Each bond may be either covalent or ionic, so that four 'structures' (cf. § 5.5) can be drawn

O	O⁻	O⁻	O⁻ ⁻
H \H	H H⁺	H⁺ \H	H⁺ H⁺
36 per cent.	24 per cent.	24 per cent.	16 per cent.
(a)	(b)	(c)	(d)

If we accept Pauling's reasoning in § 5.8, it follows that since the electronegativity difference $x_O - x_H = 1\cdot4$, each OH bond will have about 39 per cent. ionic character. It will simplify our analysis, without altering the general description, if we call this 40 per cent. This means that structures (a) and (b) must have relative weights 60 : 40, i.e. 3 : 2. The same is true for (a) : (c), and also for (c) : (d). A simple calculation now shows that the weights of (a)–(d) are in the ratio $3^2 : 3\times2 : 2\times3 : 2^2$. One way of describing all this is to say that if both OH bonds are really independent, the structures contribute in the above ratios, so that they have the final weights shown as percentages underneath the diagrams.† The chief objection to this mode of description is that, as was emphasized in Chapter V, these structures have no independent existence, so that it is strictly meaningless to speak of their

† These weights do not quite give the observed dipole moment, but that is immaterial for our present purpose. The following weights do give the observed moment 1·87 D: 41 per cent., 23 per cent., 23 per cent., 13 per cent.

weights: a second objection lies in the assumption of complete independence of the bonds. A more satisfactory view would be that if the left-hand bond is ionic, as in (c), the electronegative character of the oxygen is already saturated, so that the right-hand bond is much less likely to be ionic than would be expected from the ratio 2 : 3. The assumption of complete independence leads to a percentage for the doubly-ionic structure (d) which seems much too great.

There is yet another difficulty associated with the assignment of weights for the various structures (a)–(d) listed earlier. For it will be shown in § 8.10 that at least a part of the total dipole moment of H_2O is provided by the lone-pair, i.e. non-bonding electrons of the oxygen atom, which are forced into orbitals markedly ex-centric relative to the oxygen nucleus. These considerations, which would severely reduce the percentages of the ionic structures (b), (c), and (d) relative to the covalent structure (a), warn us once again to beware of any too naïve an interpretation even of quite simple molecules.

The point that we have just been making arises in other respects also. The assumption of a constant electronegativity x_A for an atom A may be reasonably valid for diatomic molecules; but for polyatomics it is much less satisfactory, since the polar, or ionic, effects in one bond induce corresponding effects in neighbouring bonds. In m.o. language the coefficient λ in an orbital $\psi_A + \lambda\psi_B$ does not depend solely upon the electronegativity difference $x_A - x_B$, but also upon the other groups attached to A and B.

A good example to illustrate this phenomenon[†] is the carbonyl bond $\rangle C = O$, where the high dipole moment ($\sim 2 \cdot 7$ D) shows that the valence electrons tend to congregate around the oxygen atom. As a result of this the lone-pair $(2p_y)^2$ electrons of the O atom find themselves under repulsion from more electrons than if they were in an isolated atom. They are therefore easier to remove: i.e. their ionization potential will be reduced. This is exactly what is found. For an O atom the ionization potential is 13·5 eV, yet for formaldehyde it is only about 11 eV. But we may go farther: suppose that one or more of the hydrogen atoms in formaldehyde was

† See, for example, W. C. Price, *Ann. Rep. Chem. Soc.*, 1939, **36**, 47.

replaced by some other group, of different electronegativity. This would affect the carbon atom and therefore, by inference, both the value of λ in the m.o. for the $>$C$=$O bond, and also the ionization potential of the oxygen lone-pair electrons. There ought to be some relation between λ and the ionization potential, i.e. between the polarity for the $>$C$=$O bond and the ionization potential of O. Such a relation has been found by Walsh.[†] The following table selected from a larger list in Walsh's paper, shows its nature.

TABLE 15. *Relation between polarity of carbonyl molecules and ionization potential of oxygen lone-pair electrons*

Molecule	Per cent. polarity	Ionization potential (eV)
Carbon monoxide	1	14·55
Carbon dioxide	9	13·79
Glyoxal	~30	~11·4
Formaldehyde	35	10·87
Acetaldehyde	42	10·23
Acetone	46	9·71

This kind of effect illustrates the nature of the difficulties that arise as soon as we attempt to pass from the broader aspect of approximate bond-additivity to the finer and more intimate details of non-additivity and mutual interaction. Apart from a careful study of CO and CO_2 by Moffitt,[‡] practically no theoretical calculations of such effects have yet been made.

[†] *Trans. Faraday Soc.*, 1947, **43**, 158.   [‡] *Proc. Roy. Soc.* A, 1949, **196**, 524.

VIII

HYBRIDIZATION

8.1. sp^3 tetrahedral hybridization[†]

THE discussion of directed valence in our last chapter was incomplete because it left out almost the whole field of carbon chemistry. The reason for the omission is that a study of carbon compounds introduces us to an extremely important, and rather unexpected, new concept. We can see how it arises if we ask ourselves how to explain the characteristic tetravalence of carbon as, for example, in CH_4. According to Fig. 2.7 the lowest state of a carbon atom is $(1s)^2(2s)^2(2p_x)(2p_y)$ which has two unpaired electrons and is spectroscopically described as a triplet, ^3P. Such an atom would be divalent, with a valence angle rather similar to that in water.[‡] The only way to obtain tetravalence is to excite the atom, taking one of the 2s electrons into the completely empty $2p_z$ orbital to give $(1s)^2(2s)(2p_x)(2p_y)(2p_z)$. As there are four unpaired electrons (§ 5.9), this is a quintet, ^5S. The energy for such an excitation should be discernible spectroscopically: both calculation[§] and experiment[||] seem to agree on a value about 96 kcal/mole. When this excitation has been made, we have four unpaired electrons which we may expect to pair with four attached groups, in the manner of Chapter VII. But here precisely is the difficulty: three of the electrons have p-type orbitals, and the fourth an s-type. If we assumed the formula of perfect pairing (7.25) we should expect to obtain three bonds of one kind and the fourth of a different kind: on account of the different overlapping property of p orbitals which are directional, and s orbitals which are entirely devoid of any directional character, the three bonds would be

---

[†] Hybridization was first introduced by Pauling, *J. Amer. Chem. Soc.*, 1931, **53**, 1367.

[‡] Actually we should expect a valence angle rather larger than in water, in agreement with measurements for methylene CH_2 (G. Herzberg and J. Shoosmith, *Nature*, 1959, **183**, 1801).

[§] R. F. Bacher and S. Goudsmit, *Phys. Rev.*, 1934, **46**, 948; but a rather lower value was calculated by C. W. Ufford, ibid., 1938, **53**, 568.

[||] A. G. Shenstone, ibid., 1947, **72**, 411.

different from the fourth. Also, the mutual angles would be 90°
for the p—p bonds and 125° 14′ for the s—p bonds. All these
inferences are demonstrably false for the particular molecule CH_4,
where physical evidence from the rotation-vibration spectrum
and chemical evidence from the
lack of any isomers of the form
CXY_3 or CX_2Y_2, show that the
four carbon bonds are inclined
at equal angles 109° 28′ to each
other, and are all equivalent.
It is this physical and chemical
evidence that leads us to the
next step in our mathematical
procedure. We can only get four
equivalent bonds by abandoning
the clear-cut division into atomic

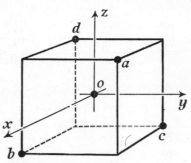

Fig. 8.1. The methane molecule
CH_4 together with its 'circum-
scribing cube'.

s and p orbitals: we must mix them. And so we arrive at the concept of mixed, or 'hybridized', orbitals.

In the case of methane this mixing must obviously include one
s and three p orbitals, and is usually called sp^3 hybridization.
We shall see later that there are plenty of other types of mixing.

There is an alternative line of thought which also leads to the
concept of hybridization. Let us, for convenience, call the carbon
a.o.'s x, y, z, s and the four hydrogen $1s$ a.o.'s a, b, c, d, as in Fig. 1,
where the x, y, z directions are parallel to the edges of the cube
through a, b, c, d, and the carbon atom is at the centre of the cube.
Then we could imagine a pairing scheme represented by the
formula (I) below: this means that hydrogen a is paired with

	a	b	c	d
I	x	y	z	s
II	y	z	s	x
III	z	x	s	y
IV	s	x	y	z

carbon x, b with y, etc. However, there are several alternative
pairings which we could consider, and which are equally satisfactory. (II), (III), and (IV) are three examples from many that

could be selected. From the geometry of the molecule, as shown in Fig. 1, none of these pairing schemes has any greater claim than any other. We must include them all in one grand wave function. If we put this in more pictorial language, we can say that the hydrogen a is paired equally often with s, x, y, and z. The same is true for b, c, and d. What could be more natural now than to suppose that instead of this partial pairing with all four carbon orbitals, there is complete pairing with some suitable combination

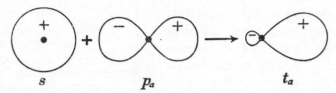

FIG. 8.2. Boundary surfaces in the formation of an sp^3-hybrid atomic orbital.

of them? In this way we are led to the idea of hybridized orbitals as a means of preserving as far as possible the fundamental principle of perfect pairing.†

The symmetry condition that we have introduced above shows that, so far as a is concerned, it is to be paired with the composite carbon orbital $s+x+y+z$. But the vector character of the p orbitals enables us to write

$$x+y+z = \sqrt{3}p_a,$$

where p_a is a $2p\sigma$ a.o. directed from the carbon atom at O towards the hydrogen a. Thus the appropriate hybrid is $s + \sqrt{3}p_a$. In normalized form this is $\frac{1}{2}(s + \sqrt{3}p_a)$. By symmetry the three other hybrids are $\frac{1}{2}(s + \sqrt{3}p_b)$, $\frac{1}{2}(s + \sqrt{3}p_c)$, $\frac{1}{2}(s + \sqrt{3}p_d)$. Let us call these $t_a,..., t_d$ respectively. Then $t_a,..., t_d$ are four composite a.o.'s directed in the four tetrahedral directions from the origin. We call this type of mixing the tetrahedral hybridization.

Once having established the existence and form of these hybrids, we can dispense with the x, y, z orbitals and axes by means of which we constructed them. In future, therefore, we shall simply

† This new pairing scheme is still not quite equivalent to the complete resonance scheme: cf. the comments on H_2O in § 7.10, and later discussion in § 14.

refer to 'tetrahedral hybrids' without reference to the complete geometry of Fig. 1.

We have already noticed that $t_a,..., t_d$ are directed towards the attached groups $a,..., d$. But a closer study shows that in fact they are very strongly directed, much more so even than the p-type orbitals. Fig. 2 shows the boundary surfaces for the tetrahedral hybrid $\frac{1}{2}(s + \sqrt{3}p_a)$ compared with those of s and p orbitals from which it is compounded. On the right-hand side of the nucleus (shown as a dot) s and p_a are of similar sign: on the left,

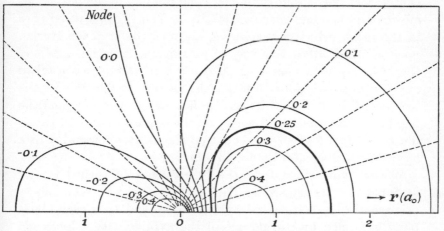

FIG. 8.3. Contours of ψ for a tetrahedral hybrid orbital of carbon. Only the top half of a section through the axis of symmetry of the orbital is shown. The complete set of contours would be obtained by rotation around the axis of x.

they are of opposite sign. So the result of adding s to $\sqrt{3}p_a$ is to accentuate the right-hand side, and diminish the left. Consequently the tetrahedral hybrid is able to overlap very strongly with an attached group, and thus gives strong binding. An accurate calculation of the contours of constant ψ yields the curves shown in Fig. 3.† ψ has axial symmetry around the direction Oa, so that the complete set of contours may be obtained by rotating those shown in the figure around the base line. The axial symmetry shows that bonds formed by direct overlap of orbitals of this kind will be σ-type bonds.

† W. E. Moffitt and C. A. Coulson, *Phil. Mag.*, 1947, **38**, 634.

It may not be immediately apparent from Fig. 3 how exceedingly effective this hybridization is in placing charge in the region where it can be used for bonding purposes. The following numerical calculation will show it. Suppose that in the hybrid $\frac{1}{2}(s + \sqrt{3}p)$ we use Slater functions (pp. 39, 40) for the $2s$ and $2p$ atomic orbitals of carbon. Then the node, shown curved in the more accurate calculations of Fig. 3, becomes a right circular cone, whose semi-vertical angle is $\cos^{-1}\frac{1}{3} = 70°\ 32'$. If an electron is now placed in the tetrahedral hybrid orbital, the total fraction of charge that lies within the nodal cone (and so is completely ineffective for bonding purposes) is only $\frac{1}{9}$. Thus $\frac{8}{9}$ of the charge lies in the region where ψ is positive, and may be used for overlap purposes. An alternative way of putting the situation is to say that whereas in a pure s or pure p orbital, there is a total of exactly $\frac{1}{2}e$ on each side of a plane (the yz-plane in Fig. 3), with the tetrahedral hybrid $\frac{7}{8}$ of the charge lies on the side in which the bond is to be formed, and only $\frac{1}{8}$ on the opposite side. All this is illustrated in § 5 when we show that the overlap integral with a hybrid is much greater than with pure s or p.

We can now understand the tetravalence of carbon in, for example, the paraffin series. Each carbon atom is imagined to be prepared in the tetrahedral hybridization, and then each C—H bond is formed by pairing one of the hybrids with a hydrogen orbital, lying along its direction: each C—C bond is formed by pairing two tetrahedral hybrids, one from each carbon atom. It does not matter for this purpose whether we use a m.o. or a v.b. wave function: the essential character is the same in either case. A similar description applies to the diamond lattice in which each carbon atom is tetrahedrally surrounded by four others. It is for this reason that the C—C distance in diamond, which can be measured by X-rays with very great precision, is often taken as the normal single C—C bond distance.

8.2. Trigonal and digonal hybrids

The tetrahedral hybrids just discussed are not the only hybrids that are important in carbon. There are two others of especial importance, called the trigonal and digonal (sometimes diagonal).

In the trigonal, or sp^2, form, we leave one of the original p orbitals unchanged (p_z, say) and mix s, p_x, and p_y. Since we are mixing three a.o.'s we can only form three distinct hybrids. As Fig. 4 shows, these three are directed in the xy-plane at angles of 120° with each other. There is, of course, no need to refer specifically to the x-, y-axes. For the three hybrids are entirely equivalent, and a trigonal orbital directed in the direction a has a wave function $s + \sqrt{2}p_a$. In normalized form this is

$$\frac{1}{\sqrt{3}}\{s + \sqrt{2}p_a\}.$$

The digonal, or sp, hybridization leaves p_y and p_z unchanged and mixes s and p_x. Fig. 5 shows that we now have two equivalent and strongly directed orbitals, this time in diametrically opposed directions. The analytical expression for a digonal orbital in the a direction is $s + p_a$; if normalized it is $\frac{1}{\sqrt{2}}(s + p_a)$. The complementary orbital pointing in the opposite direction is $\frac{1}{\sqrt{2}}(s - p_a)$.

Just as the tetrahedral hybrids were needed to describe carbon in its tetrahedral state, so the trigonal ones are needed in the ethylenic state. It is known experimentally that in ethylene all six atoms are coplanar, and the angles are not far from 120°. The description of the bonds in this molecule is therefore as follows† (see Fig. 6). The two carbons A and B are hybridized trigonally, and the overlapping orbitals A_1 and B_1 are paired: A_2, A_3, B_2, and B_3 are paired with four overlapping hydrogens. This gives six σ-bonds, and there remain the two unmixed p_z a.o.'s of A and B. These must be paired to form a π-bond, as in Fig. 4.9. This justifies us in writing the formula $H_2C{=}CH_2$, and saying that the $C{=}C$ double bond consists of a pair of trigonal σ orbitals together with a pair of π orbitals superposed. This description leads us at once to two important conclusions. First of all, in order that the bond may be as strong as possible, the separate p_z orbitals must overlap as much as possible. This requires the whole molecule to be planar, and with a bond length (1·34 A) shorter than in the single bond (1·54 A). Secondly, this description

† E. Huckel, Z. Phys., 1930, **60**, 423.

warns us that work will be needed to twist one half of the molecule
relative to the other half, on account of the reduced extent of this

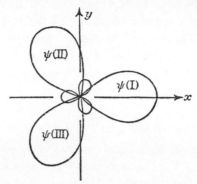

FIG. 8.4. The three trigonal sp^2-hybrids.

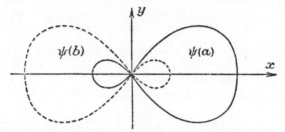

FIG. 8.5. The two digonal sp-hybrids.

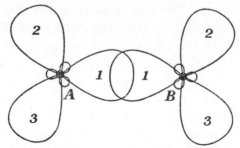

FIG. 8.6. The carbon atoms 'prepared' for binding in the ethylene molecule
$CH_2{=}CH_2$. The π orbitals on A and B are not shown to avoid confusion.
They are directed perpendicularly to the plane of the paper.

same overlap. Here is the explanation of, first, the coplanarity
around a double bond, and, second, the absence of free rotation
around it.

The digonal hybrids explain the triple bond, such as in acetylene. In the notation of Fig. 7, the two digonal hybrids A_1 and B_1 are paired to form a σ-bond: the two hydrogens are placed to overlap

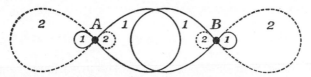

FIG. 8.7. The carbon atoms 'prepared' for binding in the acetylene molecule CH≡CH. The four π orbitals of the two atoms A and B are not shown. They are in perpendicular pairs at right angles to the line AB.

A_2 and B_2, leading to a linear molecule HC≡CH; and the un-mixed a.o.'s p_y, p_z of each atom are paired to form two π-bonds. The superposition of two perpendicular π-bonds around the same axis leads to cylindrical symmetry. So acetylene is linear, and possesses axial symmetry.

8.3. Non-equivalent hybrids

The three basic s, p hybridizations just described have the property that in each case the hybrid a.o.'s are equivalent. They are the only ones for which this is true. But all intermediate degrees of hybridization can occur, provided that not all the result-ing orbitals are to be equivalent. All that is necessary is that they shall be orthogonal. This is the point to which we referred in § 7.2. For if they are not orthogonal we cannot pair them individually with attached groups: in rough parlance we could say that they 'included a part of each other', and cannot be treated separately in the way that is required by the assumption of perfect pairing. The condition of orthogonality can be found as follows:

Any hybrid of s and p that has its maximum in the direction i must be of the form

$$s + \lambda p_i, \tag{1}$$

where λ, sometimes called the coefficient of mixing, determines the relative weights of the s and p contributions. A second hybrid associated with the direction j, will be

$$s + \mu p_j.$$

These two will be orthogonal if

$$\int (s+\lambda p_i)(s+\mu p_j)\, d\tau = 0.$$

Since s and p_i, p_j are normalized,

$$\int s^2\, d\tau = 1 = \int p_i^2\, d\tau, \quad \text{and} \quad \int p_i p_j\, d\tau = \cos\theta_{ij},$$

where θ_{ij} (Fig. 8) is the angle between the directions i and j. This latter result follows from the fact, often used before, that p_j may be treated as a vector, and resolved into $p_i \cos\theta_{ij}$ along p_i

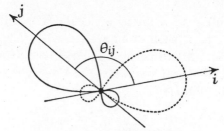

FIG. 8.8. Orthogonal hybrids.

and $p_i \sin\theta_{ij}$ perpendicular to it. On grounds of symmetry two p orbitals with perpendicular directions are orthogonal (§ 4.3). Also

$$\int sp_i\, d\tau = \int sp_j\, d\tau = 0,$$

so the orthogonality condition is simply

$$1+\lambda\mu \cos\theta_{ij} = 0. \tag{2}$$

We may now choose hybrids such as (1) in any four directions provided that appropriate λ, μ,... may be found satisfying the six conditions (2). If the hybrids are to be equivalent (2) reduces to

$$1+\lambda^2 \cos\theta_{ij} = 0. \tag{3}$$

Values of λ which satisfy this equation are summarized in Table 16 below. Evidently $\cos\theta_{ij}$ must be negative, so that no two equivalent real hybrids may make an angle less than 90° with each other. According to (2), the same is true even if they are not equivalent.

Non-equivalent hybrids are required as soon as the atoms attached to the central carbon are dissimilar. Thus in CH_3Cl, we

Table 16. *Types of s, p hybridization giving equivalent bonds*

Type of hybridization	Pure s	Digonal sp	Trigonal sp^2	Tetrahedral sp^3	Pure p
Example	..	Acetylene	Ethylene	Methane	..
Value of λ	0	1	$\sqrt{2}$	$\sqrt{3}$	..
Valence angle	..	180°	120°	109° 28′	90°

shall expect three of the hybrids to have one value (λ_1 say) and the fourth to have a different one (λ_2). Furthermore λ_1 and λ_2 will be related to the stereochemistry of the molecule according to (2).

Hybridizations of this kind are not restricted to carbon; they will apply whenever there are s and p electrons with approximately the same energy. Tetrahedral hybrids occur whenever the valence-shell electrons have a configuration similar to that in carbon; Si and Ge are obvious examples. So also is quaternary nitrogen N^+.

8.4. The valence state

When electrons of the carbon atom (or other atom) have been placed in hybridized orbitals we speak of the atom as excited, or promoted to a Valence State.† Naturally enough, since there are many different types of hybrid, there are many different valence states. Fortunately their energies (at least in the case of carbon, where the calculations are much more detailed than for other atoms) do not appear to depend greatly on the precise values of the various coefficients of mixing. The advantage of the valence state is that the various orbitals have a very strongly directed probability function, so that they can form strong bonds by perfect pairing. The disadvantage is that energy is required to form the hybridization. This energy is less in the case of carbon, where $\psi(2s)$ and $\psi(2p)$ have more nearly equal energies, than in oxygen where the difference is greater. We reap our reward for the outlay of this energy of promotion later when we find a correspondingly greater gain in energy through the formation of stronger bonds.

We may illustrate all this by a study of carbon. There are (Fig. 9) five energies of significance. The lowest of all is the energy

† J. H. Van Vleck, *J. Chem. Phys.*, 1933, **1**, 177, 219; 1934, **2**, 20; R. S. Mulliken, ibid., 1934, **2**, 782; W. E. Moffitt, *Proc. Roy. Soc.* A, 1950, **202**, 534, 548.

of solid carbon, usually taken to be graphite: a latent heat L_1 is required to sublime graphite to atomic carbon in the divalent $s^2p^2(^3P)$ state. A further energy L_2-L_1 is needed to excite the s^2p^2 atom to an $sp^3(^5S)$ atom. More energy still is needed to prepare the atom in the valence state,† and finally, with the formation of four bonds, the energy is much lowered. The numerical

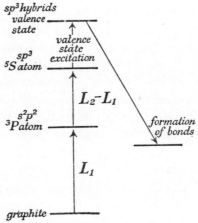

FIG. 8.9. Energies of the valence, and other, states in carbon.

values of L_1 and L_2 are still in dispute, though, as we have seen, L_2-L_1 seems to be about 96 kcal/mole, and L_1 is almost certainly 171 kcal/mole.

Confusion may easily arise concerning the Valence State. For example:

(1) It is not a spectroscopic‡ state at all. This means that a

† This has been questioned by L. H. Long, *Experientia*, 1951, **7**, 195, from considerations of experimental heats of formation. Perhaps the source of the confusion lies in the fact that even in methane the carbon atom is not restricted to sp^3 character. H. H. Voge (*J. Chem. Phys.*, 1936, **4**, 581; 1948, **16**, 984) and others have shown that the divalent s^2p^2 states also play a part, with a weight of about 30–40 per cent. Such interaction lowers the effective height of the valence state energy in Fig. 9, and reduces the height of the valence state above the ^3P ground state from a calculated value of about 162 kcal/mole for pure sp^3 orbitals to an effective 100 kcal/mole. If we are interested in the mean energy of excitation of an s to a p orbital in carbon, taking account of all possible spin multiplicities, we must use the average of all the states arising from s^2p^2 and from sp^3. As J. C. Slater has shown (*Phys. Rev.*, 1955, **98**, 1093), this gives a value close to 200 kcal/mole.

‡ A spectroscopic state is an allowed stationary state for the system and therefore directly related to possible spectroscopic observation.

carbon atom (or other atom) could not exist alone in such a condition. Thus when we speak of an excitation to the valence state, we do not describe an actual or even physically possible process. What we are trying to do is to separate the energy of the molecule into the sum of an energy for each localized-pair bond and an energy for the separate atoms. On account of the fact that the localized bonds are not pure s- or p-bonds, but are hybrids, the energy for the separate atoms will not be the energy of normal atomic ground states, but will differ from them by precisely the energy of excitation to the valence state. In the case of carbon Voge† and Van Vleck‡ calculate the valence state to lie about 7–8 eV above the s^2p^2 ^3P state.

(2) The carbon atom in, for example, methane never gets into the valence state. We could imagine the process of forming CH_4 to be achieved in an idealized fashion as follows. An isolated carbon in the ^5S state is surrounded tetrahedrally by four hydrogens at a great distance away. As these hydrogens gradually approach, keeping to their tetrahedral directions, there is a gradual change of the electronic structure around the C atom, tending to induce the four tetrahedral concentrations of charge characteristic of the valence state. The partial overlapping of these with the charge-clouds of the approaching hydrogens leads to four incipient bonds, with a contribution to the binding energy which offsets the energy required to destroy the spectroscopic ^5S atomic state. Thus the energy needed to excite to the valence state never needs to be supplied to the system. If it were possible to remove the four hydrogens in methane to infinite distance, and in some artificial way preserve the perfect pairing of their electrons with the carbon valence electrons, the final state of the carbon atom would be the valence state.§ Since the approximation of perfect

† In the strictly tetrahedral valence state, the atom may be said to be in a mixture of genuine spectroscopic states. H. H. Voge (*J. Chem. Phys.*, 1936, **4**, 581) has shown that this mixture is

$$\tfrac{1}{8}[2\sqrt{5}(sp^3,\ ^5S)+3(p^4,\ ^3P)+3\sqrt{2}(sp^3,\ ^3D)-3(s^2p^2,\ ^3P)-\sqrt{3}(p^4,\ ^1D)-$$
$$-\sqrt{2}(sp^3,\ ^1D)+\sqrt{3}(s^2p^2,\ ^1D)].$$

‡ Loc. cit.

§ This disregards resonance with certain s^2p^2 configurations (i.e. configurational interaction referred to in the footnote to p. 206), which Voge has shown may contribute from 2 to 3 eV in lowering the energy of the valence state.

pairing supposes that all electrons not actually paired together in a bond have their spins quite random relative to each other, the spins of the four electrons in the valence state must have this random character. It is chiefly for this reason that the valence state is not a spectroscopic state.

The energies of a large number of possible valence states have been calculated by Mulliken[†] and Moffitt and others.[‡] In cases where several different types of hybridization may conceivably arise, such tables are useful because the energy of excitation to the valence state measures, in an approximate way, the ease with which the corresponding hybrid a.o.'s can be formed.

8.5. Strength of hybrid bonds

The chief advantage in a hybridized a.o. is its high directional character which, according to the principle of maximum overlapping, should yield a stronger bond. Certain general features of bond strength follow at once from such considerations.

In the first place s-bonds (as in the alkali molecules $Li_2...$)[§] are almost always weak. This is because two similar s orbitals on adjacent atoms cannot possibly overlap very strongly on account of the spherically symmetrical distribution of their charge, particularly if, as in the alkali atoms, their charge-clouds are diffuse. Such bonds are weaker than p-bonds, where the directional character of the p orbital allows considerable overlap. But both should be weaker than s—p hybrid bonds, for in these latter the overlap may be very considerable. Interesting examples of these rules are the three molecules Li_2, F_2, C_2 (as in C_2H_6), where the bond energies are (Table 12, p. 185) 26, 38, and 80 kcal/mole respectively.

A reasonable expectation is that the strength of the bond between two identical atoms depends on the overlap of the two a.o.'s which are paired together. There will, of course, be other factors, some of which were mentioned in Chapter VII, but we may expect the overlap integral $\int \psi_A \psi_B \, d\tau$ to be one of the most

† Loc. cit.

‡ W. E. Moffitt, *Proc. Roy. Soc.* A, 1950, **202**, 534; L. Pauling, *Proc. Nat. Acad. Sci.*, 1949, **35**, 229; H. A. Skinner and H. O. Pritchard, *Trans. Faraday Soc.*, 1953, **49**, 1254.

Further comments on Li_2 are to be found on p. 231.

significant items in determining bond strength. In particular we may hope to compare different hybrids of s and p by a comparison of their overlap integrals. Fig. 10† shows how the overlap integral S between two atoms such as carbon depends upon the percentage s-character in the hybrids ψ_A and ψ_B, each of which is supposed to

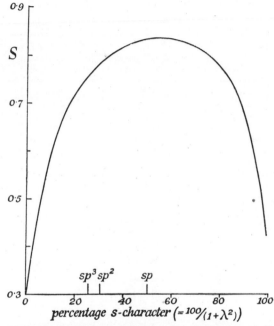

Fig. 8.10. The overlap integral S for two similar atomic hybrids of forms $s+\lambda p$, when s and p are Slater-type orbitals (eq. 2.18), and the effective nuclear charge Z is related to the internuclear distance by the condition $ZR = 8.0$.

be of the form $s+\lambda p$. The astonishing thing about this curve is that although pure s- or p-overlap amounts to less than 0.5, by suitable hybridization we can obtain an overlap exceeding 0.8. The greatest overlap occurs in the neighbourhood of sp hybridization, which suggests that sp bonds should be stronger than either sp^2 or sp^3. Data for CH bonds shown in Table 17‡ seem to support

† A. Maccoll, *Trans. Faraday Soc.*, 1950, **46**, 369.
‡ Taken from A. D. Walsh, *Trans. Faraday Soc.*, 1947, **43**, 60, but corrected in accordance with recent spectroscopic analysis.

this view. Although there may be some doubt about the precise values of the bond energies shown in the last column, there can be no doubt that the increased bond length and decreased force constant reveal a decreasing bond energy associated with the decreasing overlap of atomic orbitals as we go down the table.†

TABLE 17. *Properties of CH bonds involving differing hybridization*

Hybridiza-tion	Molecule	C—H bond length (A)	Stretching force constant (10⁵ dynes/cm)	Bond energy (kcal/mole)
sp	Acetylene	1·060	6·397	∼121
sp^2	Ethylene	1·069	6·126	∼106
sp^3	Methane	1·090	5·387	∼103
(p)	CH radical	1·120	4·490	80

A different measure of strength has been proposed by Pauling and Sherman,‡ who calculated the energies of one-electron bonds

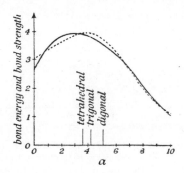

FIG. 8.11. Square of bond strength (dashed curve) and calculated bond energy values (full curve) for a one-electron bond between two identical hybrids $a\psi(2s)+(10-a)\psi(2p)$. (After Pauling and Sherman.)

between similar atoms, using the wave function $\psi_A+\psi_B$, where ψ_A and ψ_B were of the form

$$a\psi(2s)+(10-a)\psi(2p). \qquad (4)$$

Here $(10-a)/a$ replaces the coefficient of mixing λ of our earlier form (1). Thus $a = 0$ is pure p-binding and $a = 10$ is pure

† See also R. S. Mulliken, *J. Amer. Chem. Soc.*, 1950, **72**, 4493; *J. Chem. Phys.*, 1951, **19**, 900.   ‡ *J. Amer. Chem. Soc.*, 1937, **59**, 1450.

s-binding. The variation of the energy with a is shown in Fig. 11. It has its maximum near $a = 4\cdot0$, and falls to much lower values for pure s- or pure p-binding. This energy was correlated, not with the overlap integral between ψ_A and ψ_B, but with the product of the 'strengths' of the two separate orbitals ψ_A and ψ_B. The strength P_A of an orbital ψ_A is defined as the maximum value of the orbital for given r, scaled so that the value is $1\cdot0$ for pure s. It follows from (2·18) and (2·19) that the strength of a p orbital is $\sqrt{3}$ and of a d_{z^2} orbital $\sqrt{5}$. The strength of a hybrid $s+\lambda p$ is

$$P = \frac{1+\sqrt{3}\lambda}{\sqrt{(1+\lambda^2)}}. \tag{5}$$

TABLE 18. *Strength of hybrid orbital $s+\lambda p$ according to Pauling's definition*

λ	0	1	$\sqrt{2}$	$\sqrt{3}$	∞
Type	s	sp	sp^2	sp^3	p
Strength	$1\cdot0$	$1\cdot933$	$1\cdot991$	$2\cdot000$	$1\cdot732$

The maximum strength occurs for the tetrahedral hybrids $\lambda = \sqrt{3}$. Fig. 11 shows that there is a close parallelism between the energy of the bond and the product $P_A P_B$ of the two hybrid orbitals ψ_A and ψ_B.[†] Pauling has supposed that this is true in general, even when ψ_A and ψ_B are dissimilar and when interactions with other electrons present in the molecule are considered. However, a reference to Table 15 (p. 195) shows that although this concept of orbital strength is undoubtedly a valuable one, it is less satisfactory for explaining detailed variations in bond energy than is the overlap integral described at the beginning of this section. In particular it reverses the order of CH bond energy in methane, ethylene, and acetylene, and it predicts the absurd result that the energy of a π-bond should be zero. Furthermore, a better calculation[‡] of the exchange energy in an electron-pair bond such as $C-H$, similar to that described in § 6, shows a maximum value in the neighbourhood of the digonal bonds, where $\lambda = 1$.

† But see H. O. Pritchard and H. A. Skinner, *J. Chem. Soc.*, 1951, p. 945.
‡ T. Förster, *Z. Phys. Chem.* B, 1939, **43**, 58.

8.6. Calculation of valence angles

Once we have introduced the idea of hybridized orbitals, we can apply the formula of perfect pairing (7.25) and make calculations of valence angles similar to those in § 7.4. Let us consider methane† as a typical example, and imagine that we did not know that its shape was strictly tetrahedral. One possible shape would be pyramidal, in which the bonds to the three hydrogens b, c, d (Fig. 12) were equivalent, but different from that to hydrogen a.

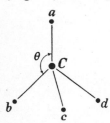

FIG. 8.12. Localized pairs in methane.

We should then imagine four hybrid orbitals α, β, γ, δ to be formed at the carbon atom, directed towards the four hydrogens. Three of these (β, γ, δ) will be equivalent, but different from the fourth (α): and all four will have coefficients of mixing which depend on the angle θ. If we neglect H—H repulsions and internal energies in the carbon atom, the exchange energy associated with the structure just described is given, analogously to (7.26), by the sum of four similar expressions, of which the first is

$$+J(a:\alpha)-\tfrac{1}{2}\{J(a:\beta)+J(a:\gamma)+J(a:\delta)\},$$

and the others are obtained by cyclic interchanges. This group of four terms arises from the fact that the orbits a and α are paired, so that the exchange integral $J(a:\alpha)$ has coefficient $+1$; and that a and β, γ, δ are not paired, so that their exchange integrals have coefficient $-\tfrac{1}{2}$. The whole of this exchange energy may be expressed quite simply in terms of θ and certain fundamental integrals involving carbon s, p and hydrogen orbitals. The precise values of these fundamental integrals are not known, but a whole range of likely values leads to the result that the exchange energy is least when the angle θ has the tetrahedral value 109° 28′. The neglected Coulomb terms are without significance, because just as in the case of H_2O (§ 7.5) they turn out to be independent of θ.

An exactly similar calculation shows that the same conclusion is reached regarding the most stable configuration of the molecule if, instead of supposing that three of the bonds are equivalent,

† J. H. Van Vleck, *J. Chem. Phys.*, 1933, **1**, 177, 219; 1934, **2**, 20.

we suppose that the four bonds are equivalent in pairs, C—a and C—b being similar, but different from C—c and C—d.

In this way the characteristic tetrahedral configuration around a carbon atom is established, not simply by symmetry considerations, but by calculation. A similar situation is found for ethane, and the paraffin series. Small differences in the equivalence of all the valence angles might be expected when, as in CH_3Cl, the attached groups are not all identical. These differences might arise because the fundamental exchange integrals with the substituted atoms are not the same as with the original hydrogens, and it might turn out more profitable to give a greater weight to the largest of these integrals at the expense of the smaller. This could be achieved by distorting the molecule from a regular tetrahedral shape. However, calculation† shows that in so far as the exchange energy is concerned, the deviations of angle are not likely to exceed 2° or 3°, in complete agreement with the accurate microwave rotation spectra of halogen-substituted methanes. It is true that these calculations are not completely convincing, because the formula of perfect pairing, on which they are based, assumes no ionic contributions to any of the bonds, and our study of diatomic molecules shows that the most characteristic result of substituting one of the hydrogens in CH_4 by a chlorine atom will be a flow of charge from the carbon towards the chlorine. The dipole moment of CH_3Cl is 1·87 D, so that if the polarity resides largely in the C—Cl region, this bond would have an ionic character of about 22 per cent. To neglect this completely is unsatisfactory: yet apparently its effect on the geometry of the molecule is very small for the HCH angle is now known to be in the range 110·5°±0·5°, only a little larger than the strict tetrahedral angle.

It appears that in CH_4 the approximation of regarding a particular carbon hybrid orbital as paired to a particular hydrogen orbital is astonishingly accurate. For the error so introduced‡ is only about 0·056 eV (1 kcal/mole). To some extent we can see this from the shape (Fig. 2) of a tetrahedral orbital. This is so strongly directed that the exchange integrals with coefficient +1

† W. G. Penney, *Trans. Faraday Soc.*, 1935, **31**, 734.
‡ M. Karplus and D. H. Anderson, *J. Chem. Phys.*, 1959, **30**, 6.

are all large and those with coefficient $-\frac{1}{2}$, corresponding to non-pairing, are particularly small. We could describe this by saying that hybridization increases the bonding because of increased overlapping with paired orbitals, and at the same time decreases the repulsion because of decreased overlapping of non-paired orbitals. Here is the explanation of the great strength of carbon bonds (see Table 12 on p. 185).

8.7. The ethylene double bond

In § 2 we described the ethylene bond $H_2C{=}CH_2$ as the super-position of a σ-bond formed by overlap of two trigonal hybrids, and a π-bond formed by overlap of two unhybridized p-type

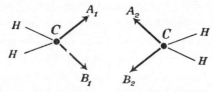

FIG. 8.13. Ethylene, a possible model.

orbitals. But before this description is accepted we ought to con-sider the possibility, historically proposed much earlier, that the carbon atoms are hybridized tetrahedrally, and are linked together by the pairing (Fig. 13) of two sets $A_1 A_2$, $B_1 B_2$ of orbitals. Two tetrahedral orbitals are inherently stronger than a trigonal plus a π orbital: but, as the diagram shows, their overlapping would be less, because the geometry of the molecule prevents them from pointing directly at each other. Calculation† using pure trigonal and tetrahedral hybrids and the v.b. type of wave function shows that the energy of the π-bond model is several eV better than that of the bent tetrahedral bonds. Some confirmation of this can be found from the fact that the HCH angle is close to 120°. This is just what would have been expected with trigonal hybridization: with tetrahedral hybridization the angle would have been close to 109° 28′.

In the simple m.o. picture the distinction between $\sigma\pi$ binding and bent tetrahedral binding is less obvious. For if we suppose that the tetrahedral

† W. G. Penney, *Proc. Roy. Soc.* A, 1934, **144**, 166; C. A. Coulson and W. E. Moffitt, *Phil. Mag.*, 1949, **40**, 1.

model is one in which the two molecular orbitals $(A_1 + A_2)$ and $(B_1 + B_2)$ are each doubly occupied, then, by an argument similar to that in small type on p. 173 (§ 7.3) involving combination of rows and columns of a determinant, it can be shown that the simple tetrahedral model and the simple $\pi\sigma$ model are entirely equivalent. They cease to be equivalent as soon as we take configuration interaction into account. But detailed calculations are not here available.

By suitable addition of higher energy orbitals, such as d and f atomic orbitals, it is possible to concentrate the charge-cloud of a hybrid even more than in a tetrahedral hybrid. But the greater overlapping power which results has had to be bought at the price of a partial excitation to $3d$ and $4f$ levels, which are energetically much less favourable. Clearly some compromise has to be reached. Some calculations by L. Pauling† suggest that the optimum mixture may involve about $2\frac{1}{2}$ per cent. each of d-character and f-character.

8.8. Hybridization and strain

The fact that the energy of the double bond in ethylene is less than twice the energy of a single bond used to be described as due to strain. This was very plausible so long as the early model of § 7 was accepted. But we now know that the explanation lies more accurately in the changes of hybridization induced by the geometry of the molecule. This raises the important question whether all strain energy, in the original language of Baeyer, can be similarly explained. The answer seems to be 'No', as the example of cyclopropane‡ will serve to show. Cyclopropane consists of three CH_2 groups arranged symmetrically with the three carbons at the vertices of an equilateral triangle. This situation is shown in Fig. 14, where the H atoms are omitted for convenience. As there are no

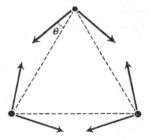

FIG. 8.14. Cyclopropane. The arrows denote the directions in which the carbon hybrids in the plane of the three carbon atoms are pointing.

double bonds in the molecule, we should expect hybridization at each carbon to be such that, so far as possible, the four hybrids

† *Proc. Nat. Acad. Sci.*, 1958, **44**, 211.

‡ C. A. Coulson and W. E. Moffitt, loc. cit.

were directed towards the attached atoms. This is easily possible for the C—H bonding electrons but it is not possible for the C—C hybrids, since, as we showed in § 3, no two real hybrids may make an angle less than 90° with each other. The best compromise is reached when $\theta = 22°$, so that the angle between the hybrids is $22°+60°+22° = 104°$. The orbitals thus obtained do not point directly towards each other, so that we could describe the bonds as 'bent'.† According to this description, the best pairing scheme for this molecule is obtained by pairing together the orbitals represented by adjacent arrows in the figure: to the extent that this scheme really does represent the electronic distribution, we are at liberty to say that hybridization is the modern form of strain for this molecule: and indeed the poorer overlap of these orbitals does correspond to a loss of energy about $7\frac{1}{2}$ eV per molecule. This value must be offset by an additional bonding due to resonance with other pairing schemes. It is not quite clear how big this is, but on general grounds it may be expected to be considerably larger than the vanishingly small value (1/20 eV) in methane. This residual energy is a type of strain (here a recovery of energy) not included in hybridization changes.‡ It is the combination of these factors, with one or two additional small terms, that represents the thermochemical strain energy of 1·09 eV (25·2 kcal/mole) measured calorimetrically.§

A case where strain energy occurs without any obvious reference

FIG. 8.15.
The phosphorus
molecule P_4.

to hybridization is found in the P_4 molecule (Fig. 15) which has the shape of a regular tetrahedron with all its angles 60°. The binding in phosphorus is similar to that in nitrogen, except that it is more nearly pure p-type. This follows because the valence angle in PH_3 (93°) is closer to 90° than in NH_3 (107°). But p orbitals must point at 90° to each other, so that the bonds in P_4

---

† On account of this bending, they may be called 'banana' bonds instead of 'sausage' bonds!

‡ See § 14 for further discussion of this residual resonance energy.

§ W. Weltner, *J. Amer. Chem. Soc.*, 1953, **75**, 4224, who corrects some numerical mistakes by Coulson and Moffitt, loc. cit.

must necessarily be bent. Simple geometry[†] shows that the angle of bending is $19\frac{1}{2}°$, and that the loss of energy due to reduced overlap, as compared with a straight P—P bond, is 0·77 eV (18 kcal) per bond. Just as in cyclopropane, however, there is a recovery of energy due to alternative pairings, leading to a final energy value for the P—P bond in P_4 about 7 kcal/mole less than for an unstrained bond.

This very much reduced overlapping may be improved by judicious admixture of a certain amount of atomic d orbital. It should be easier to add d orbitals to s and p hybrids in phosphorus than in carbon (see § 2.7) because the lowest d orbital has principal quantum number 3, and so belongs to the same shell as the phosphorus valence electrons $3s$ and $3p$, whereas in carbon the valence electrons $2s$, $2p$ are in an inner shell, with much lower energy. Pauling and Simonetta[‡] have concluded that the appropriate hybrid in P_4, which minimizes the total energy, is

$$0·987p + 0·064s + 0·15d,$$

leading to weights: $3p$, 97·4 per cent. $3s$, 0·4 per cent. and $3d$, 2·2 per cent. It is still true that the bonding is largely of p-character, but the small amount of d-character serves to alleviate the strain.

8.9. Atomic radius and electronegativity

A very rapid glance at the shape of atomic s and p orbitals shows that the p orbital projects farther from the centre than does the s. Hybrids $s + \lambda p$ will evidently project intermediate distances. We shall therefore expect that the length of a bond C—X will vary somewhat, according to the nature of the hybrid carbon orbital used. Such a situation is found in the C—H bonds, where, as Table 17 (p. 210) shows, there are differences amounting to more than 0·06 A between different CH bonds. Even the numerical magnitudes of these changes may be accounted for quite nicely by a careful study of the charge-cloud densities in these hybrid orbitals.[§] Other evidence of this effect will be found in Chapters XI and XII.

† W. E. Moffitt, *Trans. Faraday Soc.*, 1948, **44**, 987.
‡ L. Pauling and M. Simonetta, *J. Chem. Phys.*, 1952, **20**, 29.
§ C. A. Coulson, *Victor Henri Memorial Volume*, Desoer, Liége, 1948, p. 15.

Associated with this change in atomic radius is a change in electronegativity, and hence in the polarity of the bonds. For, other things being equal, the smaller the atomic radius, the closer can other electrons come before repulsive forces set in. This implies that the more s-character there is in the hybrid, the more electronegative does the atom appear, for the purposes of this particular bond. An alternative way of describing this is to say that since the ionization potential, and electronegativity, of an s electron exceeds that of a p electron,† we should expect greater electronegativity in a hybrid $s+\lambda p$ when there is a greater proportion of s, i.e. smaller λ. As mentioned at the end of § 5.8 the associated polarity differences are found experimentally in CH bonds of different types.

8.10. Dipole moments: the atomic dipole

The most noticeable distinction between a hybrid orbital and its component s, p,... orbitals is that the hybrid no longer possesses central symmetry. Fig. 2 shows very clearly that the centre of mean position in a hybrid may be at some distance from the nucleus. Thus, for a hybrid $(s+\lambda p_x)/(1+\lambda^2)^{\frac{1}{2}}$, the centre of mean position is at a distance $\bar{x}$ from the nucleus, where

$$\bar{x} = \int x \frac{(s+\lambda p_x)^2}{1+\lambda^2}\, d\tau = (1+\lambda^2)^{-1}\{\bar{x}_s+\lambda^2\bar{x}_p+2\lambda\bar{x}_{sp}\}, \quad \text{say}.$$

Now $\bar{x}_s$ and $\bar{x}_p$, which give the centroids of the s and p_x a.o.'s, are zero: and so

$$\bar{x} = \frac{2\lambda}{1+\lambda^2}\bar{x}_{sp} = \frac{2\lambda}{1+\lambda^2}\int x\psi(s)\psi(p_x)\, d\tau. \tag{6}$$

For pure s ($\lambda = 0$) and pure p ($\lambda = \infty$) $\bar{x}$ vanishes; but for hybrids of s and p, $\bar{x}$ may be quite large, with a maximum value in the digonal hybrids $\lambda = 1$. If $\psi(s)$ and $\psi(p_x)$ are the a.o.'s appropriate to carbon, $\bar{x}_{sp}$ has the numerical value‡ $0.89a_0$. This asymmetry of charge means that in the process of preparing a carbon atom for bond formation, we introduce what may be called *atomic dipoles*. The magnitude of such a dipole is $\mu = e\bar{x}$ per electron.

---

† R. S. Mulliken, *J. Phys. Chem.*, 1937, **41**, 318; W. E. Moffitt, *Proc. Roy. Soc.* A, 1950, **202**, 534, 548.

‡ C. A. Coulson, *Trans. Faraday Soc.*, 1942, **38**, 433.

Such dipoles are quite large, as Fig. 16 shows for the case of carbon, where each electron may contribute as much as 2·2 D. It is true that in a molecule like methane, the four atomic dipoles yield a zero resultant moment; but if we are solely concerned with the dipole moment of the two electrons that are responsible for one of the C—H bonds, we must evidently take account of them. This means that in equation (4.32) for the dipole moment of a polar bond, we can no longer put $\bar{x}_A = -\frac{1}{2}R$, $\bar{x}_B = +\frac{1}{2}R$, but must include (6). It is for this reason chiefly that, contrary to what would be expected on the basis of atomic electronegativity

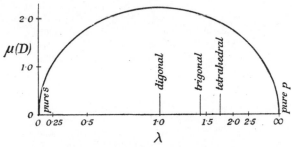

FIG. 8.16. The atomic dipole for a hybrid carbon orbital.

values, the dipole moment of tetravalent C—H has a probable direction $\overset{+\ \longrightarrow}{\text{C—H}}$, in which the direction of the arrow indicates that electronic charge has moved on to the hydrogen atom, leaving the carbon positively charged. For aromatic, ethylenic, and acetylenic carbon, on account of the greater electronegativity of C, the polarity of CH is probably reversed.†

It is important to be as clear as we can be about the chemical implications of the last few sentences. Since the only dipole moment which is directly measurable is the total moment of the molecule, our partitioning of this total among the various bonds is only on grounds of convenience (e.g. additivity rules) or of chemical behaviour (e.g. changes of dipole moment when one bond rotates relative to the rest of the molecule). Hence individual atomic dipoles have no objective reality, and it has therefore‡ been

† A review account of the CH bond polarity is given by W. L. G. Gent, *Quart. Rev.*, 1948, **2**, 383.

‡ W. C. Hamilton, *J. Chem. Phys.*, 1956, **26**, 345.

urged that when assigning bond moments they should be disregarded. If we did disregard them in C—H, the polarity would be always C^-H^+. What is being stated in the preceding paragraph is just this: that if we decide to represent a bond by the best possible single pairing scheme, then the two electrons thus paired together will have an associated charge-cloud whose dipole moment has the probable direction C^+H^- in methane, and C^-H^+ in acetylene. But this moment (see § 13) need not be the same as the apparent moment when the C—H bond rotates about C.

The atomic dipoles just described almost certainly play a larger

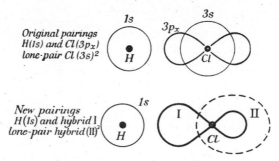

Original pairings
H(1s) and Cl(3p_x)
lone-pair Cl (3s)²

New pairings
H(1s) and hybrid I
lone-pair hybrid (II)²

FIG. 8.17. Hybridization in HCl.

part in determining the dipole moment of a molecule than has usually been supposed. Thus in HCl we have been accustomed (§§ 4.10 and 5.4) to regard the bond as arising from the pairing of $H(1s)$ and $Cl(3p_x)$ orbitals. Now it may be shown[†] that this assumption cannot give the correct dipole moment without an unexpectedly large ionic contribution. This is partly because if we use the wave function $\psi = \psi_{cov} + \lambda\psi_{ion}$ of § 5.6, the homopolar dipole (§ 4.9), which arises on account of the difference in size of H and Cl, has a magnitude (§ 6.3) of about 1·0 D with direction $\overset{\longleftarrow+}{\text{H—Cl}}$. But if we introduce a few per cent. of 3s into the orbital $3p_x$, to form I of Fig. 17, and then pair this with $H(1s)$, leaving the two lone-pair electrons in the orthogonal orbital II, the difficulty largely disappears. For the small amount of 3p in II provides a

† D. Z. Robinson, *J. Chem. Phys.*, 1949, **17**, 1022. But see D. Kastler, *J. Chim. phys.*, 1953, **50**, 556, and A. B. F. Duncan, *J. Amer. Chem. Soc.*, 1955, **77**, 2107.

sufficient asymmetry in charge to produce a substantial atomic dipole moment† in the direction $\overset{+\longrightarrow}{\text{H—Cl}}$.

A similar situation occurs in H_2O. According to the discussions in § 7.5 the angle HOH should be about 90° if pure p-binding occurs. Since H—H repulsions can only open out the angle to about 95° and the experimental value is $104\frac{1}{2}°$, it follows that the binding is not pure p. A slight admixture of s into the bonds will give much more strongly overlapping orbitals, and at the same time this (see equation (2)) will involve an opening out of the angle. As a result, the lone-pair oxygen electrons are not simply $(2s)^2$, but partake some p character, with boundary surfaces that project away from the hydrogen atoms, as in Fig. 18. It follows that a substantial part of the total moment is accounted for by the atomic dipoles of these non-bonding electrons. One result of all this is that the ionic structures discussed in § 7.11 are probably much less important than the values given there would suggest.

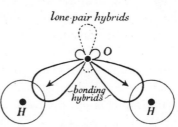

FIG. 8.18. Hybridization in H_2O.

Exactly the same situation occurs in NH_3,‡ where the angle HNH is increased from 90° to 107°. This discussion shows how exceedingly careful we must be in estimating the ionic character of a bond from its dipole moment, and how difficult it is to partition the total observed dipole moment of a molecule into contributions from the individual bonds and lone-pair electrons.

The exceedingly great importance of the lone-pair electrons in determining dipole moments is well brought out by a comparison§ of the electronic structures of NH_3 and NF_3. The bond angles at the N atom are not greatly different, being 107° and 103° respectively, so that presumably the hybridization is also much the same in the two molecules. Since we may expect the σ-bonds N—F to

---

† An illustration of the truth of the apocryphal remark: 'a little hybridization goes a very long way'.

‡ See R. S. Mulliken, *Phys. Rev.*, 1932, **40**, 55, especially p. 61.

§ V. Schomaker and Chia-Si Lu, *J. Amer. Chem. Soc.*, 1950, **72**, 1182.

be distinctly polar, it is impossible to account for the very small moment (0·2 D) of NF_3 unless there is a compensating moment from the lone-pair electrons. But in NH_3 the σ-bonds N—H are much less polar, with the result that there is no substantial moment to offset that from the lone-pair; consequently the molecular moment is quite large (1·5 D). Some detailed numerical analysis by Coulson and Greenwood,[†] using approximate wave functions, supports this conclusion. The same situation is found in H_2O and F_2O, whose dipole moments are 1·84 D and 0·18 D.[‡]

Another important conclusion from this discussion is that if we define a bond as the result of an almost exclusive pairing together, either in v.b. or m.o. terms, of two orbitals on adjacent atoms, then these orbitals are nearly always hybrids and the choice of hybrid is such as to make each separate bond only slightly polar. Thus the 'intrinsic' polarities of CH, NH, and OH are quite small. The net dipole moment of a molecule often arises almost entirely from the lone-pair electrons, and an 'apparent' moment for a bond such as N—H has its origin in the conventional method of distributing this net moment among the bonds and disregarding the non-bonding electrons. The relatively small intrinsic moment is in complete accord with some calculations by W. E. Moffitt,[§] who showed that the electronegativities of the hybrid a.o.'s of N, O, and H as they occur in the bonds of NH_3 and H_2O were all closely equal.

In a somewhat rough way we may describe the moment of the lone-pair electrons which results from hybridization, as the quantum-mechanical equivalent of the classical notion of 'polarization of non-bonding electrons'.

8.11. Structure of CO and CO_2

The molecules CO and CO_2 are sufficiently important to receive a separate treatment. The chief problems arise with CO and are

† Unpublished work: cf. also J. A. Pople, *Proc. Roy. Soc.* A, 1950, **202**, 323; *J. Chem. Phys.*, 1953, **21**, 223, for H_2O; C. A. Coulson, *Proc. Roy. Soc.* A, 1951, **207**, 63; A. B. F. Duncan and J. A. Pople, *Trans. Faraday Soc.*, 1953, **49**, 217; F. O. Ellison and H. Shull, *J. Chem. Phys.*, 1953, **21**, 1420; 1955, **23**, 2348.

‡ L. Pierce, R. Jackson and N. DiCianni, *J. Chem. Phys.*, 1961, **35**, 2240.

§ *Proc. Roy. Soc.* A, 1950, **202**, 548.

concerned with whether we should describe it as a double or a triple bond, and why its dipole moment has the negligibly small value $0 \cdot 1$ D and with polarity $C^- O^+$. It will be easiest, however, to begin with CO_2, which is known to be a linear molecule. It is at once evident that so far as σ-type electrons are concerned, the carbon atom must be hybridized approximately as in acetylene: that is to say, hybrids $s \pm p_x$ are formed out of the $2s$ and $2p_x$ orbitals, similar to those shown in Fig. 5, the x direction being along the axis of the molecule. These are paired with respective oxygen $2p_x$ orbitals (possibly containing a small amount of $2s$) so that two localized σ-bonds are formed. The remaining electrons consist of the oxygen inner $(2s)^2$ pair and a total of eight p_y and p_z electrons, three of which are associated with each oxygen and two with carbon. If the first oxygen is supposed to have non-bonding p_y^2, it may form a π-bond between its solitary p_z and the carbon p_z. Similarly the second oxygen has non-bonding p_z^2 and forms a π-bond between its p_y and the carbon p_y. This uses all the electrons, but is still not satisfactory because we can interchange the roles of p_y and p_z. Resonance between these two structures must be assumed, with the result that the molecule has complete axial symmetry.†

When we compare CO with CO_2‡ we are struck by the facts that the CO bond length is nearly the same in both molecules, and that the u.v. absorption spectra show that the net charge on the oxygen atoms is practically the same (see p. 195). This implies that the charge-cloud density in the regions between O and C and near the O nucleus must be practically the same in the two molecules. But of course it may be different near the C nucleus. We therefore describe the occupied orbitals in CO as follows:§

   (i) there are the two inner shells $C(1s)^2$ and $O(1s)^2$;

   (ii) there are three occupied σ-type m.o.'s (1σ), (2σ), (3σ); and

---

† This is the localized orbitals description. A m.o. description involving non-localized bonds has been given by R. S. Mulliken, *J. Chem. Phys.*, 1935, **3**, 720. Corresponding calculations have been made by J. F. Mulligan, *J. Chem. Phys.*, 1951, **19**, 347, 1428.

‡ L. H. Long and A. D. Walsh, *Trans. Faraday Soc.*, 1947, **43**, 342.

§ R. C. Sahni, *Trans. Faraday Soc.*, 1953, **49**, 1246, subsequently extended by B. J. Ransil, *J. Chem. Phys.*, 1959, **30**, 1113.

two occupied π-type m.o.'s $(1\pi_y)$, $(1\pi_z)$; the σ-type orbitals are compounded out of $C(2s)$, $C(2p_x)$, $O(2s)$, $O(2p_x)$, and the π-type orbitals from $C(2p_y)$, $O(2p_y)$ and $C(2p_z)$, $O(2p_z)$;

(iii) the (1σ) orbital is very tightly bonding (ionization potential about 43 eV) and is mainly composed of $O(2s)$ with a smaller amount of a nearly digonal carbon orbital $C(2s)+C(2p_x)$ chosen to overlap positively in the bond region between the nuclei. Thus the $(1\sigma)^2$ charge density is concentrated between the nuclei, on the side of the oxygen nucleus rather more than the carbon nucleus;

(iv) the (2σ) orbital is chiefly a combination $O(2s)-O(2p_x)$ concentrated near the O nucleus, but with its centre a little on the farther side away from C; these $(2\sigma)^2$ electrons contribute relatively little to the binding energy;

(v) the (3σ) orbital is almost entirely a digonal hybrid $C(2s)-C(2p_x)$ which is strongly directed away from the carbon nucleus. Since both the (2σ) and (3σ) electrons are concentrated in distinct regions of the molecule, there is relatively little interaction between them. The 3σ electrons, with ionization potential 13 eV, are the easiest to remove from the molecule;

(vi) the $(1\pi_y)$ orbital is $0.42\,C(2p_y)+0.81\,O(2p_y)$, showing that it is a double-streamer orbital, with about four times as likely a chance that the electron is near O as near C. This is quite a polar bond. The $(1\pi_z)$ orbital is, of course, just the same, but rotated through 90° around the CO axis.

The dipole moment arises from all four m.o.'s. But the contribution from the lone-pair electrons (v) is sufficiently large to compensate that arising from (iii), (iv), and (vi), leading to a calculated total moment in direction C^-O^+. Ransil shows that if we add together the total amount of each of the various atomic orbitals involved we could write for the final atomic populations†

$$\text{Carbon:}\ 1s^{2\cdot0},\quad 2s^{1\cdot68},\quad 2p_x^{0\cdot96},\quad 2p_y^{0\cdot62},\quad 2p_z^{0\cdot62}$$
$$\text{Oxygen:}\ 1s^{2\cdot0},\quad 2s^{1\cdot85},\quad 2p_x^{1\cdot51}\quad 2p_y^{1\cdot37},\quad 2p_z^{1\cdot37}$$

† R. S. Mulliken (*J. Chem. Phys.*, 1955, **23**, 1833) first introduced the use of the word population; but similar quantities had been used for some years previously.

According to this description the bond is properly described as a triple bond, since there are six bonding electrons $(1\sigma)^2(1\pi_y)^2(1\pi_z)^2$. But, particularly because of the asymmetry in the π orbitals, the strength of the bond is lower than with a normal triple bond, as in N_2. However, there is a small additional bond order coming from the relatively non-bonding $(2\sigma)^2(3\sigma)^2$. It is difficult to see how this electronic distribution could have been represented without the use of hybridized orbitals. Certainly early attempts which spoke of resonance, with approximately equal weight, between $\overset{+}{C}—\overset{-}{O}$, $C{=}O$, and $\overset{-}{C}{\equiv}\overset{+}{O}$ are far less satisfactory representations of the molecule than the more recent one reported above. In addition we can understand the electron-donor properties of CO, shown, for example, in the formation of BH_3.CO, since there are two electrons on the C atom (the lone-pair electrons (v)) which are already strongly directed away from the CO bond, and which would easily serve to complete the previously incomplete octet around the B atom.

It seems very probable that the low dipole moment in the odd-electron molecule NO (§ 6.5) is explained in much the same way as in CO. Some recent calculations[†] indicate that the m.o. corresponding to (v) in CO has a large density on the remote side of the N atom.

The description of the π electrons in CO_2 applies in a somewhat similar way to allene

$$\begin{array}{c} H \diagdown \\ \diagup \\ H \end{array} C{-}C{=}C \begin{array}{c} \diagup H \\ \diagdown \\ H \end{array}$$

The end carbons are trigonally hybridized, and the central carbon is digonal, so that the $C{=}C{=}C$ is linear, and the two π-bonds are in perpendicular directions. As a result there is no free rotation of the two CH_2 groups, which are mutually perpendicular.

8.12. Transition elements[‡]

We have so far considered hybrids of s and p a.o.'s only. One of the chief conditions necessary for effective hybridization is the

† M. Brion, C. Moser, and M. Yamazaki, *J. Chem. Phys.*, 1959, **30**, 673.
‡ A fuller account of the transition elements and their complexes is reserved for Chapter X.

close equality of the relevant a.o. energies. Now with heavier elements, as Fig. 2.6 shows, the d-type orbitals often have energies very similar to those of the s and p orbitals of the next main shell. In nickel, for example, the energies of the $3d$, $4s$, and $4p$ levels are all within about 4 eV of each other. This means that in favourable circumstances there is no reason why we should not expect hybrids involving d, s, and p orbitals. Pauling[†] was the first to show that by suitable combinations of these orbitals, very strongly directed hybrids could be formed, giving coordination numbers and valence angles quite different from those to be anticipated on the basis of pairings between s, p, or d electrons alone. A large number of such hybrids may be formed,[‡] some of which will be used in Chapters X and XII. But for our present purposes it will be sufficient to choose two or three of the most interesting for illustration.

The most important of these hybrids are the octahedral group, which arise from the selection sp^3d^2. It may be shown that these six pure orbitals may be replaced by six other equivalent ones directed octahedrally (e.g. along the $\pm$ directions of the x-, y-, z-axes). The octahedral hybrid which is directed along the positive x direction has the analytical form

$$\psi_{+x} = \frac{1}{\sqrt{6}}\{s + \sqrt{3}p_x + \sqrt{2}d_{x^2}\}. \qquad (7)$$

By changing the sign of the middle term we obtain ψ_{-x}. Definitions of the d functions are given in (2.18). The other four hybrids may be written down by symmetry. Octahedral coordination is particularly associated with the transition groups, and especially Werner's coordination complexes; we might indeed have expected this because of the need to have incompletely filled d orbitals in the central atom. Even if energy is required to form these hybrids, the fact that they are very strong provides a ready explanation of their occurrence (according to Pauling's definition of § 5 the strength of an octahedral orbital is 2·923, to be compared with 1, 1·732, and 2·236 for s, p, d respectively). Thus in $\mathrm{Fe(CN)}_6^{3-}$ we may

[†] *J. Amer. Chem. Soc.*, 1931, 53, 1367.
[‡] A list of many is given by H. Eyring, J. Walter, and G. E. Kimball, *Quantum Chemistry*, John Wiley, 1944, p. 231.

suppose at first that the extra negative charge goes to the iron atom, giving effectively $Fe^{3-}(CN)_6$. Now the neutral Fe atom (with atomic number 26) has an argon-like core $KL(3s)^2(3p)^6$ surrounded by an outer electron distribution $(3d)^6(4s)^2$. This is shown in the top line of Fig. 19. When it becomes Fe^{3-}, before hybridization, we may describe it as in the second line: and then, by an excitation of some of these electrons to slightly higher orbitals, we may form octahedral hybrids, as shown in the third line. Each of

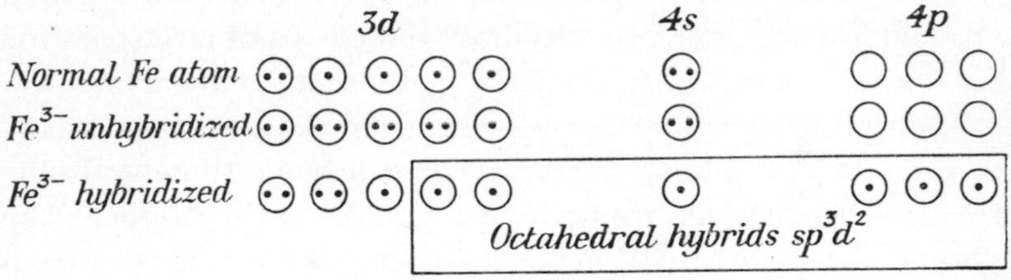

FIG. 8.19. Hybridization in Fe^{3-}.

these hybrids is paired with the free electron in one of the —CN groups, so that six bonds are formed. A similar situation exists in the cobaltammines, where, for example, the hexamminocobaltic ion $Co(NH_3)_6^{3+}$ has the same octahedral character. In this case we may imagine that each N atom gives up an electron, so that its configuration $(2s)(2p)^3$ may result in tetrahedral hybridization such as in CH_4 or NH_4^+: the Co atom $(Z = 27)$ now has $27+6-3 = 30$ electrons, of which 18 complete the argon-like core. The remaining 12 are divided into (i) 6 which completely fill three of the $3d$ orbitals, and (ii) 6 which form octahedral hybrids out of the two unused $3d$ orbitals, together with the $4s$ and three $4p$ ones. Direct pairing of these hybrids with the singly-occupied N hybrids yields six σ-type bonds.

Some comment is needed concerning the bonds in these molecules.[†] They cannot be completely covalent, for this would lead to an improbably high net charge on the central atom. In the cobaltammine ion just described, this formal charge appears to be 3. It seems most likely that polarity in the individual bonds has

---

† See Chapter X for critical comments on this model, and for a more complete and detailed description.

the effect of neutralizing this charge. Pauling† has proposed a 'postulate of neutrality' as a formal description of this. Thus in $Co(NH_3)_6^{3+}$ the electronegativity difference between Co and N ($x_{Co} = 1\cdot8$, $x_N = 3\cdot0$) leads to an ionic character for each of the Co—N bonds of about 50 per cent. Thus on the average $6 \times \frac{1}{2} = 3$ electrons have left the cobalt atom for the nitrogens. In this way the cobalt atom becomes electrically neutral. Similarly the polarity of the NH bonds results in approximate neutrality of the N atoms. But when the electronegativity of the attached groups is not sufficiently great to withdraw the excess of electrons from the central atom, as in $Fe(CN)_6^{3-}$, it seems most likely that neutrality is achieved by the use of some of the d-type orbitals for the formation of double bonds.‡ The d orbitals thus used must of course be different from those involved in the original d^2sp^3 hybrids. A similar situation occurs in the sp^2d hybrids shortly to be described. The conclusion that partial double-bond character must be associated with these bonds finds excellent support from a study of the bond lengths, which are often shorter than would be expected for a normal covalent single bond.

In the ferricyanides and cobaltammines just described the orbitals used were $(n-1)d$, ns, np, with $n = 4$. But there are occasions when we must suppose that the choice is from ns, np, and nd. An example is SF_6, where the outer shell of a normal S atom is $(3s)^2(3p)^4$; but by a double excitation to $(3s)(3p)^3(3d)^2$ we can form octahedral bonds. In this connexion some support for the introduction of d orbitals is found from the fact that in the previous row of the periodic table, where no d-type orbitals exist, such coordinations are not found. Thus there are salts containing $(SiF_6)^{--}$ and $(PF_6)^-$, but not $(CF_6)^{--}$ or $(NF_6)^-$. This is another illustration of the rule (d) in § 7.6 regarding the increase of valence by excitation of one or more electrons from closed pairs.

It is only fair to add, however, that in these 'outer-d' hybrids there are certain difficulties not yet fully understood. Thus in sulphur the mean distance of the $3d$ electron from the nucleus is

---

† *Report of International Conference*, 'Échanges isotopiques et structure molé-culaire', Paris, 1948, 2.

‡ L. Pauling, *Victor Henri Memorial Volume*, 'Contribution à l'étude de la structure moléculaire', Desoer, Liége, 1947, p. 1. See also § 10.9.

far greater than the mean distance of a $3s$ or $3p$ electron. According to Maccoll[†] this implies that its inclusion will not significantly increase the overlapping power of the hybrid. A satisfactory increase could be obtained if, for some reason, the d orbital were contracted. This may sometimes happen.[‡] However, since the outer atoms are always electronegative ones such as F, it seems probable that there is a large amount of pure ionic character in the bonds, such as would be represented in the extreme case by $S_6^+(F^-)_6$, and in less extreme ways by a series of valence-bond structures such as (I), with the negative charge being found equally on all six fluorines.

$$\text{(I)}\qquad \begin{array}{ccc} & \text{F}^- & \text{F} \\ & & \diagup \\ \text{F}\!-\!&\!\text{S}^{++}\!\!-\!&\text{F} \\ & \diagup & \\ \text{F} & \text{F}^- & \end{array}$$

Our second type of hybridization involving s, p, and d orbitals is the so-called 'square' or 'tetragonal' type. Pauling showed that the combination sp^2d was able to hybridize so that four equivalent orbitals were formed directed in a plane at 90° with each other. Instead of (7), we have the normalized functions

$$\psi_{+x} = \tfrac{1}{2}\{s + \sqrt{2}p_x + d_{x^2-y^2}\}. \tag{8}$$

The strength of these orbitals is 2.694.[§]

It was by use of these that the planar square configuration for $Ni(CN)_4^{--}$ was first predicted, and later verified experimentally. In the same way $PtCl_4^{--}$ is square.

It must not be assumed from the above that all 4-coordinated compounds of Ni have this square configuration. For example, nickel carbonyl $Ni(CO)_4$ is tetrahedral. This may be understood from our description of CO in § 11, where we showed that there

---

† *Trans. Faraday Soc.*, 1950, **46**, 369. This conclusion is supported by numerical calculations due to Craig, Maccoll, Orgel, and Sutton, *J. Chem. Soc.*, 1954, pp. 352, 354.

‡ Craig and Magnusson, ibid., 1956, p. 4895. Calculations for SF_6 by C. Zauli suggest that the $3d$ orbital contracts in such a way that its maximum occurs at approximately the S—F distance. An electron in the sulphur $3d$ orbital is then closer to the fluorines than to the sulphur nucleus. The usual concept of ionic character is scarcely applicable.

§ See also H. Kuhn, *J. Chem. Phys.*, 1948, **16**, 727.

were two electrons (the lone-pair (v) referred to as being largely $C(s-p_x)^2$) which projected strongly away from the C atom. The principle of maximum overlapping now shows that each NiCO group should be linear. If we suppose that these electrons are all shared with the Ni atoms, the $3d$-shell becomes completely full, and there remains a group of four nickel electrons which, in the form $(4s)(4p)^3$, could hybridize tetrahedrally. Electrical neutrality of the Ni atom is acquired by a partial release of the d electrons so that the NiC bonds acquire a double-bond character—perhaps as much as 75 per cent. If we are obliged to choose one single structure to represent the molecule it would therefore be (II), which is

$$
\begin{array}{c}
\text{O} \\
\parallel \\
\text{C} \\
\parallel \\
\text{(II)} \qquad \text{O}=\!\text{C}=\!\text{Ni}=\!\text{C}=\!\text{O} \\
\parallel \\
\text{C} \\
\parallel \\
\text{O}
\end{array}
$$

in good agreement with bond distances, though the force constant of the Ni—C bond is rather less than would be implied by this diagram. But almost certainly this is a case where one single structure is inadequate.

TABLE 19. *Important types of hybridization*

Coordination no. for hybrids	Atomic orbitals used	Resulting hybrids
2	sp	Linear
	dp	Linear
3	sp^2	Trigonal plane
	dp^2	Trigonal plane
	d^2s	Trigonal plane
	d^2p	Trigonal pyramid
4	sp^3	Tetrahedral
	d^3s	Tetrahedral
	dsp^2	Tetragonal plane
5	dsp^3	Bipyramid
	d^3sp	Bipyramid
	d^4s	Tetragonal pyramid
6	d^2sp^3	Octahedral
	d^4sp	Trigonal prism

A pleasant confirmation that the Ni—C bonds are largely due to the non-bonding carbon electrons (v) of CO is found in the fact that the carbonyl vibration frequency 2,144 cm^{-1} in CO is only changed to 2,040 cm^{-1} in (II). Thus the electron distribution in the CO region must be practically unaffected by the metallic coordination.

Many other forms of hybridization exist, in which some of the bonds differ from the others. A few of the more commonly used hybrids are shown in Table 19.[†]

It is important to realize that tables such as the above merely tell us what combinations are possible; they tell us nothing about which actually occur, nor which are energetically the most stable.

8.13. Other effects of hybridization

After what we have already said, there should be no difficulty in following the remaining examples of the way in which hybridization is invoked as a convenient description of chemical behaviour.

Polarization. In § 5.2 we discussed the v.b. treatment of H_2, and showed how the polarization of the atomic $1s$ orbitals around each nucleus could be allowed for, by writing (see 5.18)

$$\psi_A = \lambda_1 e^{-cr_a} + \lambda_2 x e^{-cr_a} \quad \text{instead of} \quad \psi_A = e^{-cr_a}. \qquad (9)$$

In this formula the x direction is from nucleus A to B, and λ_1, λ_2, c are certain constants. Now xe^{-cr_a} by itself could be regarded as a p-type a.o. Thus the significance of the polarized orbital (9) is that we have hybridized an s-type and p-type orbital. It is worth while putting a little energy into the two atoms in this way because the hybrids (9) are more strongly directed and overlap each other more than the unperturbed $1s$ orbitals.

Non-existence of pure s-bonds. We have described the binding in the alkali metals Li_2, Na_2,... as pure s-binding (§ 4.7). Thus, in m.o. theory, the bonding orbitals in Li_2 would be, in an obvious notation,

$$(z\sigma)^2 \equiv (2s_A + 2s_B)^2. \qquad (10)$$

It has been shown[‡] that a more accurate description would be

$$(z\sigma)^2 \equiv \{(2s_A + \lambda 2p_A) + (2s_B + \lambda 2p_B)\}^2, \qquad (11)$$

[†] For a complete list, see Eyring, Walter, and Kimball, loc. cit.

[‡] L. Pauling, *Proc. Roy. Soc.* A, 1949, **196**, 343. An alternative m.o. treatment of Li_2 by J. E. Faulkner (*J. Chem. Phys.*, 1957, **27**, 369) leads to 19 per cent. p-character.

where the existence of λ shows that some hybridization of $2s$ and $2p$ has occurred at each nucleus. The percentage of p character for these bonds is calculated to be as follows.

Molecule .	.	.	.	Li_2	Na_2	K_2	Rb_2	Cs_2
Per cent. p character		.		14·0	6·8	5·5	5·0	5·5

It follows quite simply, from the variation principle, that there are not, and never can be, any pure s-type bonds. For, taking the case of Li_2 to illustrate the argument, we can always try a wave function (11), with λ as a variational parameter. Inspection of the nature of the energy function (§ 3.6) shows that the value of λ which leads to the lowest value of the energy will seldom (if ever) be $\lambda = 0$. Consequently, the best approximate wave function of this kind will be one involving hybrids of s and p. An analogous argument holds in the v.b. description.

Sometimes this mixing is very considerable. In N_2^+, for example, the m.o. labelled $x\sigma$ on p. 102 is probably most nearly described as a 70 : 30 mixture of $2p\sigma$ and $2s$. Ratios of this kind may be estimated from a study of the absolute intensities (f-values) of band spectra, in which an electron of this kind is excited.

Valence angles in boron and beryllium. A discussion of the valence angles in boron and beryllium shows that considerable hybridization occurs. A more complete study of these electron-deficient molecules is given in Chapter XIII.

Changes of hybridization during vibration. When a molecule vibrates, so that its valence angles change from the equilibrium non-vibrating values, we may expect that the hybrids at the central atom will also change, in such a way as to 'follow' the vibrating outer atoms, so far as they are able. In fact, no complete understanding of molecular force constants is possible without some inclusion of such periodic changes of hybridization. Since (§ 9) the atomic radius depends on the coefficients of mixing in the hybrids, it follows that when a valence angle changes, there will also be forces brought into play tending to increase or decrease bond lengths. We have here the origin for some of the cross-terms in potential functions for molecular vibration.† Also, since certain

† C. A. Coulson, J. Duchesne, and C. Manneback, *Victor Henri Memorial Volume*, 'Contribution a l'étude de la structure moléculaire', Desoer, Liége, 1948, p. 33.

changes of hybridization are energetically easier than others, the hybrids are able to 'follow' the outer atoms more closely in certain types of vibration than in others: this leads† to an understanding of the relative magnitudes of many of the empirically estimated force constants.

It also clears up a difficulty‡ which arises when we use the absolute intensity of absorption of infra-red radiation to estimate the dipole moment of a given bond, such as the C—H bond. When the C—H bond, in ethylene for example, rotates about the carbon atom, in a deformation vibration, the dipole moment along one or other of the axes of symmetry will fluctuate. Now the intensity of absorption in a vibration depends on the size of the fluctuating dipole. Hence experimental intensity measurements provide a measure of the fluctuating dipole moment. It appears in this way that the apparent C—H moment is different for various normal modes. The explanation is that in certain of the normal modes the carbon hybrids can follow more freely than in others, so that the contribution from the atomic dipole (§ 10) varies differently for the different normal modes. Thus the static dipole moment for a bond may differ considerably from the dynamic moment associated with any given normal mode.

8.14. Status of hybridization

The previous discussion has brought out clearly the very wide context in which hybridization seems to be relevant. We must not, however, allow ourselves to believe that it represents any real 'phenomenon', any more than resonance between different structures such as the covalent and ionic ones of a polar bond may be called a 'phenomenon'. But we can at least say:

(a) that hybridization is the most effective way of preserving the concept of a localized bond with perfect pairing of orbitals on the two atoms of the bond;

(b) that it is a restricted form of resonance, so that a residual resonance, due to alternative schemes of pairing, still exists.

Point (a) has already been made in this chapter. If, for example, we want to regard each CH bond in methane as arising from the

---

† This has been worked out in detail by J. W. Linnett and various collaborators in a series of papers in the *Trans. Faraday Soc.*, 1948–9, of which the first is 1948, **44**, 556.

‡ C. A. Coulson and M. J. Stephen, *Trans. Faraday Soc.*, 1957, **53**, 272. A survey of some of the difficulties associated with this topic is given in C. A. Coulson, *Spectrochimica Acta*, 1959, **14**, 161.

mutual pairing of a hydrogen orbital with one definite carbon orbital, we must choose a hybrid of s and p. When the proper hybrids have been chosen, it follows from the principle of maximum overlapping that the resulting pairing scheme is so good that other pairings are almost completely excluded. But this must not blind us to the fact that other schemes of pairing do exist, giving rise to a residual resonance. This brings us to point (b); for, if we wished, we could have rejected all mention of the tetrahedral hybrids, and considered the more extensive resonance between all the pairing schemes I, II,... referred to on p. 197. Hybridization now appears as a restricted form of this resonance. The following

discussion for purely covalent binding in a molecule† B⟋ᴬ⟍C illustrates the nature of this restriction.

Let us imagine that there are two a.o.'s P and Q on atom A and that these are approximately directed toward the a.o.'s u and v of the atoms B and C. Then the most natural pairing scheme may be represented by Pu, Qv. But there are alternative schemes which should be considered, such as Pv, Qu, and also uv, PP, as well as uv, QQ and uv, PQ representing a bond between B and C. These may be represented as (i)–(v) in the diagram below. The

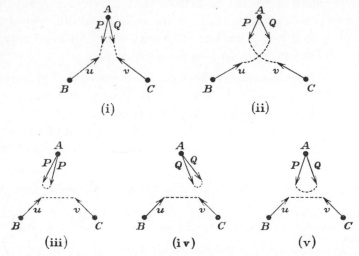

(i)   (ii)

(iii)   (iv)   (v)

† J. Guy, *Comptes Rendus*, 1946, **223**, 670. For a fuller discussion of this matter, see C. A. Coulson, *J. Chim. phys.*, 1949, **46**, 198.

true wave function must be a combination of at least the wave functions appropriate to these five structures, since the complete molecule has characteristics represented by each of them. In fact we only need (i)–(iv) since, as shown later in § 9.2, (v) reduces to a simple combination of (i) and (ii). Let us for simplicity omit any other possible structures. Then symbolically we could write

$$\psi = c_1(\text{i}) + c_2(\text{ii}) + c_3(\text{iii}) + c_4(\text{iv}), \tag{12}$$

where the constants $c_1, \ldots, c_4$ are found by a variational calculation.

Alternatively we might seek a compromise in a single scheme where some combination $\alpha_1 P + \beta_1 Q$ is paired exclusively with u, and $\alpha_2 P + \beta_2 Q$ with v. Explicit expansion of the wave function which results from this pairing shows that it is a particular case of (12) in which $c_1, \ldots, c_4$ are related to $\alpha_1, \ldots, \beta_2$ by the four equations

$$c_1 = \alpha_1 \beta_2, \qquad c_2 = \alpha_2 \beta_1, \qquad c_3 = \alpha_1 \alpha_2, \qquad c_4 = \beta_1 \beta_2.$$

Thus, whatever the values of α and β may be, there is always the relation

$$c_1 c_2 = c_3 c_4. \tag{13}$$

This means that even if we choose $\alpha_1, \ldots, \beta_2$ to minimize the energy function, we are not really allowing for a complete resonance, such as is involved in (12), but merely for a restricted form of it. A residual resonance still remains.

In many cases (e.g. CH_4, H_2O) this residual resonance is small, and we may correctly speak of the molecule as composed of localized electron-pair bonds. This is true whether we use v.b. or m.o. language. But in other cases this is not so, implying that the familiar concept of an electron-pair bond is breaking down. In m.o. language we should say that the bonds are no longer localized, but are delocalized. Such molecules include those in which strain, or other geometrical constraint, leads to what in § 8 we have called bent bonds. It is also probable that they include many of the molecules involving the transition elements discussed in § 12 and in Chapter X, as well as other cases of abnormally high valence. In this latter connexion it is interesting that such molecules are nearly always polar. This is shown by the well-known fact that the very electronegative element fluorine has a strong tendency to bring out these maximum valences (e.g., BF_4^-, SF_6, OsF_8). But if the bonds are polar their ionic character will at once imply a lack of independence between them. We have already met a simplified version of this difficulty in our description of H_2O in terms of certain covalent and ionic structures in § 7.11. The existence of one ionic bond in a structure directly affects the probability that the others are simultaneously ionic. The greater the mean polarity of the bonds, the more significant will this effect be. In the cobaltammine, $Co(NH_3)_6^{3+}$, discussed on p. 227, where the polarity is about 50 per cent., there must be considerable correlation between the electron distributions in the various bonds. Since these bonds are no longer independent of each other, the concept of localized electron-pair bonds is beginning to break down as a satisfactory description of their character. When this occurs, the language of completely delocalized m.o.'s (§ 7.1) is conceptually the simplest to use. Further discussion of this matter is deferred to our account of ligand-field theory in Chapter X.

CONJUGATED AND AROMATIC MOLECULES

9.1. Breakdown of localization: benzene

In practically all the molecules previously discussed it has been possible to localize the bonds: such delocalizations as were present were quite small. But there is an extremely large and important type of molecule for which effective localization is completely impossible. These are the conjugated and aromatic molecules which form so extensive a part of organic chemistry.

We can see this most easily if we deal with the most important of all such molecules, namely benzene C_6H_6. This is the prototype for all aromatic compounds. A large amount of evidence from X-rays and vibrational structure shows that the carbon atoms lie at the vertices of a regular plane hexagon; the six hydrogen atoms lie in the same plane directed radially outwards from the carbons, in such a way that all the valence angles are 120°. Clearly this implies that the carbon atoms are hybridized in the trigonal state. We must then arrange the directions of the hybrids as shown in Fig. 1, so that there is strong overlapping of pairs of orbitals to give localized C—C and C—H bonds, both of σ-type. These bonds may be described either in m.o. or v.b. language; their essential character is the same in either case. A simple counting of electrons shows that there are six still to be used: these are the unhybridized dumb-bell orbitals, one for each carbon atom. If the plane of the molecule is called the (x, y)-plane, these electrons are in $2p_z$ a.o.'s, all directed parallel to each other as shown in Fig. 2 (a). It is precisely at this stage that our difficulty arises: for we look for one particularly favoured scheme of pairing these orbitals together, without which localization of the bonds is impossible, and in fact there is no one single scheme more favoured than other possible alternatives.

Our quandary will appear a little different according to our choice of v.b. or m.o. language. Let us consider the v.b. language first, for historically it is much the older. There are obviously two quite distinct ways in which we might pair the π orbitals in Fig. 2 (a). They are shown in Figs. 2 (b) and 2 (c). Neither of these systems which are 'structures' in the sense of § 5.5 has any greater

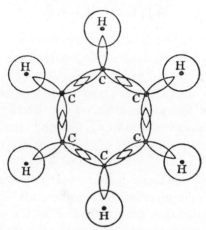

FIG. 9.1. The σ-hybrids of the carbon atoms of benzene.

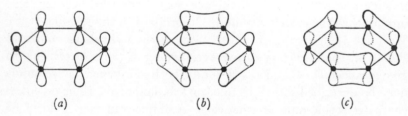

(a)   (b)   (c)

FIG. 9.2. The π-atomic orbitals in benzene (a), and the Kekulé pairing schemes (b, c).

merit than the other. Both must therefore appear in the complete wave function. Physically we may say that the benzene molecule behaves partly as if the bonds were in the one position and partly as if in the other.

This is a mathematical statement about the Schrödinger wave function. But notice what our mathematics implies. For the two schemes 2 (b) and 2 (c) are precisely what Kekulé introduced as long ago as 1865; and he supposed them to be in dynamic oscillation, interconversion taking place too quickly to be observed.

Now we see that instead of two structures alternating rapidly, we must regard the true situation as a simultaneous superposition of both. The mathematical technique of linear combinations of wave functions has taken Kekulé's original brilliant intuition, and fitted it into a formal, logical, and precise theory. This composition of the complete wave function out of the two (or more) subsidiary 'structures' is usually called resonance: an alternative name is 'mesomerism', indicating that the character of the molecule is 'in-between' that of its components. This is certainly true for the bond length which is known to be 1·40 A, lying between the values 1·54 A appropriate to a C—C single bond, and 1·34 A appropriate to a double bond. But it is not true for the energy, which, as always with linear variation functions, lies below that of the lowest separate structure. In fact, as we shall see later, the resonance energy (see § 3.6) is surprisingly large.

The m.o. description of benzene starts as before with the set of six atomic π orbitals of Fig. 2 (a). Let us call them $\psi_1, \psi_2,..., \psi_6$ in order round the ring, and look for acceptable m.o.'s found as linear combinations of $\psi_1,..., \psi_6$. It is obvious at once that we can no longer hope to take these a.o.'s in pairs, as we were able to do in § 7.1 for water. This is because each ψ_r overlaps both of its neighbours equally. We are compelled to take as our m.o.'s

$$\psi = c_1\psi_1 + c_2\psi_2 + ... + c_6\psi_6, \tag{1}$$

where the constants $c_1,..., c_6$ are found so as to make the energy function stationary. The significance of (1) is that these six π electrons have to occupy m.o.'s which extend over all six carbon atoms and are therefore completely delocalized. If we had compelled them to have m.o.'s such as $c_1\psi_1 + c_2\psi_2$, which are localized, their energy would necessarily have been greater. The amount by which the total energy of the π electrons lies below that of the localized orbitals (corresponding to one of the Kekulé structures) may now be called the delocalization energy. In many respects this name is a better description than the more conventional resonance energy, for it tells us exactly the origin of the additional binding. Fig. 3 shows, somewhat pictorially, the appearance of these new m.o.'s. The double streamers previously drawn for ethylene now stretch right round the ring, one streamer above and the other below the plane of the nuclei. Electrons of this kind, which move so freely round the molecule, have been called mobile electrons,† or sometimes unsaturation electrons.

There is an interesting contrast between the v.b. and m.o. descriptions of benzene. Both require complete delocalization, but whereas the v.b. method introduces it by superposition of Kekulé and other) structures, in the m.o. method there is nothing that

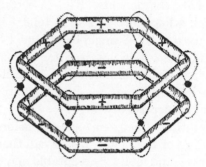

FIG. 9.3. The π-molecular orbitals in benzene (streamers).

even remotely resembles a structure. This situation warns us once more against any too literal belief in the reality of our structures.

It may be asked what justification we have for describing the superposition of two Kekulé structures as a delocalization of the π electrons. The explanation is as follows: in one of the Kekulé structures we pair together the orbitals ψ_1 and ψ_2, so that the two electrons which form this π-bond are shared by the two nuclei 1 and 2, being found equally on either nucleus. In the other Kekulé structure ψ_2 and ψ_3 are paired, so that the electrons are found either on nucleus 2 or 3. The fact that we have a super-position of the two structures implies that an electron originally on 1 may be found on 2 (due to the first structure), and then on 3 (due to the second structure). In this way it may migrate round the ring. This suggests that one possible description of the π electrons in benzene is in terms of tiny electric currents flowing round the ring. However, when one electron moves from atom 1 to atom 2, another electron moves from 2 to 1, so that normally there

† J. E. Lennard-Jones, *Proc. Roy. Soc.* A, 1937, **158**, 280.

are equal currents flowing in both directions, with no net flow of charge. It is possible to make this description much more precise if we use the language of m.o. theory; for the wave function (1) can be interpreted directly in terms of electronic flow.

Our description of benzene can be tested in at least four ways.

(1) The bond lengths are all equal, and do not alternate between short and long;

(2) electronic transitions among the mobile electrons, called $N \to V$ transitions, give rise to characteristic absorption which may be calculated, and for which quite reasonably good agreement with experiment is found;†

(3) the tiny electron currents give rise to anomalous magnetic effects. For although normally these currents flow equally in both directions, yet in the presence of a magnetic field there is a preference for one direction rather than the other, giving rise to a large diamagnetism when the field is perpendicular to the plane of the molecule.‡

(4) the mobility of these π electrons implies that electrical influences are easily propagated from one part of the molecule to another. Thus the effect of one substitution in benzene will be to exert an appreciable influence on the position of a second substitution. Detailed calculations are possible§ and provide us with the beginning of a comprehensive theory of chemical reactivity. The importance of these mobile electrons in biological processes can hardly be overestimated, for they represent the only way in which chemical and physical influences can be propagated easily along the complete length of a large molecule. In rough terms it may be said that their presence confers upon a molecule properties intermediate between those of an ordinary saturated molecule and an electrical conductor.

We have already stated that the complete delocalization of the

---

† M. Goeppert-Mayer and A. L. Sklar, *J. Chem. Phys.*, 1938, **6**, 645. But later work has shown the importance of several factors not considered by these authors.

‡ F. London, *J. Physique*, 1937, **8**, 397.

§ G. W. Wheland and L. Pauling, *J. Amer. Chem. Soc.*, 1935, **57**, 2086; G. W Wheland, ibid., 1942, **64**, 900; C. A. Coulson and H. C. Longuet-Higgins, *Proc. Roy. Soc.* A, 1947, **192**, 16; C. A. Coulson, *Research*, 1951, **4**, 307.

π electrons leads to a large energy of delocalization, and therefore to an enhanced stability. Surprisingly enough, however, this energy is not the sole agency† for the much greater stability of benzene compared with the unknown cyclobutadiene (C_4H_4), or the known cyclocta-tetraene (C_8H_8). This stability is seriously influenced by the σ-bonds. Fig. 1 showed how extremely well-suited was our trigonal hybridization for bond angles of 120°, as in the hexagon of benzene. In cyclobutadiene we should have either to choose new hybrids more nearly at an angle of 90°, or we should have to accept weaker (in this case bent) bonds as a result of decreased overlap, in a manner similar to that discussed in Fig. 8.14 for cyclopropane. It appears that‡ both possibilities lead to a loss of binding energy which more than offsets the delocalization energy of the π electrons and results in instability for the molecule. In cyclocta-tetraene, on the other hand, the bond angles would have to be opened out to 135°, in order to preserve the coplanar character necessary for any large delocalization. It turns out that it is energetically more favourable for the molecule to buckle out of a plane, and thereby to sacrifice most of the π-resonance energy. As a result the bonds are no longer all equal, but alternate between approximately normal single and double bonds. Thus the planar character of aromatic molecules is determined by a desire to have parallel π-type a.o.'s, leading to complete delocalization; and the great preference for six-rings is the result of greatest overlapping of the trigonal π-type hybrids when the valence angle is 120°.

9.2. Dewar structures

We have already introduced two pairing schemes for the π orbitals of Fig. 2. These were the quantum-mechanical versions of Kekulé's bond patterns, and are generally called Kekulé structures. But they do not represent the only possible pairing schemes. We could, for example, have paired ψ_1 and ψ_2, ψ_4 and ψ_5, ψ_3 and

† W. G. Penney, *Proc. Roy. Soc.* A, 1934, **146**, 223.

‡ C. A. Coulson and W. E. Moffitt, *Phil. Mag.*, 1949, **40**, 1. The most complete calculations for cyclobutadiene are those of S. Shida, *Bull. Chem. Soc. Japan*, 1954, **27**, 243. See also D. P. Craig, *Proc. Roy. Soc.* A, 1950, **202**, 498, and C. A. Coulson, *Chem. Soc.* (London), 1958, *Special Publication* no. 12, p. 85.

ψ_6 as shown in Fig. 4 (a). This is merely the quantum-mechanical version of the model originally proposed by Dewar. For that reason we call it a Dewar structure. There are obviously three such, shown in (a), (b), and (c). It is true that these structures have a smaller binding energy than do the Kekulé structures, on account of the 'long-bond'. But as we have already seen in Chapter V when discussing covalent-ionic resonance, that is no reason for a

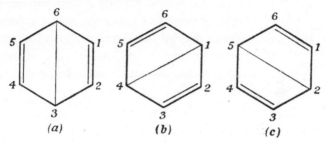

FIG. 9.4. Dewar structures for benzene.

complete neglect of them. All five structures ought to appear in our wave function. If we call the Kekulé structures I and II, and the Dewar structures III, IV, V, our wave function for the ground state should be of the form

$$\psi = C_1(\mathrm{I+II}) + C_2(\mathrm{III+IV+V}) \qquad (2)$$

where C_1 and C_2 are coefficients which must be determined from suitable secular equations (§ 3.8). We shall see in a moment how this can be done. The equality of the weights of the two Kekulé structures, and of the three Dewar structures, follows from symmetry. But before we attempt to calculate C_1 and C_2, have we any legitimate grounds for supposing that our wave function (2) includes all the covalent structures that need be considered? The answer is, yes: this arises from the fact that if we are dealing with $2n$ π electrons occupying the same number of distinct orbitals, there are exactly $(2n!)/(n!)(n+1)!$ independent structures for which the total spin is zero.† In the case of benzene, where $2n = 6$, the number is $6!/3!\,4! = 5$. Any other structure (i.e. pairing scheme) which we might set up is merely some combination of the

† A simple discussion of this is given by J. H. Van Vleck and A. Sherman, *Rev. Mod. Phys.*, 1935, **7**, 192.

original five. In particular the Claus centric formula (Fig.5) can be resolved into a combination of all five basic structures in equal proportions. We are allowed to choose any five structures provided that they are independent. In this case chemical intuition renders the choice of Kekulé+Dewar structures an obvious one.

FIG. 9.5. The Claus centric formula for benzene.

The energy of a single Kekulé structure can be written down at once by the use of the formula of perfect pairing (7.25).† Omitting the atomic energy term, and also considering only the π electrons, the energy of a structure in which atoms 1 and 2, 3 and 4, 5 and 6 are joined by double bonds is

$$E_{\text{Kek}} = Q + J_{12} + J_{34} + J_{56} - \tfrac{1}{2}(J_{23} + J_{45} + J_{61}). \tag{3}$$

In this formula Q is the Coulomb energy, and we have put all the exchange integrals between non-neighbours equal to zero. For this reason all terms such as $-\tfrac{1}{2}(J_{13} + J_{14} + J_{15})$ are omitted. If the bonds are all of equal length, (3) gives

$$E_{\text{Kek}} = Q + 1 \cdot 5J. \tag{4}$$

For a single Dewar structure (Fig. 4 a) we find, entirely similarly,

$$E_{\text{Dew}} = Q + J_{12} + J_{45} - \tfrac{1}{2}(J_{23} + J_{34} + J_{56} + J_{61}) = Q. \tag{5}$$

Since J is rather less than 2 eV this shows that a Dewar structure is about $2\tfrac{1}{2}$ eV less stable than a Kekulé structure.

A similar situation is found in other molecules. Thus in butadiene, conventionally written as $CH_2{=}CH{-}CH{=}CH_2$, we may imagine a plane configuration with angles about 120°, so that the σ-bond structure is similar to that in benzene. There remain four π electrons which we could pair in $4!/2!3! = 2$ distinct ways. These are (I) and (II) below:

I $H_2C{=}CH{-}CH{=}CH_2$,   Energy $Q + 1 \cdot 5J$.

II $H_2C{-}CH{=}CH{-}CH_2$,   Energy Q.
       |_____|

Formula I may be called a Kekulé-like or simply Kekulé structure. Formula II is a Dewar-like, or Dewar, structure.

† Provided that we neglect all overlap integrals and exchange between π electrons and σ electrons!

In naphthalene (Fig. 6), with 10 π electrons, there is a total of $10!/5!\,6! = 42$ independent structures, comprising 3 Kekulé structures, no less than 16 Dewar structures, 19 structures with two 'long-bonds', and 4 with three 'long-bonds'. Some of these are shown in the diagram. The number of long-bonds is sometimes called the degree of excitation of a structure, so that a Kekulé structure is unexcited, a Dewar structure is singly-excited, and so

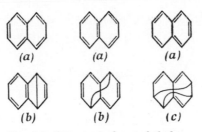

(a)   *(a)*   *(a)*

(b)   *(b)*   *(c)*

FIG. 9.6. Structures for naphthalene.

(a) Kekulé, or unexcited, structures.
(b) Dewar, or singly-excited, structures.
(c) Doubly-excited structure.

on. This nomenclature is singularly unfortunate because there is no connexion whatever between this use of the word 'excitation' and that which represents the excitation of the molecule as it occurs in absorption or emission of light. It may easily lead us into confusion if we are not careful. For in the ground state of benzene both unexcited and singly-excited structures occur: but in at least one of the excited states, only unexcited structures (Kekulé) can be used, on account of symmetry.

9.3. Calculation of the weights in v.b. method

If we have decided to use the v.b. method, our problem is essentially reduced to a calculation of the relative weights of each of the various selected structures. Suppose that we call these structures I, II,..., K, and their related wave functions Ψ_1, Ψ_2,..., Ψ_k. We have used a capital Ψ_1 to denote the wave function of structure I, because it is most important to distinguish these many-electron functions from the single-electron orbitals ψ, ψ_1,... used in (1). This notation will apply right through the present chapter.

For the same reason we use C_r for the coefficient of Ψ_r and c_r for the coefficient of ψ_r.

According to the v.b. method, the best linear variation function may be written in the form

$$\Psi = C_1\Psi_1 + C_2\Psi_2 + \ldots + C_k\Psi_k. \tag{6}$$

According to (3.43) the coefficients C_r and the energy E are given by the secular equations, k in number, of which the rth member is

$$C_1(H_{1r}-ES_{1r})+C_2(H_{2r}-ES_{2r})+\ldots+C_r(H_{rr}-ES_{rr})+\ldots$$
$$+C_k(H_{kr}-ES_{kr}) = 0. \tag{7}$$

In this equation

$$H_{rs} = \int \Psi_r H \Psi_s \, d\tau = H_{sr}, \tag{8}$$

$$S_{rs} = \int \Psi_r \Psi_s \, d\tau = S_{rs}, \tag{9}$$

and H is the Hamiltonian operator for the system of π electrons.

In calculating $H_{rr}-ES_{rr}$, we note that H_{rr}/S_{rr} is the energy of structure r, which may be found from the approximation of perfect pairing just as in (4) and (5). The calculation of $H_{rs}-ES_{rs}$ is a little more difficult, and we shall content ourselves with describing the simplest of several possible procedures, but without giving any proof.† We suppose that all overlap and exchange integrals between a.o.'s which are not nearest neighbours may be neglected. To find $H_{rs}-ES_{rs}$ we first draw separately the bond diagrams represented by the two structures, omitting all mention of the basic σ-bonds. Thus if r and s denote the Kekulé and Dewar structures

we draw them in the simplified forms $\langle\,|$ and $|\,|\,\,|$ respectively.

Next we form the superposition pattern $\langle\!|\,\,\|$ by placing the two

---

† A proof is given by L. Pauling, *J. Chem. Phys.*, 1933, **1**, 280. This article should be consulted before using these methods in more general cases, since there may be otherwise unexpected powers of -1 in H_{rs} and S_{rs}.

simplified diagrams on top of each other. Such a pattern will always consist of a certain number i of closed contours, called 'islands'. In the example which we have chosen $i = 2$, since a double line $\parallel$ counts as a closed contour for this purpose. It may now be shown that

$$H_{rs} - ES_{rs} = \frac{1}{2^{N-i}}\{Q - E + bJ\}, \tag{10}$$

where $2N$ is the total number of electrons, Q and J are the familiar Coulomb and exchange integrals, and b is a quantity defined by:

b = number of pairs of neighbour orbitals (whether bonded or not) in the islands of the superposition pattern $-\frac{1}{2}\times$ number of pairs of neighbour orbitals on separate islands. (11)

In our particular example, the number of pairs of neighbour orbitals in the islands is $3+1 = 4$, since the long vertical line joins two atoms which are not nearest neighbours. Similarly there are just two pairs of neighbours on separate islands. The various coefficients of the exchange integrals are shown against their bonds in the diagram below:

In our case therefore

$$H_{rs} - ES_{rs} = \frac{1}{2^{3-2}}\{Q - E + (4 - \tfrac{1}{2}\times 2)J\} = \tfrac{1}{2}(Q - E + 3J).$$

Other matrix components may be found in precisely the same way. The method works equally well for $H_{rr} - ES_{rr}$, and then the coefficients $1+$ and $-\frac{1}{2}$ in formula (11) become the same as the coefficients $1+$ and $-\frac{1}{2}$ in the formula (7.25) for perfect pairing.

Once we have calculated all the matrix components in (7) we can eliminate the C_r and reduce our problem to the solution of a secular determinant of degree k in E. The lowest root will correspond to the ground state of the molecule: the other roots to excited states. Corresponding to each energy E, we can obtain from (7) the ratios of the coefficients C_1, C_2,..., C_k. The squares of these quantities give the relative weights. And the resonance energy is the difference between the energy of one of the Kekulé structures and E.

Ideally we ought to use all possible structures. But with large molecules this becomes prohibitively complex, so that a choice of the simplest is usually made. Thus for small molecules we generally content ourselves with Kekulé and first-excited structures: for large molecules, when the number of excited structures is often enormous, we group the totality of structures into Kekulé, first-excited,... and suppose that every structure in each group has the same coefficient. This reduces the degree of the secular determinant to 3 or 4, and appears to introduce very little absolute error.†

Ideally also we ought to include ionic structures, such as $\bigcirc^+_-$ for benzene: but with a few simple exceptions‡ this is too cumbersome.

9.4. Particular case of benzene

The rules just described can best be illustrated by reference to benzene. Suppose first that we consider only the two Kekulé structures I and II in equation (2). In the ground state the wave function is obviously

$$\Psi_1 + \Psi_2,$$

and the energy may be found from the secular equations (7) by putting $C_1 = C_2$ and $C_3 = C_4 = C_5 = 0$. It is

$$E = \frac{H_{11} + H_{12}}{S_{11} + S_{12}}.$$

Using the values of the matrix components found according to (10) this gives

$$E = Q + 2 \cdot 4J.$$

Now we have seen in (4) that the energy of a single Kekulé structure is $Q + 1 \cdot 5J$. Resonance between the two Kekulé structures reduces the energy by $0 \cdot 9J$, i.e. about $1\frac{1}{2}$ eV.

Another possible simplification is to consider simply the three

† J. Sherman, *J. Chem. Phys.*, 1934, **2**, 488.

‡ D. P. Craig, *Proc. Roy. Soc.* A, 1950, **200**, 272, 390, 401. Some very general formulae for the various matrix components have been given by R. McWeeny, *Proc. Roy. Soc.* A, 1954, **223**, 306.

Dewar structures, with a wave function $\Psi_3+\Psi_4+\Psi_5$. If we put $C_1 = C_2 = 0$, $C_3 = C_4 = C_5$ in (7) we can show that

$$E = Q+2{\cdot}0J. \tag{12}$$

Thus the two Kekulé structures are a better approximation to the true wave function than are the three Dewar structures, but the difference is nothing like so great as is usually believed.

Finally, let us take all five structures, with a wave function

$$\Psi = C_1\{\Psi_1+\Psi_2\}+C_3\{\Psi_3+\Psi_4+\Psi_5\}. \tag{13}$$

The secular determinant is a quadratic

$$\begin{vmatrix} \tfrac{5}{2}x+6J & 3x+9J \\ 3x+9J & \tfrac{9}{2}x+9J \end{vmatrix} = 0,$$

where $x = Q-E$. When expanded this takes the form

$$x^2-2Jx-12J^2 = 0.$$

The lowest root gives

$$E = Q+J(\sqrt{13}-1) = Q+2{\cdot}6055J, \tag{14}$$

leading to a resonance energy $1{\cdot}1055J$. (But of course only the first two figures are really significant.) We can summarize these various results in the table below:

TABLE 20. *Energies for different combinations of structures in benzene*

Structures used	Wave function	Energy	Resonance energy
Single Kekulé	Ψ_1	$Q+1{\cdot}5J$	..
Both Kekulé	$\Psi_1+\Psi_2$	$Q+2{\cdot}4J$	$0{\cdot}9J$
Single Dewar	Ψ_3	Q	..
All three Dewar	$\Psi_3+\Psi_4+\Psi_5$	$Q+2{\cdot}0J$	$0{\cdot}5J$
All five structures	$C_1\{\Psi_1+\Psi_2\}+C_3\{\Psi_3+\Psi_4+\Psi_5\}$	$Q+2{\cdot}606J$	$1{\cdot}106J$

There is one further point which is of interest in this connexion. In the ground-state wave function (13) $C_3/C_1 = 0{\cdot}4341$, showing that the relative weights of each Dewar and Kekulé structure are $0{\cdot}4341^2 : 1$, i.e. $0{\cdot}19 : 1$. We may therefore assign weights 39 per cent. to each Kekulé structure and 7 per cent. to each Dewar structure. This shows us, better than any of the previous work, precisely how much more important are the Kekulé than the Dewar structures.

TABLE 21. *Resonance energies in selected hydrocarbons*

Compound	v.b. resonance energy‡	m.o. resonance energy‡	Observed† values kcal/mole
Benzene . . .	1·106J	2·00β	37
Naphthalene . .	2·04J	3·68β	75
Anthracene . .	2·95J	5·32β	105
Phenanthrene . .	3·02J	5·45β	110
Diphenyl . .	2·37J	4·38β	79
Butadiene . .	0·23J	0·47β	3·5 ·
Hexatriene . .	0·48J	0·99β	..

A large number of calculations have been made by this method for hydrocarbons in condensed or linear form. Table 21 shows a selection, from which it will appear that the resonance energy is much greater for the cyclic molecules than for the linear ones. The reason for this is that in a linear molecule there is only one Kekulé structure, and resonance arises from interaction between this and other structures of considerably greater energy. But with the aromatic compounds there are several Kekulé structures which, because of their equal energy, interact strongly. This resonance energy is approximately proportional to the number of closed rings, though the staggered arrangement, as in phenanthrene, is a little more stable than the straight one, as in anthracene.

9.5. Compression energy

The last column in Table **21** shows the so-called 'observed resonance energies'. These are obtained from the total heat of formation of the molecules by subtracting the energy of one of the Kekulé structures. This latter energy is calculated on the

† Taken chiefly from L. Pauling, *The Nature of the Chemical Bond*, Cornell University Press, 3rd edn., 1960, p. 195. The most accurate resonance energies are obtained from observed heats of hydrogenation, though assumptions such as that all C—C single bonds have the same energy render any precise estimate of resonance energies rather artificial. Earlier values were often obtained from heats of combustion, and were as much as 10 per cent. larger than the values in Table 21. An alternative set of 'observed values' is given by F. Klages, *Chem. Ber.*, 1949, **82**, 358. See also T. L. Cottrell and L. E. Sutton, *J. Chem. Phys.*, 1947, **15**, 685, for a critical discussion of the appropriate double-bond energy to take for the purpose of calculating resonance energies.

‡ Calculated on the assumption that all exchange integrals J and resonance integrals $β$ between neighbouring atoms are equal. This is acceptable for the ring compounds, but not for the chains, where it exaggerates the resonance energy.

assumption of bond additivity, taking the single and double C—C bonds to have the same energies as in ethane and ethylene. If, for the moment, we accept this approximation, we must choose the exchange integral J so that one of the observed values (usually benzene) is reproduced. When this is done, the other values are found to be reproduced with considerable success. It would, of course, be more satisfactory if an *ab initio* calculation of J were possible. Such is not the case, on account of certain other difficulties shortly to be listed, and we are therefore obliged to have recourse to experiment. Values of J in the region of 1·6 eV seem to give good results for the resonance energies of most hydrocarbon molecules. For the calculation of u.v. spectra, however, a larger value, about 1·9 eV, appears more suitable.

It is well, at this stage, to remind ourselves once more of the approximations involved in column 2 of Table 21. These are (i) lack of orthogonality of all a.o.'s, (ii) assumption of equal exchange integrals for all bonds, (iii) assumption that all exchange integrals between non-adjacent atoms are negligible, (iv) neglect of all ionic structures, (v) neglect of higher permutations (exchanges), (vi) neglect of all interactions between σ- and π-bonds,† (vii) the assumption that all C—H bonds are equivalent, whether the carbon be primary or secondary. This is a formidable list, even though it does not include the following serious difficulty.

When we discuss resonance between certain structures, as, for example, the Kekulé structures of benzene, and deduce a resonance hybrid, we must pay careful attention to the positions of the nuclei. For our resonance is an electronic resonance; that is to say, we may only properly include structures in which the nuclei are in the same relative position. Now in one of the Kekulé structures for benzene, three of the bonds are short, and three are long. In the other structure, the positions are reversed. There is effectively no resonance between these two structures. We must first distort them both, so that all the bonds are equal, and then allow the distorted structures to interact. This means that work

† Their importance has been proved by S. L. Altmann, *Proc. Roy. Soc.* A, 1952, **210**, 224, I. G. Ross, *Trans. Faraday Soc.*, 1952, **48**, 973, A. D. McLean, *J. Chem. Phys.*, 1960, **32**, 1595, and many others.

has had to be supplied to the structures, compressing one set of three bonds and extending the other set, before resonance becomes operative. The 'observed resonance energies' of Table 21 are the net values, so that the true resonance energy as measured by the second column should be considerably greater than the values in the fourth column. We ought to include what is termed the 'energy of compression' of the basic σ-bonds.† This energy is sometimes quite large. For benzene‡ it may be as much as 35 kcal/mole so that the true resonance energy should lie between 65 and 75 kcal/mole. For the straight polyene chain of butadiene, on the other hand, the compression energy is only 2–3 kcal/mole.

These considerations should warn us against too literal an identification of theoretical and experimental resonance energies. Yet there can be no doubt that our understanding of the large resonance energies found for the cyclic condensed systems is qualitatively correct.

9.6. Molecular-orbital description

We must now return to the m.o. description of these molecules, and elaborate the discussion of p. 239. Again let us choose benzene as a particular example. Each of the six π electrons is supposed to move under the influence of a potential field provided by the attractions of the nuclei and the repulsions of the σ electrons and the remaining π electrons. This means that we can discuss each electron separately, introducing an effective Hamiltonian **H** to govern its behaviour. The explicit form of **H** is very difficult to write down, since it is obtained by an averaging process taken over all the other electrons, whose wave functions must therefore be already known! For most purposes, therefore, we make little or no attempt at an explicit formula for **H**, but reckon to estimate the essential quantities which depend upon **H** by an appeal to experiment for one particular molecule. In this respect there is an empirical character about the final energy values similar to that

† J. E. Lennard-Jones, *Proc. Roy. Soc.* A, 1937, **158**, 280.
‡ R. S. Mulliken *et al.*, *J. Amer. Chem. Soc.*, 1941, **63**, 41. However, an estimate by C. A. Coulson and S. L. Altmann (*Trans. Faraday Soc.*, 1952, **48**, 293) gives only 27 kcal/mole. See also R. S. Mulliken and R. G. Parr, *J. Chem. Phys.*, 1951, **19**, 1271.

with the v.b. method. It is, however, absolutely imperative to recognize that the Hamiltonian **H** here introduced is entirely different from the Hamiltonian H used in § 3. Our present Hamiltonian **H** is an operator involving only one of the π electrons; the former Hamiltonian H involved all of them. But both are approximate in that they neglect all the σ electrons. A similar care is needed to distinguish between the matrix components $\mathbf{H}_{rs}$ and H_{rs}. The coefficients c_r in the m.o. $\psi = c_1\psi_1 + \ldots + c_6\psi_6$ are found from the secular equations. In the usual way these will be six in number. The first of the set has the form

$$c_1(\mathbf{H}_{11} - ES_{11}) + c_2(\mathbf{H}_{12} - ES_{12}) + \ldots + c_6(\mathbf{H}_{16} - ES_{16}) = 0, \quad (15)$$

where

$$S_{rs} = \int \psi_r \psi_s \, d\tau = S_{sr}, \qquad \mathbf{H}_{rs} = \int \psi_r \mathbf{H}\psi_s \, d\tau = \mathbf{H}_{sr}. \quad (16)$$

If the a.o.'s are normalized, $S_{11} = S_{22} = \ldots = 1$; and if we neglect overlap even of adjacent orbitals, $S_{12} = \ldots = 0$. $\mathbf{H}_{rr}$ is then the energy which one of the π electrons would have if it had been compelled to stay on nucleus r, with a wave function ψ_r, and $\mathbf{H}_{rs}$ is the resonance integral, usually written β_{rs}. It is customary to neglect all β_{rs} except between neighbours, and also to give all the non-vanishing integrals the same value β. Similarly all the $\mathbf{H}_{rr}$ are supposed to be equal, with a value E_0.† With these assumptions the six secular equations are

$$
\begin{aligned}
c_1(E_0 - E) + c_2\beta & & & & & + c_6\beta & = 0 \\
c_1\beta & + c_2(E_0 - E) + c_3\beta & & & & & = 0 \\
& c_2\beta & + c_3(E_0 - E) + c_4\beta & & & & = 0 \\
& & c_3\beta & + c_4(E_0 - E) + c_5\beta & & & = 0 \\
& & & c_4\beta & + c_5(E_0 - E) + c_6\beta & & = 0 \\
c_1\beta & & & & + c_5\beta + c_6(E_0 - E) & & = 0
\end{aligned}
$$
$$(17)$$

If we eliminate the coefficients c_r, we obtain a secular determinant of degree 6 in $E_0 - E$, whose roots may be shown to be

$$E = E_0 + 2\beta, \quad E_0 + \beta \text{ (twice)}, \quad E_0 - \beta \text{ (twice)}, \quad E_0 - 2\beta. \quad (18)$$

† This treatment is due originally to E. Hückel, see, e.g., *Z. Phys.*, 1931, **70**, 204: or the *International Conf. Phys.*, Physical Soc., 1935, vol. 2, p. 9.

Since β is negative, these are in ascending order of magnitude. The lowest m.o. is therefore single, with energy $E_0+2\beta$, and will hold two electrons with opposed spins. The next m.o. is double, with energy $E_0+\beta$, and will hold four electrons. These orbitals are called bonding, since $E < E_0$; the others are anti-bonding. The high resonance energy of benzene is now attributed to the fact that there are just six electrons to fit into the orbitals (18), so that the bonding levels are just completely full. Thus the total π energy, in this simple approximation, is

$$2(E_0+2\beta)+4(E_0+\beta) = 6E_0+8\beta. \tag{19}$$

If we had localized an electron in the region of one bond (e.g. between atoms 1 and 2) its wave function would have been $\psi_1+\psi_2$, with energy $E_0+\beta$. Six electrons of this kind, comprising one Kekulé structure, would have total energy $6E_0+6\beta$. The difference between this and the energy (19) is the delocalization energy 2β. This is the quantity which we have shown in the third column of Table 21. This table also shows values for other aromatic molecules obtained in the same manner, and ready to be compared with the alternative v.b. calculations. Despite the many approximations involved in both treatments, the agreement is surprisingly close. Indeed, if β/J is given the value 0·54 so that β is about -20 kcal/mole, the two columns differ by less than 10 per cent. This is the more remarkable when it is realized that resonance, or delocalization, energy is obtained as a relatively small difference between two nearly equal large quantities.

In the case of benzene, the lowest m.o. has a normalized wave function

$$6^{-\frac{1}{2}}\{\psi_1+\psi_2+\psi_3+\psi_4+\psi_5+\psi_6\}. \tag{20}$$

But because of the double degeneracy, a large number of possible alternatives exist for the second m.o.'s. One purely real version is

$$c_1 = c_4 = 0, \quad c_2 = c_3 = -c_5 = -c_6 = \tfrac{1}{2}, \tag{21 a}$$
$$c_1 = -c_4 = 1/\sqrt{3}, \quad c_2 = -c_3 = -c_5 = c_6 = 1/\sqrt{(12)}. \tag{21 b}$$

But the most symmetrical version, which involves complex c_r, and which shows the immediate equivalence of all six carbon atoms, is:

$$c_r = \sqrt{\tfrac{1}{6}}e^{r\pi i/3}, \tag{22 a}$$

and
$$c_r = \sqrt{\tfrac{1}{6}}e^{-r\pi i/3}. \tag{22 b}$$

A large number of calculations have been made by this method, even for very big molecules: and many improvements have been added to the simple form of the theory described above. But although these refinements do certainly change the numerical values in Table 21, they do not change the essential significance of our conclusions.

One simple way of illustrating the distribution of energy levels (18) is by plotting them on a vertical energy line, as in Fig. 7. Here

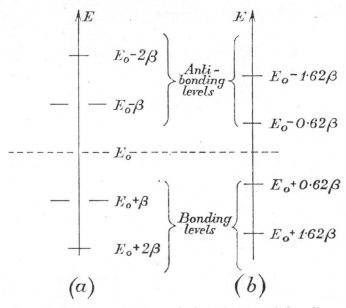

FIG. 9.7. Molecular-orbital energies in (a) benzene, (b) butadiene.

each horizontal line represents one molecular orbital, with the lower ones more stable than the upper ones. Since an isolated π electron would have energy E_0 we can label all the levels below the dotted line as bonding, and all those above it as anti-bonding. A diagram of this kind shows immediately that benzene, with six π electrons occupying the three bonding m.o.'s, is much more stable than butadiene where the four π electrons occupy the two bonding m.o.'s.

9.7. Heterocyclic molecules, v.b. description

We must now consider the changes that take place in our previous discussion when one or more of the carbon atoms is replaced by some other atom, such as nitrogen. The particular case of pyridine will serve to illustrate the argument.

In the first place we may imagine pyridine to be obtained in a

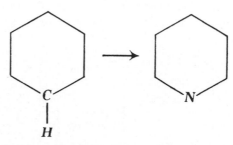

Fig. 9.8. Schematic relation between benzene and pyridine.

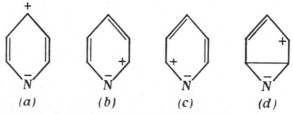

Fig. 9.9. Ionic structures in pyridine.

purely formal way by compressing one of the H atoms into the adjacent carbon nucleus, as shown in Fig. 8. The number of π electrons does not change in this process, the two electrons that formerly constituted the C—H bond becoming lone-pair electrons of the N atom. Nor, on account of the valence angles, does the hybridization change.† So the lone-pair electrons will have orbitals of approximately trigonal form directed away from the ring. We can still discuss the six π electrons separately from the σ electrons, and pair them together in the same manner as in the Kekulé and Dewar structures for benzene. However, an essential difference arises on account of the fact that nitrogen is more electronegative

† This neglects a small change in valence angles, e.g. the CNC angle in pyridine is 116° 50′ instead of 120°. But this makes no effective difference to our analysis.

than carbon, so that there is a definite tendency for the π electrons to move on to it. In v.b. language this means that in addition to the five covalent structures previously mentioned, we must include ionic structures such as those of Fig. 9 a–c. There are, of course, other structures in which the N atom is positively charged, and yet others in which both the positive and negative charges are on carbons. But all of these are energetically less favoured than the three shown in Fig. 9. The positive charge is placed on either the o or the p carbons since if it is placed on a *meta*-carbon, as in 9 (d), we cannot pair the remaining four π electrons in any satisfactory manner: the particular structure (d), which only contains one proper π-bond, will be of too great energy to participate in the resonance as effectively as (a)–(c), and may be neglected. Resonance between the five covalent structures and the three ionic structures in a manner similar to that discussed in § 5.7 will result in an additional lowering of the energy, and a net flow of charge from the *ortho*- and *para*-positions on to the nitrogen atom. In principle there is nothing to prevent us from making the necessary calculations: all that is required are a few more exchange and Coulomb integrals. But in practice the evaluation of these terms proves too difficult, and usually semi-empirical methods have to be adopted.† This limitation renders the method qualitative rather than quantitative. All that we can do is to obtain an approximate estimate for the weights of the various ionic structures. If the weights of the Kekulé, Dewar, and ionic structures (a), (b), and (c) are w_k, w_d, w_a, w_b, w_c, so that $w_b = w_c$, and

$$2w_k + 3w_d + w_a + w_b + w_c = 100, \qquad (23)$$

it follows at once that the fractional net charge on the N atom is $(w_a + w_b + w_c)/100$, and on each *ortho*- and *para*-carbon $w_b/100$ and $w_a/100$ electrons respectively.

9.8. Heterocyclic molecules, m.o. description

The m.o. description of a heterocyclic system can be made a little more precise. The essential feature which distinguishes such

† See, e.g., A. Pullman, *Ann. Chim.*, 1947, **2**, 5; R. Daudel and A. Pullman, *J. de Phys.*, 1946, **7**, 59, 74, 105; B. Pullman, *Bull. Soc. Chim. France*, 1948, **15**, 533. Serious attempts to include ionic structures are by M. Simonetta, *J. Chim. phys.*, 1952, **49**, 68, and C. Zauli, *J. Chem. Soc.*, 1960 2204

a molecule from the corresponding hydrocarbon is the changed electronegativity at the hetero-atom. In terms of the effective Hamiltonian for each individual π electron, the matrix element H_{rr} (equation (16)) for the hetero-atom will now differ from that for the remaining carbon atoms. The corresponding resonance integrals β_{rs}, where r is the hetero-atom, will also differ slightly, but the difference, particularly when nitrogen replaces carbon, is

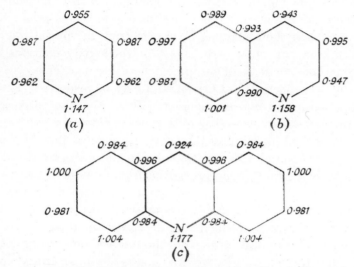

Fig. 9.10. Charge distributions in (a) pyridine, (b) quinoline, and (c) acridine.

small, and it may be shown to exert only a second-order effect on the final charge distribution. In the case of pyridine, calling the N atom number 1, the secular equations will be identical with (17) except that the term E_0 in the first line is altered. This alteration depends on the electronegativity change, and may be taken to be proportional to the difference of the electronegativities of the two atoms, using the scale explained in § 5.8. In the case of nitrogen it used to be customary to replace E_0 for the N atom by $E_0+2\beta$, but later work† suggests that $E_0+\tfrac{1}{2}\beta$ is a rather more likely value.

† L. E. Orgel, T. L. Cottrell, W. Dick, and L. E. Sutton, *Trans. Faraday Soc.*, 1951, **47**, 113; A. Lofthus, *Molec. Phys.*, 1959, **2**, 367; P.-O. Löwdin, *J. Chem. Phys.*, 1951, **19**, 1333; R. McWeeny and T. E. Peacock, *Proc. Phys. Soc.* A, 1957, **70**, 41.

The corresponding changes for other atoms may now be found by simple proportion. The secular equations have next to be solved; first the energies, and then the coefficients c_r in the various m.o.'s are thus obtained.

To find the resulting charge distribution we must remember that in m.o. theory all the π electrons have orbitals extending over the complete molecular framework. We have therefore to determine the charge distribution for each orbital separately, and then sum these distributions for all the occupied orbitals. In a particular m.o.

$$\psi = c_1\,\psi_1 + \ldots + c_n\,\psi_n, \tag{24}$$

the normalization condition is

$$\sum c_r^2 = 1,$$

and the familiar interpretation of ψ^2 as a density shows us that we may associate fractional charges c_1^2, c_2^2,..., c_n^2 of an electron with the nuclei 1, 2,..., n. The normalization condition ensures that the complete electron is thus accounted for. By summing c_1^2 for each occupied orbital, we obtain the total electronic charge on nucleus 1. Fig. 10† shows a few values calculated in this manner.

9.9. Pyrrole, aniline, and other substituted aromatic molecules

Some interesting points about the role of π electrons, and the preference for a ring system containing six of these, follow from a comparison of pyrrole (Fig. 11 a) and aniline (Fig. 11 b).

In pyrrole the four carbon atoms are hybridized in approximately trigonal style, and together contribute four π electrons. Nitrogen contains five electrons in its valence shell. If we suppose that these are also hybridized trigonally, then the use of one electron in each of the three σ-bonds joining it to its three neighbours will leave two π electrons (the lone-pair). If the molecule is coplanar, these two will augment the total number of π electrons

---

† Taken from G. W. Wheland and L. Pauling, *J. Amer. Chem. Soc.*, 1935, **57**, 2086, and H. C. Longuet-Higgins and C. A. Coulson, *Trans. Faraday Soc.*, 1947, **43**, 87, but scaled down to agree with the more recent electronegativity parameter for nitrogen. Very similar results have been obtained by T. E. Peacock in some unpublished calculations.

to six, which will therefore completely occupy the three lowest
m.o.'s. These turn out to have the same general character as in
benzene (Fig. 7). This means that there is just room for six bonding electrons, and the stability of the molecule is assured. It will
be noticed that this description requires the three bonds at the
N atom to be coplanar. If we had tried to find an alternative
description in which the bonds made angles similar to those in
ammonia, the hydrogen atom would have been either above or

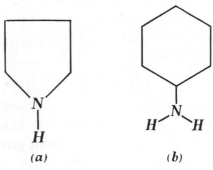

(a)   (b)

FIG. 9.11. (a) Pyrrole, and (b) aniline.

below the plane of the ring, and the lone-pair electrons could not
have had the π character necessary for the large amount of delocalization which our earlier description required. Now, as Table 21
shows, the delocalization energy for a closed ring is much greater
than that for an open system of four carbon atoms. The most
stable arrangement is therefore the planar one.† The chief difference between pyrrole and pyridine is that in pyrrole the nitrogen
atom contributes two π electrons; and in pyridine only one. In
both cases the total number of π electrons is six. A second difference, however, arises from the fact that since the N atom contributes two π electrons, the only way in which we may introduce
this atom into the v.b. resonating system will be by ionic structures
in which the nitrogen is positively charged. This implies that
pyrrole resonates between the covalent structures Fig. 12 (a, b)
and ionic structures such as 12 (c, d). As a result, the nitrogen
atom carries a net positive charge instead of a net negative charge,

† This has been established experimentally using pure rotation spectra, by
W. S. Wilcox and J. H. Goldstein, *J. Chem. Phys.*, 1952, **20**, 1656.

as in pyridine. The more electronegative the atom, the less favourable energetically and therefore presumably the less significant are the ionic structures in the resonance hybrid. Pauling[†] has suggested that in the five-membered heterocyclic molecules furan, pyrrole, and thiophene (the electronegativities of oxygen, nitrogen, and sulphur are 3·5, 3·0, and 2·5 respectively) the total weight of the ionic structures such as 11 (*c*, *d*) are 8, 24, and 28 per cent., respectively. [The case of thiophene may be different from the

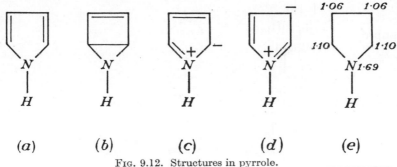

(*a*)   (*b*)   (*c*)   (*d*)   (*e*)

Fig. 9.12.   Structures in pyrrole.

(*a*) (*b*) covalent;
(*c*) (*d*) ionic;
(*e*) final charge distribution (m.o. method).

others, since sulphur has possible *d*-type a.o.'s with π symmetry, and somewhat different hybridizations may conceivably occur, involving these *d* orbitals.[‡]] In the m.o. treatment of these molecules, we do not speak of ionic structures, but we can calculate the charge distribution in the manner previously outlined for pyridine. The results show just the same positive net charge on the nitrogen as was implied in the v.b. treatment. Fig. 12 (*e*) shows the values thus obtained.

There is an interesting confirmation of the difference between pyrrole and pyridine in a study of their dipole moments. The dipole moment of pyrrole[§] is 1·80 D in a direction which makes the N atom positive. Not more than about 0·4 D of this can be due to the σ electrons in the C—H, C—N, and N—H bonds, so that

† *Nature of the Chemical Bond*, 1st edn., p. 208.
‡ H. C. Longuet-Higgins, *Trans. Faraday Soc.*, 1949, **45**, 173. See also C. Zauli, *J. Chem. Soc.*, 1960, p 2204.
§ H. Kofod, L. E. Sutton, and J. Jackson, *J. Chem. Soc.*, 1952, p. 1467.

approximately 1·4 D arises from the π electrons. The value obtained from the π-electron distribution in Fig. 11 (e) is about 1·9 D and in the correct direction. In pyridine, on the other hand, the observed dipole moment is 2·15 D† in a direction that makes the N atom negative. This is precisely what is required from the charges in Fig. 10 (a), which lead to a π-moment (sometimes called the resonance moment‡) $\mu_\pi = 1·2$ D. When we add to this the C—H and C—N σ-bond moments, and the moment of the two

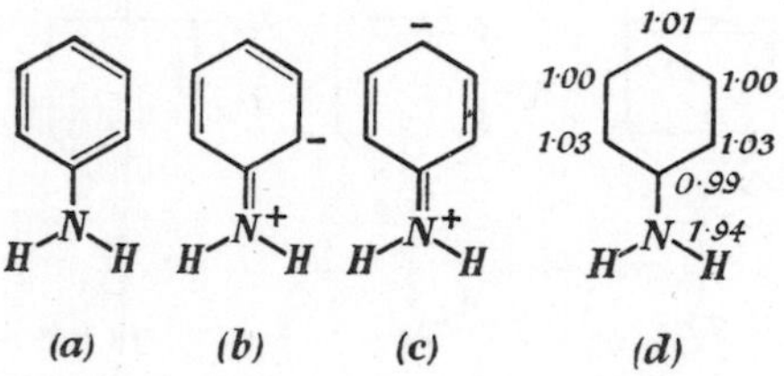

FIG. 9.13. Structures in aniline.

(a) covalent;   (b) (c) ionic;
(d) final charge distribution (m.o. method).

lone-pair electrons on the nitrogen atom (cf. Fig. 8.16), we get approximately the observed value.

A somewhat similar situation occurs in aniline (Fig. 13). If the molecule had been completely coplanar, then there would have been two π electrons on the nitrogen, which could enter into resonance with the other π electrons of the ring. However, dipole-moment studies of *para*-phenylenediamine (*p*-amino-aniline) show that the valence angles at the nitrogen atom do not differ greatly from those in ammonia (§ 7.2) This means that when we draw the ionic structures such as Fig. 13 (b, c) there is not very efficient overlap between the π orbital on the carbon and the nearly tetrahedral lone-pair hybrid on the nitrogen which together constitute the second half of the $\diagup C{=}\overset{+}{N}\diagdown$ bond. The resonance and exchange integrals will therefore be smaller, and the weights of the ionic structures correspondingly less. But we can assert that (1)

† B. B. DeMore, W. S. Wilcox, and J. H. Goldstein, *J. Chem. Phys.*, 1954, 22, 876.

‡ L. E. Sutton, *Proc. Roy. Soc.* A, 1931, 133, 668; *Trans. Faraday Soc.*, 1934, 30, 789.

the resonance moment will be such as to feed electrons into the ring, leaving the nitrogen atom with a small residual positive charge, and (2) structures in which the excess ring charge resides on the *meta*-carbons are much less important energetically than (*b*) and (*c*), in which it is on the *ortho*- and *para*-carbons. The final charges, according to the m.o. method,† are shown in Fig. 13 (*d*).

It is interesting to enquire why the molecule is not planar. If it were so, it would be necessary to change the hybridization at the nitrogen atom from the approximately tetrahedral character found in ammonia to the trigonal type. This would involve energy, the amount of which may be estimated from a study of the vibration spectrum of ammonia. In the so-called 'inversion' spectrum, the N atom passes right through the plane of the three hydrogens to a position of minimum energy symmetrically placed on the other side. It appears that about 7 kcal/mole are required to effect this inversion;‡ this is therefore the energy that is required to flatten the original pyramid into a plane. In the planar state, the bonds are trigonal, so that we conclude that about 7 kcal/mole are needed to change the hybridization. Presumably much the same would be true for aniline, and this energy would have to be set against the gain in resonance as a result of coplanarity. Now the observed resonance energy in aniline is about 6 kcal/mole over and above the value for benzene. So in order that the molecule

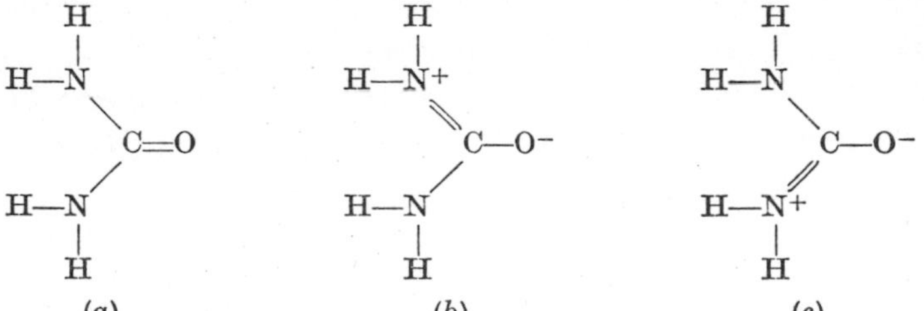

FIG. 9.14. Structures in urea, showing (*a*) covalent; (*b*) (*c*) ionic.

should be planar, the resonance energy would then have to be at east 6+7 (i.e. 13) kcal/mole. It is not surprising that the inclusion

† I. Fischer-Hjalmars, *Arkiv Fysik*, 1962, **21**, 123.

‡ J. F. Kincaid and F. C. Henriques, *J. Amer. Chem. Soc.*, 1940, **62**, 1474; see also J. D. Swalen and J. A. Ibers, *Bull. Amer. Phys. Soc.*, 1962, **17**, 43.

of polar structures such as Fig. 13 (b, c) is not able to provide so much energy. But the balance of energy terms must be close, since in urea (Fig. 14) in addition to the covalent structure (a) there are ionic structures (b) and (c) which do not break up the benzenoid ring resonance as in aniline, and which also place the negative charge on a more reactive atom (oxygen rather than carbon), and which lead to a completely planar molecule.†

We can now see at once why aniline is a much weaker base than ammonia. For the addition of a proton to give $C_6H_5 . NH_3^+$ requires us to sacrifice the additional resonance energy which we have just been describing. No such sacrifice is needed in the reaction $NH_3 + H^+ \rightarrow NH_4^+$. In this way we have a simple understanding of the difference of about 6 in the pK_b values of the two compounds; not more than about one-quarter of this difference can apparently be attributed to an induction effect arising from the differing polarity of N—H and N—C bonds.‡

According to the above, any atom, or group of atoms, which is adjacent to a π-electron system and which possesses electrons with orbitals of π symmetry, may be expected to enter in the conjugation already present. In chlorobenzene, for example—taking the z-axis perpendicular to the benzene plane—the chlorine atom possesses two $2p_z$ a.o.'s, otherwise not engaged in bonding, but which could participate in the conjugation round the ring. In m.o. language we should say that the π orbitals extended over seven nuclei instead of over six. In v.b. language we should say that in addition to structures such as (i) below, we must consider others such as (ii) and (iii). Three conclusions follow from such considerations. The first is that since structures (ii) and (iii) are only possible when the Cl is positively charged, we shall anticipate that the π-electron distribution (but not, of course, the σ-electron distribution) will be such as to give a flow of electronic charge into the ring. The second is that this charge must flow preferentially to the *ortho*- and *para*-positions. Thirdly it may be inferred that the C—Cl bond possesses a partial double-bond character distinct

---

† P. Vaughan and J. Donohue, *Acta Cryst.*, 1952, **5**, 530 (X-rays); D. R. Waldron and R. M. Badger, *J. Chem. Phys.*, 1950, **18**, 566 (infra-red).

‡ For further discussion see G. E. K. Branch and M. Calvin, *The Theory of Organic Chemistry*, Prentice-Hall, 1945, chap. vi.

from what it would have in a system such as CH_3Cl, where there are no conventional π electrons. All three conclusions are also

reached by the application of m.o. theory.[†] They are also verified by direct experiment, as follows.

The charge displacement is shown by the existence of a resonance moment, originally introduced by L. E. Sutton.[‡] This is the difference between the dipole moments of the corresponding aromatic and aliphatic molecules. Thus we may compare the dipole moments of CH_3X and C_6H_5X. The table below[§] gives values for several distinct substituents X. It will be observed that for the first four molecules (the other two molecules will be dealt with later) the resonance moment, determined as the difference of corresponding figures in the two rows, is always such as to make the substituent atom less negatively charged in the aromatic molecule than in the aliphatic.

Table of dipole moments (in Debye units)

X =	F	Cl	Br	OH	NO$_2$	CN
$\mu(CH_3X) =$	1·81	1·87	1·80	1·70	3·44	3·97
$\mu(C_6H_5X) =$	1·58	1·72	1·77	1·45	4·23	4·42

The second conclusion to be verified experimentally is that the charge which flows into the ring is concentrated at the *ortho*- and *para*-positions. This is shown from the fact that all four of these substituents are *ortho-para* directing,[||] i.e. they direct a positively charged approaching radical (e.g. NO_2^+) to substitution preferentially in the *ortho*- or *para*-positions. Without doubt this is chiefly

---

† C. A. Coulson and H. C. Longuet-Higgins, *Proc. Roy. Soc.* A, 1947, **191**, 39; F. A. Matsen, *J. Amer. Chem. Soc.*, 1950, **72**, 5243.

‡ *Proc. Roy. Soc.* A, 1931, **133**, 668.

§ Mostly taken from *Table of Dielectric Constants and Electric Dipole Moments of Substances in the Gaseous State*, U.S. Dept. of Commerce, N.B.S. Circular 537, 1953.

|| For a review see C. K. Ingold, *Chem. Rev.*, 1934, **15**, 225; or A. E. Remick, *Electronic Interpretations of Organic Chemistry*, John Wiley, 1943; or M. J. S. Dewar, *The Electronic Theory of Organic Chemistry*, Oxford, 1949.

due to the electrostatic attraction arising from the excess negative charge at these places, which facilitates the approach of the ion.

The third conclusion—that the 'single' bond acquires a partial double-bond character—is shown by a small contraction of the bond length. However,† accurate microwave spectroscopy has since shown a lack of cylindrical symmetry around the bond axis, which can most satisfactorily be interpreted as the acquisition of some π-character. In the particular case of chloroethylene $CH_2{=}CHCl$, the charge distribution around the C—Cl axis is distorted in such a way as to correspond to about 5 per cent. double-bond character. In this way all the major claims of the theory have been verified experimentally. There is also an additional delocalization, or resonance, energy, amounting to about 5 kcal/mole, but the experimental calorimetric data are hardly yet sufficiently precise to establish the true value with great accuracy.

It still remains for us to discuss the last two groups in the table of dipole moments given earlier. These differ from the others in that they are *meta*-directing instead of *ortho-para*. In nitrobenzene, for example, the extra ionic structures that correspond to (ii) and (iii) in chlorobenzene, are (iv) and (v), in which charge has flowed out of the ring instead of into it; and in which this charge has come from the *ortho*- and *para*-positions, leaving the *meta*-positions unaffected. Such molecules will therefore be unreactive for positively charged radicals (e.g. NO_2^+, Br^+), and their reactivity towards negatively charged radicals (e.g. OH^-, NH_2^-) will be at the *o*- and *p*-positions. With these groups the resonance moment is in the opposite direction to the others, as is shown by a comparison of the second and third rows of the table.

(iv)   (v)

9.10. Fractional bond order

We have already referred to the fact that as a result of resonance between the Kekulé and Dewar structures, all six C—C bonds in

† E. B. Wilson, *Faraday Soc. Discussions*, 1950, no. 9, p. 108.

benzene are equivalent, and have a bond length intermediate between those of a normal single and double bond. This suggests that we should assign them a fractional order. If we use the v.b. method this may be calculated† from a knowledge of the weights of each constituent structure. Thus the percentage double-bond character of any chosen bond is the total weight, measured in percentages, of all the structures in which this bond is shown as double. Consider, for example, the 1–2 bond in benzene. This appears as double in one of the Kekulé structures (Fig. 2) and in one of the Dewar structures (Fig. 4 *a*). Its percentage double-bond character is therefore

$$39+7 = 46.$$

All six bonds have precisely the same character. We can convert this into fractional bond order by saying that the C—C bonds have a total order 1·46. Alternatively their mobile bond order is 0·46.

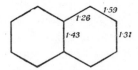

Fig. 9.15. Bond orders in naphthalene (v.b. method).

Similarly, in pyridine, using the notation of (23), the percentage double-bond characters of the N—C_1, C_1—C_2, and C_2—C_3 bonds are respectively w_k+w_d, $w_k+w_d+w_a+w_b$, $w_k+w_d+w_b$. From these values the bond orders are soon obtained. In aniline, the existence of the ionic structures is shown by a partial double-bond character of the N—C bond, since, as Fig. 13 shows, every ionic structure involves this bond as double. In naphthalene, on the other hand, there are no important ionic terms, but the forty-two covalent structures (Fig. 6) do not by any means contribute equally. When the order of the bonds are calculated from the weights of these various structures, the values shown in Fig. 15 are obtained. This diagram shows that the $\alpha\beta$ bond has a much higher bond order than the others, and therefore most closely resembles a normal double-bond.

† L. Pauling, L. O. Brockway, and J. Y. Beach, *J. Amer. Chem. Soc.*, 1935, **57**, 2705.

One important application of these bond orders is in the prediction of bond lengths. If a smooth curve is drawn through the basic points corresponding to single, double, and triple bonds, it is possible to read off the anticipated length from a knowledge of the order, and vice versa. Indeed, it was by use of the experimental bond lengths that the ionic characters of furan, pyrrole, and thiophene (p. 261) were estimated.

The m.o. definition of fractional bond order† is somewhat different from that just described in v.b. terms. Since each mobile electron has an orbital extending over several nuclei, we must regard it as contributing to all the bonds in the aromatic framework. The total bond order of any given bond is then the sum of contributions from each of the occupied m.o.'s. Consider a particular orbital

$$\psi = c_1\psi_1 + c_2\psi_2 + \ldots + c_n\psi_n.$$

An electron in this orbital may be expected to contribute to the bond between atoms 1 and 2, which we suppose to be neighbours, if it has a large probability of being found in the region of the bond 1–2. This requires that both c_1 and c_2 shall be large, and of the same sign (cf. Chapter IV). It is clearly not sufficient that one of c_1 and c_2 should be large, for that would imply that the electron was chiefly located around one of the nuclei, and was not between them. Indeed, it is the coefficient of $\psi_1\psi_2$ in the density function ψ^2 that may properly be taken to measure the contribution of this electron to the bond 1–2. We therefore define the partial bond order of this orbital as c_1c_2, and the total mobile order of the 1–2 bond is the sum of contributions c_1c_2 from every mobile electron. If the coefficients c_r are complex, c_1c_2 is replaced by $\frac{1}{2}(c_1c_2^* + c_1^*c_2)$. This definition gives mobile bond orders 1 and 2 —and therefore total bond orders 2 and 3—for ethylene and acetylene, so that the fixed points on the order-length curve are correctly described.

An example will show how this is applied. In equations (20), (21 a), (21 b) we have given the normalized m.o.'s for benzene. It follows at once that an electron in the lowest orbital contributes

† C. A. Coulson, *Proc. Roy. Soc.* A, 1939, **169**, 413.

$\frac{1}{6}$ to the bond order of each of the six C—C bonds: and that the contributions from the other occupied orbitals are as shown below.

Bond	1–2	2–3	3–4	4–5	5–6	6–1
m.o. equation (20) . .	$\frac{1}{6}$	$\frac{1}{6}$	$\frac{1}{6}$	$\frac{1}{6}$	$\frac{1}{6}$	$\frac{1}{6}$
m.o. equation (21 a) . .	0	$\frac{1}{4}$	0	0	$\frac{1}{4}$	0
m.o. equation (21 b) . .	$\frac{1}{6}$	$-\frac{1}{12}$	$\frac{1}{6}$	$\frac{1}{6}$	$-\frac{1}{12}$	$\frac{1}{6}$
Total mobile order, 2 electrons per orbital . . .	$\frac{2}{3}$	$\frac{2}{3}$	$\frac{2}{3}$	$\frac{2}{3}$	$\frac{2}{3}$	$\frac{2}{3}$

In the bottom line we have added together the contributions from all the occupied orbitals, remembering that there are two electrons in each. The result shows, as we should have expected, that all six bonds are equivalent, with total bond order $1\frac{2}{3}$. It will be noticed that some contributions are positive and others negative. This is important because a similar calculation can be made for excited states in which an electron has been moved from one of the lower orbitals to a higher one. The various bond orders are no longer the same as before, and we can tell which ones have been strengthened, and which ones weakened, by the excitation. Thus in butadiene, conventionally written as

$$CH_2\!=\!CH\!-\!CH\!=\!CH_2,$$

the orders of the C—C bonds in the ground state are 1·894, 1·447, and 1·894 respectively. [This shows that the central C—C bond is an acceptor bond, acquiring bond order at the expense of the two end donor bonds.] But in the first excited state, the three bond orders become 1·447, 1·671, and 1·447, indicating that excitation weakens the end links, and strengthens the central one.†

Fig. 16 shows the curve relating order and length for C—C bonds. From this curve we predict that the bond length in benzene (order $1\frac{2}{3}$) should be 1·40 A, in almost complete agreement with experiment (1·397 A). Values for naphthalene are shown in Table 22. Despite the many approximations involved in the theory, the agreement is sufficiently good to give us confidence in the general validity of the method. This is particularly true for the shortest bond 1–2.

† These bond orders are based on equal resonance integrals β for all three bonds. A more careful allowance for different β's changes the values slightly but does not alter the general result. Its chief effect is to reduce the central bond order to about 1·2. (See, e.g., C. Moser, *J. Chem. Soc.*, 1954, p. 3454.)

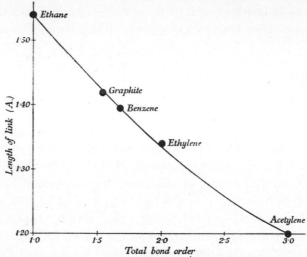

FIG. 9.16. Order-length curve for carbon–carbon bonds.† This is the curve appropriate to bond orders calculated by the m.o. method. A slightly different curve applies with bond orders calculated by the v.b. method.

TABLE 22. *Bond lengths (A) in naphthalene*

Bond	1–2	2–3	1–9	9–10
Length (calc.) .	1·38	1·41	1·42	1·42
Length§ (obs.) .	1·36	1·42	1·42	1·42

§ D. W. J. Cruickshank and R. A. Sparks, *Proc. Roy. Soc.* A, 1960, **258**, 270.

It will be recognized that the two definitions of bond order, as given by the m.o. and v.b. theories, are not identical, and that therefore the corresponding order-length curves will not quite coincide. In all significant cases, however, the agreement between the bond lengths estimated by the two methods is within the range of validity of either theory alone.‡

† Other order-length curves have been given by A. Lofthus, *Molec. Phys.*, 1959, **2**, 367, for CN and NN bonds; E. C. Cox and J. W. Jeffrey, *Proc. Roy. Soc.* A, 1951, **207**, 110, for CO, CN, and CS bonds. A more refined account of CC bonds is due to C. A. Coulson, 1948, *Victor Henri Memorial volume*, Contribution à l'étude de la structure moléculaire, p. 15, Liége: Desoer.

‡ Further details are given by C. A. Coulson, *Proc. Roy. Soc.* A, 1951, **207**, 91, and by Cruickshank and Sparks (loc. cit.).

9.11. Free valence

The concept of fractional bond orders has proved very useful not only in predicting bond lengths, but also in providing a quantum-mechanical version of Thiele's theory of partial valency. Let us illustrate this in terms of butadiene, for which the simple m.o. theory calculates C—C bond orders 1·894, 1·447, 1·894. Consider (Fig. 17) the carbon atom C_1. This atom is involved in two C—H

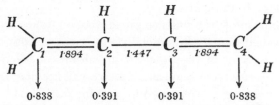

FIG. 9.17. Bond orders and free valences in butadiene.

bonds which may be assigned an order 1·0, and in one C—C bond of order 1·894. We could define a total bond number N_1 as

$$N_1 = 2 \times 1\cdot0 + 1\cdot894 = 3\cdot894.$$

N_1 measures the total degree of bonding of this atom. Similarly

$$N_2 = 1\cdot0 + 1\cdot894 + 1\cdot447 = 4\cdot341.$$

Clearly C_2 is much more deeply engaged in bonding than C_1, and has therefore a smaller free valence. Now it may be shown that for a carbon atom (excluding triple bonds) the greatest possible value of N is $N_{max} = 3 + \sqrt{3} = 4\cdot732$.

It is natural to describe

$$F_r = N_{max} - N_r \tag{25}$$

as the free valence of atom r. For butadiene

$$F_1 = F_4 = 4\cdot732 - 3\cdot894 = 0\cdot838,$$

$$F_2 = F_3 = 4\cdot732 - 4\cdot341 = 0\cdot391. \tag{26}$$

F_r measures the maximum conceivable increment in N_r, and therefore corresponds to Thiele's partial valency, or Werner's residual affinity. It has this advantage over Werner's theory, that a definite numerical magnitude may be assigned, and the way in which this free valence changes when a substitution, or other change, is made in the rest of the molecule, may be discussed quantitatively. If we use the m.o. definitions of bond order, it turns out that values of F_r greater than 1·0 are usually associated with free radicals, and values in the neighbourhood of 0·8 with the terminal carbon of a chain; values near 0·4 apply to aromatic carbons (in benzene $F = 0·40$) and very small values of F to the internal atoms of a condensed molecule. A convenient way of representing free valence is by an arrow diverging from the nucleus and with the numerical value of F_r written at its head. Fig. 17 shows this for butadiene.

The definition of free valence given above applies both to m.o. and v.b. calculations, though the numerical values may differ slightly on account of the different definitions of fractional bond order. An alternative v.b. measure of free valence may be obtained in a manner similar to that used in § 10 for fractional bond order. If we admit that the 'long bonds' which appear in excited structures are so weak that the electrons at either end of the bond are effectively free to engage in other binding, then F_r can be defined as the total weight of all structures in which one long bond terminates on atom r. In the case of benzene, the weights given at the foot of p. 249 show that $F_r = 0·07$. In general it appears that although the numerical values may differ considerably, the relative values are usually much the same, whatever definition one uses.†

9.12. Molecular diagrams and chemical reactivity

A convenient method of summarizing the significant numerical magnitudes for conjugated and aromatic molecules is by means of a molecular diagram. In such a diagram the bond orders are written along the bonds, the net charge on each atom (in units of one electron) is written near the atom, and the free valence is shown by an arrow as described in the last sections. Examples of the molecular diagram for benzene, naphthalene, pyridine, and benzoquinone are given in Fig. 18. No free valence is attached to the nitrogen or oxygen atoms in the two heterocyclic molecules because the presence of a lone-pair of electrons renders this concept less convincing.

† For a comparison, with references, see C. A. Coulson and P. and R. Daudel, *Rev. Sci.*, 1947, **85**, 29.

The principal uses to which molecular diagrams can be put may be listed as follows:

(1) bond orders allow us to infer bond lengths;
(2) bond orders enable us to recognize the degree of bond fixation. Fig. 18 shows that this is much more nearly complete in the quinone than in any of the other molecules;
(3) charges on atoms enable us to estimate the most likely places of attack† by charged radicals (e.g. cations like NO_2^+ in nitration or anions like NH_2^- in amination). The cations,

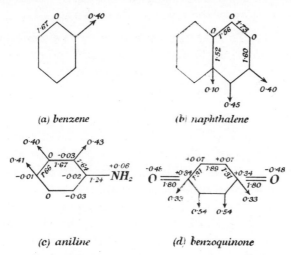

(a) benzene   (b) naphthalene

(c) aniline   (d) benzoquinone

Fig. 9.18. Molecular diagrams for some common molecules.

for example, are attracted most strongly to places of high electronic charge, the anions to places of low charge. This principle must be used with discretion, since in the activated-complex transition stage, considerable forces of a non-electrostatic nature may exist;‡

(4) charges on atoms enable us to estimate π-electron dipole moments, which we have earlier called resonance moments,§

† C. A. Coulson and H. C. Longuet-Higgins, *Proc. Roy. Soc.* A, 1947, **192**, 16.
‡ G. W. Wheland, *J. Amer. Chem. Soc.*, 1942, **64**, 900; W. A. Waters, *J. Chem. Soc.*, 1948, p. 727.
§ L. E. Sutton, *Proc. Roy. Soc.* A, 1931, **133**, 668; *Trans. Faraday Soc.*, 1934, **30**, 789.

and to see how they change as a result of substitution or further conjugation;

(5) free valence determines to some extent the ease of attack by neutral free radicals. In such homolytic reactions there are no important electrostatic interactions as in the case of the heterolytic reactions discussed in (3), and the forces which start off the reaction will be largely due to the residual affinities of the approaching atoms in the two reacting groups. These affinities permit the formation of incipient bonds, and thereby a lowering of the energy, without any severe deformation of the reagents themselves.

After this brief introduction to the theory of chemical reactivity we shall conclude our discussion of aromatic and conjugated compounds with a brief comparison between the m.o. and v.b. treatments developed in this chapter.

9.13. Comparison of the two theories

The most important point regarding the m.o. and v.b. treatments of conjugated and aromatic systems is the astonishingly large measure of agreement between them. This includes resonance energy, bond lengths, and charge distributions. When it is realized that the m.o. method almost completely neglects any electron-correlation (§ 6.4) and that the v.b. method grossly exaggerates it, there is some justification for accepting those common conclusions as correct. At the same time there are many minor matters, such as the small differences between bond lengths in the larger molecules, and other more important ones, such as the interpretation of u.v. spectra, in which the theories sometimes disagree, and in which we cannot say which is the more reliable.

There is one way in which these larger molecules differ from the diatomic molecules discussed in Chapter VI. We saw there that the inclusion of ionic structures in v.b. calculations, or configurational interaction in m.o. calculations, was able to convert the two theories into complete equivalence. With larger molecules this is still theoretically true: in practice it is quite impossible to include anything like sufficient structures, or configurations. In anthracene, for example, it is clearly impossible to include all the

429 covalent structures, even if we exploit to the full the symmetry of the molecule; and this neglects an even larger number of ionic structures. The choice of the particular structures to be included has to be made on the basis of chemical intuition, or mathematical convenience. There are many cases in which the choice is by no means as unequivocal as in benzene, particularly in view of the established fact that with larger and larger molecules the excited structures become progressively more important than the unexcited ones. It seems as if a definite limit is placed on the size of the molecule that may be dealt with conveniently. And even for small molecules the inclusion of ionic structures presents almost insuperable technical difficulties.

With the m.o. theory, on the other hand, it is relatively easy to introduce hetero-atoms: but it is far more difficult to deal properly with electron-correlation.[†] Some refinements in which this is explicitly included suggest that configurational interaction is more important than in the diatomic H_2 discussed in § 6.4. For that reason, if for no other, we cannot hope ever to make satisfactory *ab initio* calculations, and we must be content with general outlines such as those developed in this chapter. These outlines do, however, enable us to understand a very large part of the field of organic chemistry, and to organize it and correlate its different sections: they provide us with at very least a qualitative understanding of the essential processes at work. Taken as a whole, both the v.b. and m.o. approximations seem about equally good; and any theoretical conclusion cannot be regarded as substantiated unless it is predicted by both.[‡]

[†] See, for example, R. G. Parr, D. P. Craig, and I. G. Ross, *J. Amer. Chem. Soc.*, 1950, **18**, 1561; and P.-O. Löwdin, *Advances in Chemical Physics*, 1959, **2**, 207, Interscience Publishers.

[‡] The most complete account (for the period up to 1950) of the material discussed in this chapter is in the book *Les Théories Electroniques de la Chimie Organique* by B. and A. Pullman, 1952, Masson, Paris. For more recent ideas see R. Daudel, R. Lefebvre, and C. Moser, *Quantum-mechanical Methods and Applications*, 1959, Interscience Publishers.

LIGAND-FIELD THEORY†

10.1. d-electrons in the transition elements

IT is well known that the transition elements form a very wide variety of complexes. These vary from largely ionic compounds such as $[FeF_6]^{3-}$ to hydrated complexes such as $[Ti(H_2O)_6]^{3+}$. It seems almost inevitable that this wide variety of behaviour should be related in some way to the chief characteristic of the transition elements, that they all possess d electrons. Apart from Pauling's use of d orbitals to form hybrids, as discussed in § 8.12, we have not so far found them useful in the formation of bonds. This chapter, however, will be concerned with the behaviour of atoms having varying numbers of d electrons. It is important, therefore, that we should understand their distribution and properties in the gaseous atoms. After that we can see how this distribution is affected by the presence of surrounding groups—which we shall call ligands—placed around the atom in some definite pattern.

We saw in § 2.9 that there are five distinct d orbitals, so that in any shell an atom can accommodate not more than ten d electrons. As we pass from scandium to copper in the first long period we progressively fill up the $3d$ sub-shell. Thus the table below shows the electron distribution outside an argon-like core $(1s^2 2s^2 2p^6 3s^2 3p^6)$ when the atom is in its ground state. At the

Atom	K	Ca	Sc	Ti	V	Cr	Mn	Fe	Co	Ni	Cu	Zn
Electron distribution	s	s^2	ds^2	d^2s^2	d^3s^2	d^5s	d^5s^2	d^6s^2	d^7s^2	d^8s^2	$d^{10}s$	$d^{10}s^2$

beginning of this series the $4s$ electron (designated simply as s) is more stable than the $3d$ electron (designated simply as d). But as we move across the table the $3d$ electron drops relative to the $4s$ electron, though the energy differences are nowhere very large. Thus the mean size of the $4s$ and $3d$ charge-clouds must be similar at the beginning of the table: but at the end of the table, the

† For a fuller and excellent account of the material in this chapter see L. E. Orgel, *An Introduction to Transition-metal Chemistry*, 1960, Methuen.

d electrons are more compressed than the s ones. In neutral Fe, for example,† self-consistent-field calculations show that the outer maximum of the $4s$ orbital is about 4·5 times as far out from the nucleus as the maximum of the $3d$ orbitals. These latter orbitals have approximately the same size as the $3p$ orbitals, so in many respects they may be treated as if they belonged to an inner core, not greatly perturbed by chemical and other bonding. Thus‡ within the distance (about $2\cdot5a_0$) which represents one-half

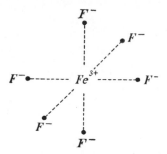

Fig. 10.1. Octahedral arrangement in $[FeF_6]^{3-}$.

of the interatomic distance in metallic iron, no less than 95 per cent. of the d-electron charge-cloud is to be found. In $[FeF_6]^{3-}$ (Fig. 1), therefore, it will be a reasonable approximation to think of a ferric ion Fe^{3+} with a total of five $3d$ electrons at the centre of an octahedron of six fluoride ions F^-. Similarly in the hydrated ferrous ion there will be six $3d$ electrons around the central atom: and in $[Cr(NH_3)_6]Cl_3$ these will be the three d electrons of Cr^{3+} surrounded by six neutral ammonia molecules.

10.2. Crystal-field, or electrostatic, splitting

In the isolated atom all five d orbitals have the same energy. But when the atom is perturbed, due to surrounding ligands, this is no longer true. It becomes of the greatest importance to know how the degeneracy is split. If the perturbation can be represented by an electrostatic field we can speak of this as electrostatic splitting. Such situations arise particularly in ionic crystals (e.g. NaCl which could be represented, as in Ch. XI, by Na^+Cl^-) and

---

† M. F. Manning and L. Goldberg, *Phys. Rev.*, 1938, **53**, 662.
‡ F. Stern, *Phys. Rev.*, 1956, **104**, 684.

it was in connexion with this that Bethe† first studied the splitting of orbitals of any symmetry type. For this reason it is frequently referred to as crystal-field splitting. Different crystal types give rise to electrostatic fields which possess different symmetries. The way in which the degeneracy of the d electrons is split depends on this symmetry. A knowledge of group theory is desirable in order to understand the details of all this; but we shall find that considerable progress is possible by the aid of a few simple pictorial concepts.

10.3. A simple example: the square planar complex

A simple example will show the way in which this is achieved. Let us consider (Fig. 2) a central atom with d orbitals placed

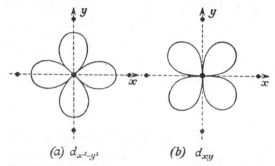

(a) $d_{x^2-y^2}$ (b) d_{xy}

FIG. 10.2. Splitting in a planar square complex. The outer dots denote the four ligands symmetrically placed along the x- and y-axes.

symmetrically between four ligands on the x- and y-axes. In all cases in which we shall be interested the ligands either possess a net negative charge (e.g. F^-) or align themselves so that a negative region of charge (e.g. oxygen in H_2O) is nearest to the central atom. Thus the electrostatic field will be such as to repel electrons from the directions of the x- and y-axes.

We must now choose the five appropriate d orbitals. Following the argument in § 2.9 we shall obviously take these to be $d_{x^2-y^2}$, d_{z^2}, d_{xy}, d_{yz}, d_{zx}. The unique z-axis almost forces the choice of d_{z^2}: and then the rest follows at once.

Fig. 2 (a) shows that in the $d_{x^2-y^2}$ orbital, all four lobes of

† H. Bethe, Ann. Physik, 1929, 3, 133. But the first molecular application appears to be by J. H. Van Vleck, J. Chem. Phys., 1935, 3, 807.

charge are unfavourably placed relative to the ligands, shown as large dots. So the energy of this orbital is raised very considerably by the electrostatic repulsion from the ligands. But in Fig. 2 (*b*) we can see that the d_{xy} orbital is rather less raised. The remaining three orbitals are scarcely affected, since their greatest concentrations of charge lie in regions remote from the perturbation. Calculations do not settle their order unambiguously, since this depends on the detailed shape of the *d*-orbital wave functions. But from

symmetry the d_{xz}, d_{yz} pair must always be degenerate. Thus the original five-fold degeneracy is split into one doublet level and three distinct singlet levels. The magnitudes of the splittings are proportional to the electrostatic field. But their ratios depend solely on the symmetry of the crystal field, and therefore only need to be calculated once for each type of symmetry, and each central atom. Fig. 3 shows this splitting diagrammatically.

One simple deduction can be made from Fig. 3. Since each orbital will accommodate two electrons, with paired spins, there should be a tendency for systems with eight or nine *d* electrons to form square planar complexes, though this tendency should be much greater when there are eight electrons than when there

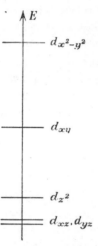

Fig. 10.3. *d*-electron energies in a planar square complex.

are nine. This is because, with eight or nine electrons, we can leave the unfavourable orbital $d_{x^2-y^2}$ either completely, or at least half, empty. An example of this tendency is in the nickel cyanide ion $[Ni(CN)_4]^{--}$ where, if we suppose it to be in the form $Ni^{++}(CN^-)_4$, we see that there are eight *d* electrons. The ion is square planar. But with Fe instead of Ni, there would only be six *d* electrons. As a result the ferrocyanide ion is $[Fe(CN)_6]^{4-}$, with an octahedral arrangement.† It is a general rule, however, that Ni, Pd, and Pt tend to form planar complexes when there are eight *d* electrons.

† But see § 11 for a reference to the role played by π electrons in stabilizing some of these complex ions.

10.4. Other symmetries

The most important geometrical symmetry found in molecular complexes is the octahedral one, as in Fig. 1. If we choose the directions from the central metal atom to the ligands as the x-, y-, z-axes, then our choice of d orbitals will be the same as in § 3. A simple diagram, similar to Fig. 2, shows that now the splitting is such that d_{xy}, d_{yz}, d_{zx} remain degenerate, and considerably lower in energy than d_{z^2}, $d_{x^2-y^2}$, which also remain degenerate. The fact that d_{z^2} behaves in the same way as $d_{x^2-y^2}$ can be seen if we realize (equation 2.23) that d_{z^2} is a linear combination of $d_{z^2-x^2}$ and $d_{z^2-y^2}$. Now by symmetry $d_{z^2-x^2}$ and $d_{z^2-y^2}$ must behave just as $d_{x^2-y^2}$. So any linear combination of them—and in particular d_{z^2}—must behave similarly.

This splitting into a triplet and a doublet can be proved by the use of group theory. The correct description is that

$$d_{z^2} \text{ and } d_{x^2-y^2} \text{ are of symmetry } e_g \quad \text{(sometimes } d\gamma\text{)}$$
$$d_{xy}, d_{yz}, d_{zx} \text{ are of symmetry } t_{2g} \quad \text{(sometimes } d\varepsilon\text{)} \quad (1)$$

We shall frequently have occasion to refer to them by their symmetry names—in which the subscript g has the same significance as in § 4.5, and in which we no longer need to distinguish between the x-, y-, and z-axes.

It is desirable to have some scale on which the changes of energy can be represented. In the octahedral case, as in all others, it is convenient to take the zero of energy in the perturbed system to be such that the centroid of all five d-levels remains unchanged as a result of the ligand field.[†] Since there are 3 lower levels and 2 upper ones, it follows that their separate displacements are in the ratio $2 : 3$. It has become conventional to represent the overall splitting either by the symbol Δ, or (in older work) by $10Dq$, where $Dq > 0$. We therefore say that the e_g levels are raised $6Dq$ ($= \frac{3}{5}\Delta$) and the t_{2g} levels are lowered $4Dq$ ($= \frac{2}{5}\Delta$).

Similar calculations may be made for other types of symmetry. Fig. 4[‡] shows the results for the main symmetries. This is an

---

[†] At this stage we are chiefly interested in the sequence of energy levels and their mutual separation. Their absolute positions are of less importance.

[‡] Adapted from J. S. Griffith and L. E. Orgel, *Quart. Rev.*, 1957, **11**, 381, and R. G. Pearson, *Chem. & Eng. News*, 1959, **37**, 72.

exceedingly important diagram, on which much of the rest of our discussion will depend.

The question may be asked: what would have happened if we had not used the particular choices of axes, and hence of d orbitals, shown in Fig. 4? The answer to this question is that if we had

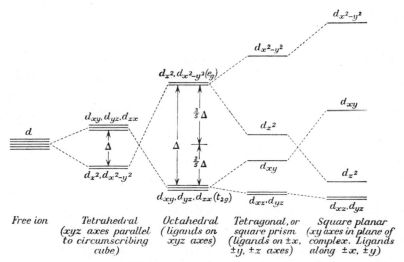

Fig. 10.4. Approximate d-electron energies in fields of different symmetries.

chosen quite different directions for the five fundamental d orbitals, we should have had to consider linear combinations of these orbitals, and when the detailed analysis was carried through, we should have found that we had been led to those particular combinations corresponding to equation (1) for the octahedral group, and similarly for the others in Fig. 4. It is fortunate, however, that by simply drawing diagrams such as those of Fig. 2, we were able to avoid recourse to the full mathematical techniques of group theory.

10.5. The spectrochemical series

Experimentally most Δ-values lie in the range

$$10,000 < \Delta < 30,000 \text{ cm}^{-1}.$$

Since 8,068 cm^{-1} is approximately 1 eV, this means that usual values of Δ are in the range from 1 to 4 eV. It would be very nice if we could make absolute calculations of this crystal-field splitting. Unfortunately this is not possible—nor would it be sufficient, even if we could do it. It is not possible since even now our knowledge of the sizes of d orbitals in complex atoms is still very incomplete, and our power of calculating the polarizability of an orbital is yet smaller! It is reasonable enough to argue, for example, that since the core in Na^+ is much more compact than in Au^+, therefore the polarizability is smaller. But this does not distinguish between the d electrons in Fe and Ni, since in these atoms the d electrons lie well inside the outer shell of electrons. Nor, indeed, would it be sufficient to know the numerical value of Δ, as we shall see later, since other effects beside the purely electrostatic crystal-field splitting play a part in the complete electronic description.

It has been found empirically that many of the more frequent ligands can be arranged in a series such that Δ increases as we pass along this series. The precise values of Δ depend, of course, on the choice of central metal atom, but the spectrochemical series,† as it is called, is almost independent of this choice. The order of increasing Δ is

I^-, Br^-, Cl^-, F^-, C_2H_5OH, H_2O, NH_3, ethylenediamine, NO_2^-, CN^-

The most effective means for measuring Δ is from a study of the energy required to excite an electron from one of the d-levels to another. The wavelength of light absorbed frequently lies in the visible region, a situation responsible for the colour of many of these complexes. Perhaps the simplest example is the aquo-complex of titanium, $[Ti(H_2O)_6]^{3+}$. Here the central metal atom has just one d electron, in an octahedral environment, so that the lowest state (see Fig. 4) should be the triply-degenerate t_{2g} level. Excitation of this to the doubly-degenerate e_g level should require energy Δ, and be associated with an absorption frequency ν, where $\Delta = h\nu$. Experiments show a band at 5,000 A, i.e. 20,000 cm^{-1}, which may be shown to arise from this transition $t_{2g} \to e_g$. Thus $\Delta = 20,000$ cm^{-1} approximately. With more than one d electron, there are other factors to be considered, as will appear later: but the essence of the method is the same.

† R. Tsuchida, *Bull. Chem. Soc. Japan*, 1938, **13**, 388.

It may be mentioned that, partly on account of their larger size and greater polarizability, values of Δ for the second and third transition series (involving the $4d$ and $5d$ orbitals respectively) are 40 to 80 per cent. larger than for the first transition series (involving $3d$ orbitals).

10.6. Strong and weak fields: high and low spin

We must now look at some of the additional factors that arise when more than one d electron is involved. For the present we shall neglect all interaction with the ligands other than that represented by a crystal field of appropriate symmetry. Later we shall relax this restriction.

Consider first the octahedral vanadium complex $[V(H_2O)_6]^{3+}$ in which we represent the central atom as V(III) or V^{3+}. Neutral vanadium has five valence electrons; so V^{3+} has two. According to Fig. 4 we must put these two electrons into the three lowest t_{2g} levels. According to Hund's rules (p. 35) they should go into different members of the degenerate set, and should have parallel spins. In the corresponding chromium complex $[Cr(H_2O)_6]^{3+}$ with three d electrons we shall expect one in each of the three t_{2g} orbitals, and with parallel spin. Since each electron carries a magnetic moment of $\frac{1}{2}$ Bohr magneton, this means that these two complexes will appear to have magnetic moments of 1 and $1\frac{1}{2}$ units respectively. But when we come to the fourth d electron, as in $[Cr(H_2O)_6]^{++}$ involving Cr(II), it is not clear whether we should put it in one of the t_{2g} orbitals, with opposite spin to the previous three electrons; or whether it is better to put it in one of the e_g orbitals. It is true that this orbital lies higher than the t_{2g} orbitals, by an amount Δ, but if Δ is not too big, we may regain this energy by separating the electrons as much as possible and keeping their spins parallel. For then their mutual Coulomb repulsion is small, and their exchange interaction lowers the total energy. It all depends on the magnitude of Δ. If Δ is small we continue by putting up to two further electrons in the e_g orbitals—all with parallel spin—and then, when the number of d electrons exceeds five, we begin to complete the t_{2g} levels with opposed spins. If Δ is large we complete the t_{2g} sub-shell before starting the e_g sub-shell. In the first case the spin has a high value: in the second it has a low one. This is the origin of the terms high-spin and low-spin complexes. Table 23 shows the two situations, and the resultant spin. In general, for a given metal atom high-spin complexes are associated with small Δ, and low-spin complexes with large Δ.[†] In the case of $[Cr(H_2O)_6]^{++}$, which we mentioned earlier, the fourth electron goes into the e_g orbital ($\Delta = 14,000$ cm^{-1}) leading to a high-spin complex. But in the case of $[Co(H_2O)_6]^{3+}$ with six $3d$ orbitals in Co(III) we have a low-spin complex represented by t_{2g}^6. Table 23 shows that it is

TABLE 23. *Spins in octahedral complexes*

No. of d electrons	Arrangement in weak-field high-spin case (t_{2g} ⋯ e_g)		Result-ant spin	Arrangement in strong-field low-spin case (t_{2g} ⋯ e_g)		Result-ant spin
1	↑		$\frac{1}{2}$	↑		$\frac{1}{2}$
2	↑ ↑		1	↑ ↑		1
3	↑ ↑ ↑		$1\frac{1}{2}$	↑ ↑ ↑		$1\frac{1}{2}$
4	↑ ↑ ↑	↑	2	↑↓ ↑ ↑		1
5	↑ ↑ ↑	↑ ↑	$2\frac{1}{2}$	↑↓ ↑↓ ↑		$\frac{1}{2}$
6	↑↓ ↑ ↑	↑ ↑	2	↑↓ ↑↓ ↑↓		0
7	↑↓ ↑↓ ↑	↑ ↑	$1\frac{1}{2}$	↑↓ ↑↓ ↑↓	↑	$\frac{1}{2}$
8	↑↓ ↑↓ ↑↓	↑ ↑	1	↑↓ ↑↓ ↑↓	↑ ↑	1
9	↑↓ ↑↓ ↑↓	↑↓ ↑	$\frac{1}{2}$	↑↓ ↑↓ ↑↓	↑↓ ↑	$\frac{1}{2}$
10	↑↓ ↑↓ ↑↓	↑↓ ↑↓	0	↑↓ ↑↓ ↑↓	↑↓ ↑↓	0

only for the cases of $d^4 - d^7$ that the high-spin and low-spin situations differ. This magnetic criterion for distinguishing these two situations was recognized very early as being of the greatest importance.[‡]

[†] For this reason the two types of complex have sometimes been called weak-field and strong-field complexes.

[‡] L. Pauling, *Nature of the Chemical Bond*, Cornell Univ. Press, 2nd edn., 1960, chap. 5.

A particular example of the distinction between high-spin and low-spin complexes is illustrated in Fig. 5† which shows the crystal-field splittings in two different octahedral complexes of the ferric ion. In the fluoride, with small Δ, we have a high-spin complex; but in the cyanide, with large Δ, a low-spin complex.

There are two other effects of a purely electrostatic crystal-

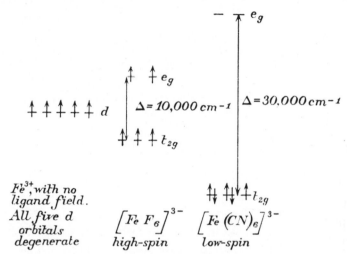

FIG. 10.5. *d*-orbital splitting in octahedral complexes of the ferric ion.

field which must be briefly mentioned. Both have the result of complicating the simple picture just described. In the first, called spin-orbit coupling, we notice that there is an interaction between the magnetic effect of the electron in its orbit (orbital magnetic moment) and the spin. In the case of a single electron, such as our previous example of Ti(III) as in $[Ti(H_2O)_6]^{3+}$, spin-orbit interaction lifts the degeneracy of the t_{2g} levels. Fortunately, however, this splitting is not usually large except for heavy atoms.‡ The second effect is known as the Jahn–Teller effect.§ These authors showed that in symmetrical non-linear molecules, a system cannot remain in equilibrium in an orbitally-degenerate state, but will inevitably distort in such a way that the degeneracy is lifted. The

† Taken from R. S. Nyholm, *Records of Chem. Prog.*, 1958, **19**, 45.
‡ For a full account see E. U. Condon and G. H. Shortley, *Theory of Atomic Spectra*, Cambridge Univ. Press, 1951.
§ H. A. Jahn and E. Teller, *Proc. Roy. Soc.*, A, 1937, **161**, 220.

case of Ti(III) will serve as an illustration.† Here the single electron is in a triply-degenerate orbital level t_{2g}. The result is an unstable system, which distorts in such a way that the octahedron is compressed or extended along the x-, y-, or z-direction. Fig. 6 shows how one of the three t_{2g} levels separates out below the others. Fortunately this effect also is usually quite small.

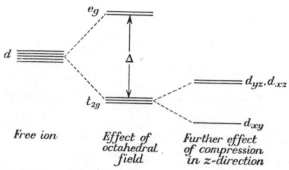

FIG. 10.6. Jahn–Teller splitting of a d-level (t_{2g}) in an octahedral field.

10.7. Ligand-field theory

Our discussion has hitherto been entirely in terms of the crystal field provided by the ligands. No other participation of ligand electrons has been considered. But this is a serious omission, since there are many cases where electrons from the ligands take part in some form of covalent bonding to the central metal atom. There are two ways in which this bonding takes place, via σ-bonds and via π-bonds. Since the σ-bond contribution is usually the more important we shall discuss it first.

Our problem may be put in the following way. Given that there are five d orbitals on the metal atom, and one orbital on each of the ligands, what molecular orbitals can be formed from their linear combination? The ligand orbitals will be taken to have axial symmetry relative to the directions joining each ligand to the metal atom. In the case of the fluoride ion, as in $[FeF_6]^{3-}$, represented in Fig. 1, the σ orbital is the $2p\sigma$ fluorine orbital whose axis lies along the line joining the Fe and F nuclei. In the case of the cobaltammines, such as $[Co(NH_3)_6]^{3+}$, the σ orbitals are the

† A. Carrington and H. C. Longuet-Higgins, *Quart. Rev.*, 1960, **14**, 427.

lone-pair hybrids of each ammonia molecule, as described in § 8.10. In the case of a chelating ligand such as ethylenediamine, $NH_2.CH_2.CH_2.NH_2$, which occupies two of the coordinating sites (see Fig. 7), the ligand orbitals are the lone-pair orbitals of the two

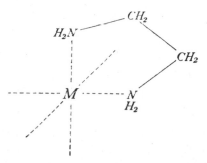

FIG. 10.7. The chelating property of ethylenediamine.

end nitrogen atoms. The m.o.'s that we are now going to form will obviously be completely delocalized, so that, from the mathematical point of view, we have a situation similar to that dealt with in Chapter IX, where we formed delocalized m.o.'s for aromatic and conjugated molecules. The difference now is that each separate ligand orbital has local σ-character, and not π.

Let us return to the case of a square planar complex represented in Fig. 2. We want to know how to combine four ligand orbitals in such a way that these combinations may have the right symmetry to combine with suitable s, p, d orbitals on the central atom. This is a problem that is very easy to solve by the methods of group theory.† But we have already met a simple case of this problem in our m.o. description of water (p. 168) where the ligand orbitals are the two $1s$ orbitals of the hydrogen atoms, H_1 and H_2. We found that the only allowed combinations were $H_1 \pm H_2$. Of these, $H_1 + H_2$ had the right symmetry to combine with one of the $2p$ orbitals of the central oxygen atom, and $H_1 - H_2$ with a different $2p$ orbital. The third $2p$ orbital of oxygen could not combine with any of the hydrogen orbitals. This discussion provides the clue for our planar square complex.

† See, for example, J. H. van Vleck, *J. Chem. Phys.*, 1933, **1**, 181, 219; J. H. van Vleck and A. Sherman, *Rev. Mod. Phys.*, 1935, **7**, 168 (especially p. 219).

Let us define the ligand orbitals in such a way that each of them is positive in the region where they approach the central atom.

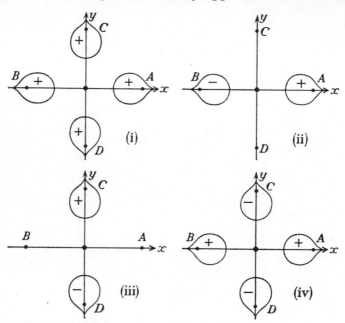

FIG. 10.8. Correct combinations of ligand orbitals (σ-type) for a planar square complex. The correct symmetry labels are (i) a_{1g}, (ii) e_u, (iii) e_u, (iv) b_{1g}.

Then if, as in Fig. 8, we refer to these ligand orbitals as A, B, C, D we can see that the allowed combinations are as follows:

(i) $A+B+C+D$, which has the full symmetry of the complex, and will combine with a central s orbital;

(ii) $A-B$, which has the same symmetry as a p_x orbital at the centre, and will therefore combine with it;

(iii) $C-D$, which has the same symmetry as a p_y orbital at the centre, and will therefore combine with it;

(iv) $A+B-C-D$, which has the same symmetry as a central $d_{x^2-y^2}$ orbital (see Fig. 2a), and will combine with it.

On account of the almost zero overlap between A, B, C, D the energies of these four combinations of $A...D$ will all be the same, and effectively equal to that of A alone. The correct group-theory designations of these four combinations, which will also

apply to the m.o.'s formed by them, are shown in Fig. 8. Thus
we have m.o.'s of the following forms:

$$\{A+B+C+D\}+\lambda_1 s+\lambda_2 d_{z^2} \qquad \text{Symmetry } a_{1g}$$

$$\left.\begin{array}{l}\{A-B\}+\mu p_x \\ \{C-D\}+\mu p_y\end{array}\right\}\text{Symmetry } e_u$$

$$\{A+B-C-D\}+\nu d_{x^2-y^2} \qquad \text{Symmetry } b_{1g}$$

$$\left.\begin{array}{l}d_{xz} \\ d_{yz}\end{array}\right\}\text{Symmetry } e_g$$

$$d_{xy} \qquad\qquad\qquad\qquad \text{Symmetry } b_{2g}$$

The numerical values of the coefficients λ, μ, ν must be found by
the use of the variation method. In each of the e_u and b_{1g} symmetries there will be two levels, one of which (see § 3.10) lies above
the higher of the energies of the separate halves, and the other
lies below the lower. We have also included in this table the central

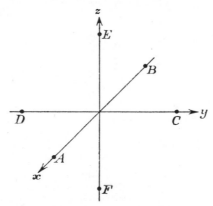

FIG. 10.9. Labelling of octahedral ligand orbitals.

atom orbitals d_{xy}, d_{yz}, d_{zx}, though they have the wrong symmetry
to combine with the hydrogens: and we have added d_{z^2} to the
a_{1g} line, since, as Fig. 2.10 shows, its symmetry is correct for
combination with $\{A+B+C+D\}$.

The octahedral situation can now be dealt with in the same way.
On account of its great importance we have listed in Table 24
the orbitals on the central atom, and the particular combinations
of the ligand groups A, B,...F (Fig. 9) with which an LCAO
molecular orbital can be built. We may now form these linear

combinations. A typical situation is shown in Fig. 10, where the metal orbitals are on the left, the ligand group-orbitals are on the right, and in the middle there are the full molecular orbitals. Since the ligand orbitals are usually more electronegative than the metal orbitals, we have drawn the right-hand energy level below any of the left-hand ones.

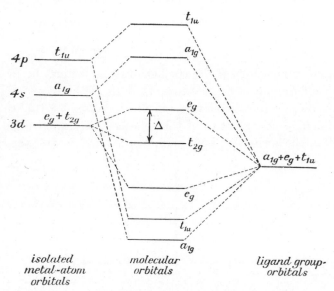

FIG. 10.10. Formation of molecular orbitals in octahedral complexes, energy being measured upwards.

a-type are non-degenerate
e-type are doubly-degenerate
t-type are triply-degenerate.

We can now see how the new diagram in Fig. 10 modifies the picture previously presented in Fig. 4. Formerly we considered only the d electrons in the central atom: but now we include the ligand electrons, and also s and p electrons of the metal. There are normally two electrons in each ligand orbital $A...F$, so that, according to Fig. 10, they will completely fill the three lowest molecular orbitals. (On account of their degeneracy, it can be seen that there is accommodation for exactly 12 electrons in the a_{1g}, t_{1u} and e_g molecular orbitals.) But these 'ligand' electrons have migrated partly into the metal-atom orbitals $3d$, $4s$, $4p$. And, of

TABLE 24. *Molecular orbitals in the octahedral group*

Central atom orbital	Appropriate combination of ligand σ orbitals	Group symmetry name	Appropriate combination of ligand π orbitals
s	$A+B+C+D+E+F$	a_{1g}	none
p_x	$A-B$		$C_{\pi x}+D_{\pi x}+E_{\pi x}+F_{\pi x}$
p_y	$C-D$	t_{1u}	$A_{\pi y}+B_{\pi y}+E_{\pi y}+F_{\pi y}$
p_z	$E-F$		$A_{\pi z}+B_{\pi z}+C_{\pi z}+D_{\pi z}$
$d_{x^2-y^2}$	$A+B-C-D$	e_g	none
d_{z^2}	$-\{A+B+C+D\}+2\{E+F\}$		
d_{xy}			$A_{\pi y}-B_{\pi y}+C_{\pi x}-D_{\pi x}$
d_{yz}	none	t_{2g}	$C_{\pi z}-D_{\pi z}+E_{\pi y}-F_{\pi y}$
d_{zx}			$A_{\pi z}-B_{\pi z}+E_{\pi x}-F_{\pi x}$

course, the previous purely-metal orbitals such as t_{2g} and e_g will now involve a fraction of the ligand orbitals. Thus the separation Δ, which is marked in the figure, is not quite the same as before. It is much more difficult to calculate this Δ, since both metal-atom and ligand orbitals are involved. However, if, as often happens, the ligand orbitals lie a long way below the metal-atom orbitals, these e_g and t_{2g} orbitals will correspond quite closely with those calculated on the electrostatic crystal-field basis.

Diagrams such as that of Fig. 10 may be drawn for each type of symmetry represented in Fig. 4. They enable the allocation of electrons to be made to the various orbitals. Further, the distinction between strong-field and low-field complexes is unaffected by the inclusion of the ligand orbitals.

The theory just described is usually known as ligand-field theory, to distinguish it from the less accurate but simpler electrostatic crystal-field theory, with which we started.

10.8. Relation with Pauling's octahedral hybrids

We are now in a position to relate our ligand-field theory description of an octahedral complex to the hybridization theory of Linus Pauling, which we outlined in § 8.12. Let us consider the ferricyanide $[Fe(CN)_6]^{3-}$ of page 227 as our example. In the third line of Fig. 8.19 we supposed that the Fe^{3-} ion was in the form

$$\underbrace{d_{xy}{}^2 d_{yz}{}^2 d_{xz}}_{\text{remaining atomic}} \quad \underbrace{d_{z^2} d_{x^2-y^2} s\, p_x p_y p_z.}_{\text{forming octahedral hybrids}}$$

The first three d orbitals, holding five electrons, remained atomic. Their group-theory label is t_{2g}. The remaining d^2sp^3 atomic orbitals formed six octahedral hybrids, which then formed σ-bonds with the ligand orbitals. If these σ-bonds were pure covalent, we should have $Fe^{3-}(CN)_6$; if they were pure ionic, we should have $Fe^{3+}(CN^-)_6$. In view of the high electronegative character of the CN group as compared with Fe we expect the latter to be more nearly correct. If it were indeed absolutely correct, we should have the case of an electrostatic crystal field, and it would not be very reasonable to begin our description in terms of octahedral Fe hybrids, and then find them to be of no use. Ligand-field theory, however, automatically allows for the right amount of polarity, which will usually be fairly high. It seems, therefore, a more sensible description. But of course the two descriptions agree in predicting that the remaining atomic d electrons are of type d_{xy}, d_{yz}, d_{zx}, subsequently becoming t_{2g} in the presence of the octahedral field. There is, however, this difference, that if in the simple Pauling theory the d_{z^2}, $d_{x^2-y^2}$ metal orbitals are used in the formation of covalent bonds, they will not be available to be the e_g levels at height Δ above the t_{2g}. In the ligand-field theory they exist very naturally, being largely metal $3d$ orbitals, but with a small amount of ligand orbitals mixed with them. It is possible to modify the resonating-bond picture so that these e_g orbitals appear; but this destroys the simplicity of that picture. Our general conclusion, therefore, is that the low-lying ligand-field theory orbitals $a_{1g}t_{1u}e_g$ are the counterpart of the Pauling octahedral hybrid bonds, but no simple explanation is provided in this latter account for the presence of the ligand-field e_g orbitals, or for the delocalization of the magnetic electrons t_{2g} on to the six ligands. For these reasons the ligand-field theory description is to be preferred.†

10.9. π-bonding with the ligands

We have so far dealt only with σ-bonding between the metal atom and the ligands. But quite evidently there will be π-bonding also. Fig. 11 shows one type of π-bonding in the planar square complex. It is clear from this diagram that the combination of

† J. S. Griffith and L. E. Orgel, *Quart. Rev.*, 1957, **11**, 381, and particularly pp. 391–2.

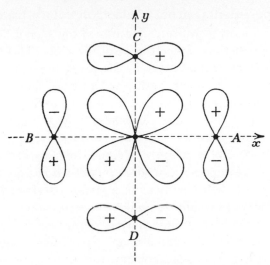

Fig. 10.11. An example of π-bonding in square complexes. The central atom orbital is d_{xy}, which overlaps strongly with the appropriate combination of π orbitals $A \cdots D$.

ligand orbitals

$$A_{\pi y} - B_{\pi y} + C_{\pi x} - D_{\pi x}$$

is of precisely the right symmetry to overlap strongly with d_{xy} of the central atom. Reference to page 289 will show that d_{xy} was one of the atomic orbitals, with symmetry b_{2g}, not previously used in a delocalized m.o. But now it becomes at least partly delocalized. Similar descriptions apply to the other orbitals. We show, in the last column of Table 24, those combinations of π ligand-orbitals which combine with p and d central atom orbitals in octahedral complexes. Since, however, this π-bonding, already referred to on page 286, complicates the analysis without adding anything essentially new, we shall not describe any further the nature of the resulting modifications to Fig. 10. Its most important application so far lies in the cyanide and carbonyl complexes. For further details the reader is referred to the books by L. E. Orgel† and J. S. Griffith,‡ and to two important conference reports.§

† Loc. cit.
‡ *The Theory of Transition Metal Ions*, Cambridge, 1961.
§ *Rep. 10th Solvay Conference*, Brussels, 1956; *Faraday Society Discussions*, 1958, no. 26.

10.10. Experimental proof of electron delocalization

One of the most significant features of our ligand-field description is the prediction of electron delocalization. This occurs from the ligands to the metal atom in the low-lying $a_{1g}t_{1u}e_g$ levels, all of which are doubly-filled; and it occurs from the metal atom to the ligands in the partly-filled sub-shells t_{2g} and e_g (Fig. 10). As Table 24 shows, the t_{2g} m.o. consists mainly of a metal d orbital, which, however, borrows π orbitals from the ligands; similarly the e_g borrows only σ orbitals. Fortunately, by the use of very high accuracy techniques in modern physics, it has proved possible to confirm these delocalizations in a striking fashion.† There are three chief ways in which this is done.

When there is both orbital motion giving rise to tiny electrical currents, with their associated magnetic moments, and also electron spin, with its magnetic moment, the ratio of the total angular momentum and the total magnetic moment obtained by summing the orbital and spin contributions, has a value, called the Landé splitting factor, or g-value, which can be determined spectroscopically. Now if a d electron spends only a fraction of its time on the central atom, it will contribute correspondingly less to the orbital moment. The g-value will then change. By measuring the g-value it is possible to work backwards to the distribution of the magnetic electrons. Thus in the case of the $[\mathrm{IrCl_6}]^{--}$ ion, where the central atom has a low-spin configuration t_{2g}^5, the π electrons of the ligand chloride ions will partly flow into the hole in the t_{2g}^6 shell. It seems‡ that this 'hole' is about 68 per cent. on the Ir atom and 32 per cent. on the Cl atoms.

The second proof of delocalization comes from the ligand hyperfine structure. For if, in the previous example, there is a deficit of π electrons around the chlorine atoms, there will be a resultant electron spin around each ligand. Thus there will be interaction between the spin of the 'hole' and the spin of the chlorine nuclei, giving rise to a hyperfine structure superposed upon the main iridium hyperfine structure. When this situation is properly un-

---

† See A. Carrington and H. C. Longuet-Higgins, *Quart. Rev.*, 1960, **14**, 427, for references. ‡ K. W. H. Stephens, *Proc. Roy. Soc.* A, 1953, **219**, 542; E. Cipollini, J. Owen, J. H. M. Thornley and C. Windsor, *Proc. Phys. Soc.*, 1962, **79**, 1083.

ravelled† it appears that the distribution of the hole is about 74 per cent. on the Ir atom and 26 per cent. on the Cl atoms. This figure differs from the g-value estimate, but no significance attaches to this since the calculation in both cases depends on wave functions which are not known very exactly.

Finally, if magnetic electrons migrate from the metal atom to the ligands, there will be a smaller effective net magnetic moment near the metal nucleus, and so there will be a reduced interaction with the magnetic moment of the nucleus. Such reductions have been found experimentally: they reveal themselves in a smaller hyperfine spacing of the observed transition energies than if the whole of the magnetic electrons had been around the central nucleus.

These techniques are essentially physical ones. But they amply confirm the general picture provided by our chemical arguments, particularly in the ground state of these complexes. Finally, further evidence of delocalization is obtained from a study of excited states, where, as Jorgensen has shown for a series of hexa-halide complexes,‡ there are strong absorption bands in the visible and near ultra-violet. These may be interpreted as due to charge-transfer transitions, where an electron originally chiefly in π orbitals on the six halide ions jumps into an orbital of d- or s-type chiefly concentrated on the metal atom. Fig. 10 shows that there will normally be vacant orbitals in one or both of the e_g and a_{1g} symmetries. Detailed analysis shows that they are used.

We must now leave this topic of ligand-field theory. But before doing so we may remind ourselves that the three concepts of d-orbital splitting, high- and low-spin complexes, and delocalization of ligand orbitals have brought a sense of order and pattern which was previously lacking in this important section of inorganic chemistry. And yet it is doubtful whether any one of these three concepts would have been developed without the simplifying ideas of wave mechanics. It must be regarded as one of the major triumphs of wave mechanics in the period 1945–60 that it has provided this enormous degree of understanding.

† J. H. E. Griffiths, J. Owen, and I. M. Ward, *Proc. Roy. Soc.* A, 1953, **219**, 526.
‡ C. K. Jørgensen, *Molec. Phys.*, 1959, **2**, 309.

10.11. π-electron ligands

Our previous complexes have been chiefly dependent upon the use of σ electrons for coordination. But in the last few years many new complexes have been discovered, in which the π electrons of molecules such as butadiene and benzene appear to be involved

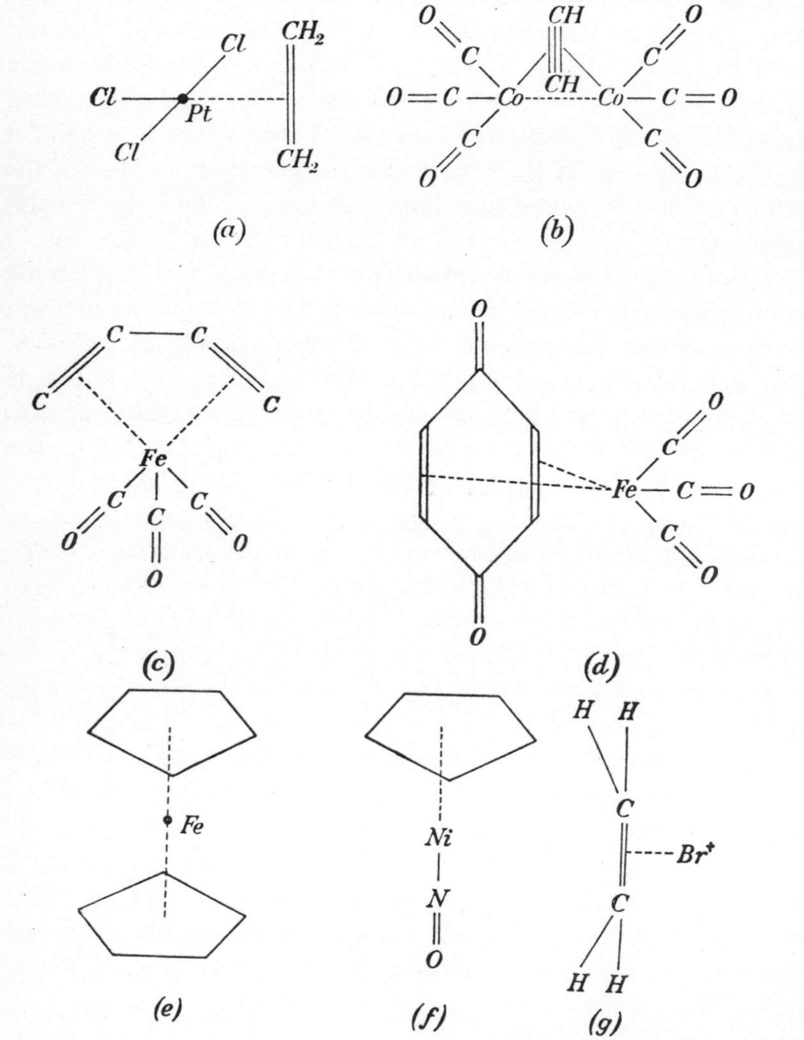

(a)

(b)

(c)

(d)

(e)

(f)

(g)

(a) $PtCl_3C_2H_4$ (b) $Co_2(CO)_6C_2H_2$ (c) $Fe(CO)_3C_4H_6$ (d) $Fe(CO)_3C_6H_4O_2$
(e) $Fe(C_5H_5)_2$ (f) C_5H_5NiNO (g) $C_2H_4Br^+$

in coordinate-link formation. Thus there is the ethylene complex (*a*) of platinum, the acetylene complex of dicobalt hexacarbonyl (*b*), the butadiene complex (*c*), and the *para*-benzoquinone complex (*d*) of $Fe(CO)_3$. One of the most interesting examples of these π-electron ligands is dicyclopentadienyl iron (*e*), now called ferrocene.[†] This substance forms orange crystals, which are sufficiently stable to permit vaporization without decomposition.

The two cyclopentadienyl rings are not necessary for coordination as is shown by the existence of (*f*). There is obviously a close parallel between the ability of π electrons in these molecules to act as ligand orbitals in a complex, and the formation of so-called π-complexes[‡] such as between ethylene and Br^+ (*g*), which are postulated as intermediates in many chemical reactions.

There is no great difficulty in understanding some of these molecules. Thus in (*a*) and (*g*) we may suppose that the double-streamer charge-cloud of the π-bond shown in Fig. 4.9 is distorted in such a way (Fig. 12) as to overlap more effectively with the metal atom. There will be certain small compensating changes, since the sharp division into σ and π electrons in ethylene was dependent upon the plane of symmetry, now removed. Thus in the butadiene[§] complex (*c*) all three C—C distances appear to be almost equal, with a value 1·45 A corresponding to relatively little

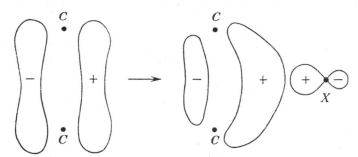

FIG. 10.12. Schematic representation of change in π orbital on formation of a π-complex. *M* denotes the orbital of the metal atom.

† T. J. Kealy and P. L. Pauson, *Nature*, 1951, **168**, 1039; S. A. Miller, J. A. Tebboth, and J. F. Tremaine, *J. Chem. Soc.*, 1952, p. 632.

‡ See, for example, M. J. S. Dewar, *The Electronic Theory of Organic Chemistry*, Oxford Univ. Press, 1949.

§ O. S. Mills and G. Robinson, *Proc. Chem. Soc.*, 1960, p. 421.

double-bond character. Furthermore, in the acetylenic complex (*b*), there are two sets of double-streamer orbitals, and the geometry of the molecule is such that the centre of the C≡C triple bond lies off the line joining the two cobalt nuclei. Fig. 12 represents dona-

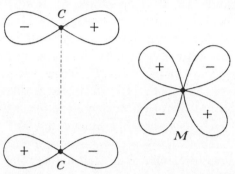

Fig. 10.13. Showing overlap between a metal *d* orbital and the empty anti-bonding π molecular orbital in a double bond.

tion of an electron from the olefine to the metal atom. But, as Fig. 13 shows, there may also be migration back to the empty anti-bonding π orbital of the double bond, which overlaps strongly with the appropriate *d* orbital on the metal atom. The situation is thus very similar to that which we described earlier in this chapter for octahedral and other similar molecular complexes. We shall not therefore discuss it further.

10.12. Sandwich molecules, ferrocene†

The dicyclopentadienyl iron molecule ferrocene (*e*) is not by

Fig. 10.14. Superposition of relevant sections of three-dimensional Fourier series to give composite picture of dicyclopentadienyl iron.

† A survey of the properties of ferrocene is given by P. L. Pauson, *Quart. Rev.*, 1955, **9**, 391. See also L. E. Orgel, *Introduction to Transition-Metal Chemistry*, Methuen, 1960, chap. 10.

any means unique. There is now a large family of these 'sandwich' molecules. Thus the Fe atom may be replaced by Ti, V, Cr, Mn, Co, Ni, Ru, Os, or Mg. And the five-membered cyclopentadienyl rings may be replaced (though not in every case) by 4, 6, 7, and 8 membered rings C_nH_n. It was originally supposed, in the case of ferrocene, that on account of the desire of the five-membered ring to establish an aromatic sextet, there would be charge migration, leading to $C_5H_5^-.Fe^{++}.C_5H_5^-$. But this cannot be correct, since the molecule behaves as a typical covalent compound. It is probable that the C_5H_5 rings are almost neutral since[†] the first acid dissociation constant of ferrocene dicarboxylic acid is the same as that of benzoic acid. On the other hand, in nickelocene $Ni(C_5H_5)_2$, where the central atom has two more d electrons, proton nuclear magnetic resonance spectra[‡] indicate that all the carbons are equivalent and carry a net charge of $0.14e$, leading to a Ni atom $Ni^{+1.4}$. This suggests that we should apply the principles of ligand-field theory to these complexes, forming molecular orbitals of appropriate symmetry by combination of the m.o.'s of the π electrons of each C_5H_5 ring, and also the s, p, d orbitals of the metal atom. Now we know from the X-ray analysis of Dunitz, Orgel, and Rich[§] (see Fig. 14) that the two C_5H_5 rings are parallel, with the metal atom lying symmetrically between them, and the rings in a staggered formation. As a result the molecule possesses a centre of symmetry. This latter property tells us at once that all our m.o.'s must have either u- or g-symmetry (p. 85).

Let us start[||] with the π orbitals of the two rings. There are only three bonding π m.o.'s for each ring, and we neglect completely the anti-bonding ones. Calling these I, II, III and I', II', III' as in Fig. 15, we see that there will be combinations of the form $I \pm I'$, $II \pm II'$, $III \pm III'$. Three of these six combinations will be g-type, and three will be u-type. In the iron atom we consider

---

† R. B. Woodward, M. Rosenblum, and M. C. Whiting, *J. Amer. Chem. Soc.*, 1952, **74**, 3458.

‡ H. M. McConnell and C. H. Holm, *J. Chem. Phys.*, 1957, **27**, 314.

§ J. D. Dunitz, L. E. Orgel, and A. Rich, *Acta Cryst.*, 1956, **9**, 373.

|| This follows closest to W. E. Moffitt, *J. Amer. Chem. Soc.*, 1954, **76**, 3386, but more detailed numerical estimates are due to R. E. Robertson and H. M. McConnell, *J. Phys. Chem.*, 1960, **64**, 70. A pictorial but only partly delocalized description is in J. W. Linnett, *Trans. Faraday Soc.*, 1956, **52**, 904.

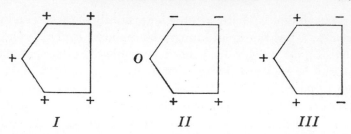

Fig. 10.15. The three bonding π m.o.'s in a cyclopentadienyl ring. The + and − signs show the sign of the coefficient c_r in the usual LCAO expression $\Sigma c_r \phi_r$. II and III are degenerate, with a higher energy than I.

only the $4s$ and the $3d$ orbitals, omitting the $4p$ as being energetically too high. Since both $4s$ and $3d$ are g-type, this tells us at once that the u-type combinations $I-I'$, etc., remain unaffected by the presence of the metal atom. Their energies will, therefore, be almost the same as the energies of I, II, and III (the last two are degenerate: compare equations (9.21 a) and (9.21 b) for benzene). This leaves us with the three g-type combinations $I+I'$, $II+II'$, $III+III'$ and the metal orbitals $4s$, $3d_{z^2}$, $3d_{x^2-y^2}$, $3d_{xy}$, $3d_{yz}$, $3d_{xz}$, in which the z-axis is the axis of molecular symmetry, and the y-axis lies from left to right across the page. The symmetry of the d orbitals is such that:

d_{xy}, $d_{x^2-y^2}$ cannot combine with any ring orbital (other than the high-energy ones, which we are neglecting),

d_{z^2} combines, but only rather weakly, with $I+I'$,

d_{yz} combines strongly with $III+III'$,

d_{xz} combines strongly with $II+II'$.

The last three of these are illustrated in Fig. 16. Just as in § 4.7 every combination of two orbitals gives rise to a bonding and an anti-bonding mixture. The result of all this is that the bonding levels will be:

$$I-I', \; II-II', \; III-III', \; d_{xy}, \; d_{x^2-y^2}, \; d_{z^2}+(I+I'),$$
$$d_{yz}+(III+III'), \; d_{xz}+(II+II'),$$

where the notation $d_{z^2}+(I+I')$ stands for a bonding combination of d_{z^2} and $(I+I')$, though not necessarily with equal weights. Including the metal atom $4s$ will lead to a mixing with $d_{z^2}+(I+I')$,

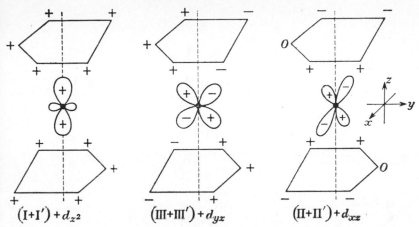

$$\left(\mathrm{I+I'}\right)+d_{z^2} \qquad \left(\mathrm{III+III'}\right)+d_{yz} \qquad \left(\mathrm{II+II'}\right)+d_{xz}$$

FIG. 10.16. Diagram showing overlapping of orbitals of different symmetries in ferrocene. But the numerical values of the LCAO coefficients will not be exactly ± 1.

which is the only m.o. with this symmetry, so that this level splits into two which we could write symbolically as

$$s+d_{z^2}+(\mathrm{I+I'}), \quad s-d_{z^2}+(\mathrm{I+I'}).$$

It is likely that the final order of levels is as shown in Fig. 17. The details of this diagram are not quite certain, and may well vary from molecule to molecule. But we notice that there are nine bonding m.o.'s, requiring eighteen electrons to fill them. Now there are exactly eighteen electrons in ferrocene, and in many of the most stable of these sandwich molecules. Indeed, it was on this basis of eighteen electrons that Longuet-Higgins and Orgel[†] made the proposal that the unstable π-electron molecule cyclobutadiene C_4H_4 could exist in the complex $C_4H_4.M.X_2$, where X is a univalent ligand and M is Ni, Pd, or Pt. This prediction was subsequently verified by Criegee and Schröder,[‡] who prepared the dimer of $C_4H_4.Ni.Cl_2$ and showed it had the expected structure. We can also see from Fig. 17 that the ferrocene molecule should be diamagnetic, but the cobalt analogue, with its extra electron in the anti-bonding level, should be paramagnetic and less stable. Nickelocene, with two additional electrons, will locate them in the degenerate orbital $(\mathrm{II+II'})-d_{xz}$, $(\mathrm{III+III'})-d_{yz}$,

[†] *J. Chem. Soc.*, 1956, p. 1969.
[‡] R. Criegee and G. Schröder, *Ann. der Chem.*, 1959, **623**, 1.

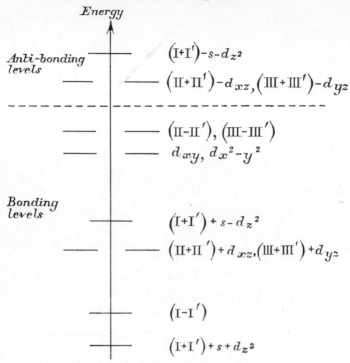

FIG. 10.17. Approximate location of m.o. energies in ferrocene-type molecules.

and so, by Hund's rules, should have resultant spin unity, on account of its two unpaired electrons. In this way we can understand the relative stabilities and magnetic properties of these complexes.

However, there are still some unsolved problems in this highly interesting field. One example is dibenzene chromium $Cr(C_6H_6)_2$, which has been prepared and an X-ray analysis of it made. This analysis shows that, although in ferrocene the C—C bonds in the five-membered ring are all equal, with a value $1.40+0.02$ A, in dibenzene chromium the bonds alternate in the manner of an isolated Kekulé structure, with lengths[†] 1.353 ± 0.014 and 1.439 ± 0.014 A. No explanation is available to show why this should be so.[‡]

[†] F. Jellinek, *Nature*, 1960, **187**, 871.
[‡] D. H. W. den Boer, P. C. den Boer and H. C. Longuet-Higgins, *Molec. Phys.*, 1962, **5**, 387.

XI

NON-METALLIC SOLIDS

11.1. The four main types of solid

OUR previous discussions have been concerned almost exclusively with molecules. Yet we may rightly expect that some at least of the principles applicable to separate molecules in the gas phase will also apply to solids. But before we attempt to make such application we must distinguish four main types of solid. We shall see that in every case the theory of valency so far developed contributes to our understanding. But new emphases appear in each successive type, and in the case of metals these are sufficiently important and novel to require a separate chapter. The four types of solid are:

(1) molecular crystals (and liquids);
(2) covalent crystals, with equal or similar atoms;
(3) ionic crystals;
(4) metallic conductors, and alloys.

These four classes are not absolutely clear-cut, and there are several intermediate types such as the hydrogen bond (Chapter XIII) which is intermediate between (1) and (3); or graphite, intermediate between (2) and (4). Some of these will be referred to in our subsequent discussion, but the classification (1)–(4) will serve most conveniently as the basis of our account. In a field as large as the Structure of the Solid State, this account cannot be anything like complete. Rather, our object must be to explain and justify the main principles which are effective.†

11.2. Molecular crystals

When a non-polar substance such as I_2 is cooled sufficiently, it crystallizes into a solid form. But X-ray studies show that the unit out of which the crystal is built is still the single diatomic molecule. It is true that as Fig. 1 shows, there is a definite scheme

† An excellent account of the experimental results is given by A. F. Wells, *Structural Inorganic Chemistry*, Clarendon Press, Oxford, 2nd edn., 1950.

in which the units are packed together, and it is equally true that the bond length is increased from 2·66 A in the gas to 2·68 A in the solid. But this distance is still much less than the least distance 3·54 A between atoms on adjacent molecules. It is quite evident that the forces responsible for the crystal formation are quite different from the valence forces responsible for each I_2 unit. They are thus van der Waals, or polarization, forces. Their weakness compared with valence forces is shown by the relatively low temperature at which melting takes place, and the small energies involved in melting and evaporation. In Cl_2, for example, where

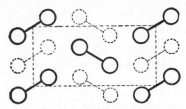

Fig. 11.1. The crystal of iodine, showing the presence of pairs of atoms formed by diatomic I_2 molecules. The dotted molecules lie below the plane of the solid molecules.

the same situation obtains, the heat of dissociation of the molecule is 57 kcal/mole which may be compared with 4–5 kcal/mole for the heat of sublimation.

Forces of this kind will have a tendency to be non-directional, so that the molecules will pack together as closely as possible. It is for this reason, of course, that the rare gases Ne, A, Kr,..., which are extreme examples of this phenomenon, crystallize in the way in which spheres can be packed together most tightly. In this cubic close-packing, each atom has twelve nearest neighbours. A similar arrangement exists for crystalline HCl, HBr, H_2S, CH_4, and in most of such systems, at temperatures not too far below the melting-point, the individual molecules are actually able to rotate. If, however, the shape of the molecule is very far from being spherical, as in benzene, the packing will still be such as to allow as many near neighbours as possible to each separate molecule. Fig. 2 shows what actually happens in benzene. The planes of the molecules are perpendicular to the plane of the paper, and

any one molecule (say the centre one of the figure) is surrounded
by twelve neighbours, four unshaded ones at the same horizontal
level, and four shaded ones above and below. By virtue of the two
directions in which the planes of the molecules lie, a closer packing
is possible than if all were parallel to the same plane. It is not
surprising that molecules of this kind show almost the same internal
vibrations in the solid, liquid, and gas phases. For the individuality

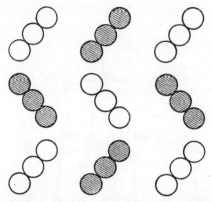

FIG. 11.2. The structure of crystalline benzene.
Each circle represents a CH group, the plane
of the molecule being perpendicular to the paper.
Shaded molecules are displaced both above and
below this plane through one-half of the unit
cell height.

of the molecules is always preserved, and the internal binding is
only very slightly weakened by the regular association in the
solid, or the irregular association in the liquid. The figures below
show how little change there is in two of the benzene frequencies.
A similar situation holds for all crystals of this class:

ν (gas)	ν (liquid)	ν (solid)
3099	3090	3089 cm^{-1}
3045	3035	3034 cm^{-1}

It is obvious that the theory of valence only exerts a minor influence on the structure of such crystals; the important factor is
essentially geometrical. Further, the chief distinction between the
liquid and the solid is the regular and permanent association in
the solid, to be contrasted with the largely random and constantly
changing association in the liquid.

11.3. Covalent crystals

The second class of crystals is termed covalent, because the forces that operate to maintain the structure are almost identical with those already explained for covalent binding. If, for example, we are told that a carbon atom, when hybridized in sp^3 style, can form four strong bonds at a tetrahedral angle, we must not be surprised that carbon atoms arrange themselves in an infinite tetrahedral pattern, such as diamond (Fig. 3). It is obvious that

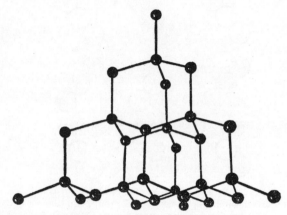

Fig. 11.3. An element of the diamond crystal, in which each carbon atom is surrounded tetrahedrally by four others.

each bond is effectively localized, just as in methane or a larger paraffin chain. Such solids are really little more than huge molecules. Since every atom is strongly bound to all its neighbours, these crystals will be very hard, with a very high melting-point and large latent heat. Silicon, germanium, and grey tin are of the same type as diamond. Carborundum (SiC) also has a tetrahedral arrangement around each atom, and again we can speak of effectively localized bonds, alternate atoms being C and Si. The difference in electronegativity of the two atoms is so small that these bonds are not significantly polar.

Tetrahedral structures of this kind are very open, and correspond to a large atomic volume (i.e. volume per atom). This is only possible if directional forces play a considerable part, thus providing further evidence that the bonds have an essentially molecular and valence character. In fact we may infer this type of binding whenever we find tetrahedral angles, even if, as in zinc sulphide ZnS, this may not be obvious on other grounds. In the case of ZnS it seems probable that each 'bond' is formed from sp^3 tetrahedral hybrids at both atoms. If such bonds were purely covalent, we should have a situation represented by $Zn^{--}S^{++}$; if they were purely ionic, we should have $Zn^{++}S^{--}$, though of course in this latter case it would not be easy to understand the open tetrahedral structure. It seems reasonable, therefore, to suppose that the bonds are partly covalent, partly ionic. Detailed calculations[†] suggest that the ionic character in this crystal—and in most other similar tetrahedral crystals—is such that the more electronegative element (here sulphur) carries a small excess of electrons, of the order of $e/3$. But the degree of covalency is sufficiently large for directional valence forces to determine the stereochemistry, and we can therefore speak of these as valence crystals. They are often referred to in terms of the group (or ordinal, see p. 182) number of the atoms involved. Thus diamond is IV–IV, and so is carborundum; but ZnS is II–VI, and the exceedingly important intermetallic semi-conductors such as GaAs or InSb are III–V. A related system, ZnO, which is of hexagonal close-packed type, shows[‡] the concentration of electrons along some of the Zn—O bonds just as would be expected for a model of covalent-ionic resonance.

There are other solids of this same general type, but with different geometrical shapes. For example, sulphur, which is by nature divalent, forms long chains with the characteristic valence angle of 105°, when it is heated to about 200° C (plastic sulphur). These chains contain essentially localized covalent S—S bonds, and the chains are held together partly by van der Waals polarization forces, and partly by the fact that when they are sufficiently long they may thread in and out of one another to give a disorderly 'matted' effect. Similarly (Fig. 4) crystalline Se and Te form parallel zigzag chains in which each atom has two neighbours, and SiS_2 consists of infinite chains of SiS_4 tetrahedra with weak van der Waals forces between the chains. There does not seem to be

† C. A. Coulson, L. Redei, and D. Stocker, unpublished calculations.
‡ H. M. James and V. A. Johnson, *Phys. Rev.*, 1939, **56**, 119.

any simple reason, however, why CS_2 remains molecular and does not form chains similar to SiS_2. This example reminds us that in solids various structures often differ by only a very small energy.

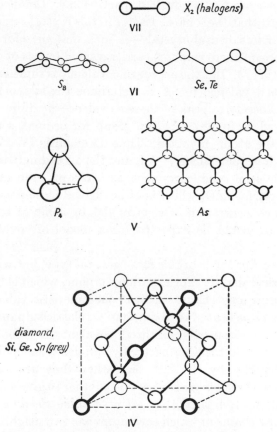

It is because of this that polymorphism is so common, a given substance existing in two or more forms according to the external

Fig. 11.4. Typical bonding in atoms of Groups IV–VII.

conditions of temperature and pressure. For the same reason it is much easier to understand a given structure *a posteriori* than to predict it in advance.

Arsenic is interesting in this connexion because it crystallizes in double layers (see Fig. 4) in which each As atom has three neighbours at a distance of 2·51 A. The distance between the layers is rather greater, 3·15 A, showing that though the bonds are almost as localized as in a molecule such as AsH_3, there is still a small degree of resonance involving inter-layer bonds. This particular solid is therefore intermediate between types (2) and (4 of § 1. Antimony and bismuth show a similar effect, but the

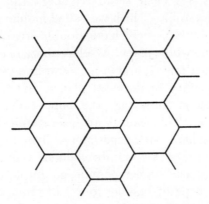

FIG. ·11.5. A layer of graphite, in which each carbon atom is surrounded trigonally by three others. Planes above and below are displaced one bond length relative to the first.

layers become closer together, indicating an increasing shift from localized bonds towards a metallic structure.

There are plenty of other examples of this covalent type of binding. They all illustrate what is called the $8-N$ rule. This is that each atom has $8-N$ nearest neighbours, where N is the ordinal number of the Periodic Group (i.e. 4 for C, 5 for N, etc.). It will be recognized that this is merely another version of the octet rule of molecular chemistry. The applicability of this rule to a crystal-line solid may be regarded as strong evidence that the bonds are localized ones, of molecular-valence character.

We have seen that the crystal structure of diamond results essentially from the tetrahedral hybridization of its sp^3 orbitals: confirmation is obtained from the fact that the interatomic distance 1·54 A is almost exactly the same as occurs in ethane and the heavier paraffins. It is a very natural step from here to associate the trigonal hybridization discussed for aromatic molecules in Chapter IX with graphite; and indeed the very structure of graphite (Fig. 5), in which each layer is built in hexagonal fashion, reminds one strongly of a set of huge aromatic compounds. The distance between successive planes is 3·35 A, a value so large that it can only arise from van der Waals forces. But within any one plane, there is a basic set of trigonal localized sp^2 σ-bonds; the remaining electrons—which we called mobile when discussing benzene in Chapter IX—will have double-streamer type m.o.'s extending over the whole plane. We have here reached a situation half-way towards a metal; and in fact graphite does show a small electrical conductivity in its basal planes, but not across them. Explicit calculations show that the bond order (§ 9.10) of the C—C bonds is 1·53. This leads to an interatomic distance 1·42 A, in complete agreement with experiment. Just as diamond represents the extension to an infinite solid of the type of binding found in saturated carbon compounds, so graphite represents the extension of the type of binding found in aromatic molecules.

We could, if we wished to do so, equally well describe graphite in terms of resonance between structures, both covalent and ionic. The chief difficulty in such a description is that there are far too many structures to enumerate, and we have reasons for believing that the more highly-excited ones are collectively the most important.

We have seen on page 307 that ZnS possesses a diamond structure, but is held together by both covalent and ionic forces. In the same way boron nitride BN forms a layer lattice (I) just like graphite. In this lattice the σ-bonds will be partly covalent and partly ionic, just as in ZnS, except that the hybrids are sp^2 trigonal rather than sp^3 tetrahedral. And the π electrons will have double-streamer type m.o.'s extending over the whole plane, just as in graphite. Here again we have a solid intermediate between types (2), (3), and (4) of § 1.

It is interesting to note that, just like carbon, boron nitride forms not only a layer lattice, but also a tetrahedral diamond-

like lattice, of great hardness.† All the electrons now form localized σ-type bonds, as in a typical III–V compound.

(I)

$$
\begin{array}{c}
\diagup \qquad \diagdown \\
\text{N—B} \qquad \text{N—} \\
\diagup \qquad \diagdown \qquad \\
\text{—B} \qquad \text{N—B} \\
\diagdown \qquad \diagup \\
\text{N—B} \qquad \text{N—} \\
\diagup \qquad \diagdown \qquad \diagup
\end{array}
$$

11.4. Ionic crystals

The third type of solid enumerated in § 1 occurs when the atoms
involved have very different electronegativities. The most out-
standing examples are the alkali halides where for the alkali atom
x is small and for the halide x is large. If the two atoms were

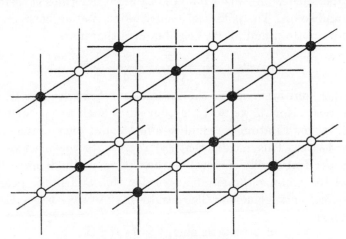

FIG. 11.6. The cubic crystal of NaCl. The open circles are Na atoms, the
closed circles are Cl atoms.

forming a diatomic aggregate the polarity would be great. Thus
in NaCl, $x_{Cl} - x_{Na} = 3 \cdot 0 - 0 \cdot 9 = 2 \cdot 1$, so that, according to (5.33)
the ionic character would be expected to be just under 50 per
cent. Now suppose, as actually occurs, that we may place Na
atoms and Cl atoms on adjacent corners of a simple cubic lattice,
as in Fig. 6. Then each sodium atom is under attraction from no
less than six neighbouring chlorines, and every chlorine from six

† R. H. Wentorf, *J. Chem. Phys.*, 1957, **26**, 956.

sodium atoms. It is almost inevitable to conclude that under such circumstances the solitary outer electron ($3s$) of each Na atom would be passed over to its neighbouring Cl atoms, with the result that the lattice was effectively composed of Na$^+$ and Cl$^-$ units. In such a lattice there would be little or no covalent bonding. We can make the contrast between the diatomic molecule and the infinite crystal more precise if we calculate the energies of Coulombic attraction between the charges in the two systems. If the interatomic distance is taken to be R in both cases, then the potential energy due to charges $\pm e$ in the molecule is simply $-e^2/R$. But in the crystal, any one central sodium atom with charge $+e$ is surrounded first with six chlorine atoms with charge $-e$ at distance R, and then by twelve sodium atoms with charge $+e$ at distance $\sqrt{2}R$, this is followed by eight chlorines at distance $\sqrt{3}R$, and so on. The potential energy of interaction between this one sodium atom and all its neighbours is therefore

$$-e^2\left\{6 \times \frac{1}{R} - \frac{12}{\sqrt{2}R} + \frac{8}{\sqrt{3}R} \cdots \right\}. \tag{1}$$

A similar sum arises from the interactions between one Cl and all the rest. Now if we add together sums such as (1) for every Na and every Cl atom we shall in effect count every interaction energy twice. This means that (1) represents the electrostatic energy per NaCl unit. Several mathematical methods have been devised for making the summations for this and other possible geometrical arrangements. The results may always be expressed in the form

$$\text{electrostatic energy} = -Ae^2/R, \tag{2}$$

where A has a value, here 1·75, depending on the crystal structure. Values of A for a few important structures are given in Table 25.

TABLE 25. *Values of the Madelung constant*

Structure	Example	A
Simple cubic . . .	NaCl	1·748
Body-centred cubic . .	CsCl	1·763
Fluorite	CaF$_2$	5·039
Wurtzite	ZnS	1·641
Rutile	TiO$_2$	4·816

In every case R is the closest anion-cation distance and the energy (2) refers to one stoichiometric molecule. The constant A is called the Madelung constant for a particular structure.†

It is obvious from this table that any tendency towards an ionic molecule will be considerably enhanced in the crystal, with the result that there is almost complete charge transfer. This transfer cannot, however, be quite complete. For we may regard the wave function for the whole crystal as a linear combination of ψ_{ion} representing the purely ionic state, and ψ_{cov} representing a set of covalent structures. The energy function will be stationary when a small, but non-vanishing, coefficient is attached to ψ_{cov}.

The above conclusion can be tested quite simply by a study of X-ray diffraction. X-rays are chiefly scattered by the electrons, so that the experimental scattering curves can be used to infer the charge distribution which was responsible for the scattering. Not only do we thus determine the crystal structure, but we can also estimate how many electrons are associated with each nucleus. In NaCl, for example, the total area under the radial distribution curve (§ 2.3) shows that 17·85 electrons are round the Cl atom. Neutral Cl would have 17 electrons, from which it follows that 0·85 of the valence electron in each sodium atom has migrated to the chlorine atoms. As a result the total electrostatic energy per NaCl is

$$-\frac{Ae^2}{R} \times (0\cdot85)^2,$$

with $A = 1\cdot75$. With the more electronegative fluorine, the degree of ionicity is even greater. Further confirmation of this interpretation of NaCl as effectively pure-ionic can be found from a study of the overlap integrals $\int \phi(Na^+)\phi(Cl^-)\, d\tau$, where $\phi(Na^+)$ and $\phi(Cl^-)$ are any pair of one-electron a.o.'s in Na^+ and Cl^-. The greatest value of any such integral is only 0·06, indicating an almost complete independence of the two ions so far as covalent bonding is concerned.

It appears from this discussion that a rough approximation when dealing with ionic crystals is to suppose that charge transfer

† For further details see J. Sherman, *Chem. Rev.*, 1932, **11**, 93.

is complete. In accurate work, however, we ought to distinguish five effects. These are:

(1) ionic contribution to the energy, measured by (2) with an appropriate charge distribution;

(2) residual covalent bond energy;

(3) polarization of the ions that are formed (e.g. Na^+, Cl^-). Of these, the anion is so much more polarizable than the compact cation that it alone needs to be considered;

(4) repulsive forces due to partial overlapping of adjacent charge-clouds. These forces are important, since otherwise the first (ionic) contribution would draw all the ions closer and closer together;

(5) zero-point vibrational energy. In § 3.4 we showed that every simple-harmonic oscillator has an energy at least equal to $\frac{1}{2}h\nu$, where ν is the frequency that would be expected on purely classical grounds. This energy is called the zero-point energy, since it is always present, even at the absolute zero of temperature. Now a crystal of N atoms will have $3N-6$ internal vibrations, each of which will contribute to the total zero-point energy of the system. In the table of energy values for H_2 near the end of Chapter I, we showed that this energy may amount to several per cent. of the bond energy. With heavier atoms the percentage is less, and can be estimated from the lattice frequencies.

A few comments on the above list of energy values is necessary. The first contribution has already been discussed, and the second one follows from bond energies if we already know the ionicity of the solid. In most calculations this is assumed, though often without complete justification, to be 100 per cent. The polarization contribution (3) is relatively small because the symmetry of the electric field around any one ion is very high, so that only a small residual polarization occurs. This is in contrast to a diatomic molecule, where the field around each atom is very far from symmetrical. In really accurate work a further energy related to this has to be included. This is the London dispersion force between the polarizable anions,† which varies as R^{-6} if the ions are several

† J. E. Mayer, *J. Chem. Phys.*, 1933, **1**, 270.

diameters apart. In those cases (see later) where the anions are actually in contact with each other, this energy becomes quite significant. There remain the repulsive forces (4). These forces fall off very rapidly at large distances, and careful quantum-mechanical calculations[†] suggest an exponential form $be^{-R/\rho}$, where b and ρ are two constants chosen so that (i) the minimum total energy occurs when R has the observed value and (ii) the correct compressibility is obtained. For the alkali halides we may put this in the form

$$ce^{-(R-r_1-r_2)/\rho}, \tag{3}$$

where $c = 4 \times 10^{-12}$ ergs, $\rho = 0.345$ A, and r_1, r_2 are ionic radii shown in Table 26. These values of r_1 and r_2 are rather smaller

TABLE 26. *Basic radii (A units) for use in equation* (3)

Li+	0·475	F-	1·110
Na+	0·875	Cl-	1·475
K+	1·185	Br-	1·600
Rb+	1·320	I-	1·785
Cs+	1·455		

than the conventional ionic radii which we shall describe later. An alternative form for the repulsive energy, used in early calculations, was b/R^n, with $n \sim 9$. When summing these repulsive forces, only nearest neighbours are really significant, though Lennard-Jones and Ingham[‡] have shown how to make the necessary summations over all the atoms. The way in which these various energies add up to give the observed lattice energy is

TABLE 27. *Binding energies in* NaCl

Electrostatic energy . . .	+8·92 eV
Polarizabilities	+0·13
Repulsion energy . . .	−1·03
Zero-point vibration energy .	−0·08
Total lattice energy (calc.) . .	+7·94 per NaCl unit.
(obs.) . .	7·98

† M. Born and J. E. Mayer, *Z. Phys.*, 1932, **75**, 1; J. E. Mayer and L. Helmholz, ibid., 1932, **75**, 19; M. L. Huggins and J. E. Mayer, *J. Chem. Phys.*, 1933, **1**, 643; M. L. Huggins, ibid., 1937, **5**, 143.

‡ *Proc. Roy. Soc.* A, 1925, **107**, 636.

shown for the case of NaCl in Table 27.† The agreement between theory and experiment is so astonishingly close that there can be no doubt regarding the essential validity of the interpretation. In general, agreement may be expected to within about 2 per cent. of the total lattice energy.

11.5. Ionic radii

The fact that in ionic crystals the separate atoms all acquire an inert rare-gas structure with closed electronic shells suggests that it should be possible to formulate a set of ionic radii such that the equilibrium distance between adjacent ions in such a crystal is approximately equal to the sum of the appropriate radii. Now as we have already seen for neutral atoms, no strict boundary exists for any atomic wave function. Yet the charge-cloud density does fall quite rapidly towards zero after a certain radial distance, and thus at least a relative estimate of effective radii may be obtained. Let us consider first univalent ions such as Na^+, Cl^- in which the net charge is $\pm e$. It follows from the explicit forms of the a.o.'s given in (2.18) that for electrons in the L-shell, $2/(Z-S)$ is a measure of the spread of the charge-cloud, where Z is the atomic number and S is the screening constant. The corresponding measure for electrons in the M-shell is $3/(Z-S)$. Now consider K^+ and Cl^-, both of which have an argon-like structure. In each case $S = 11.25$ so that $Z-S$ has the values 7.75 and 5.75 respectively. But the experimental KCl distance in the crystal is 3.14 A. If we divide this in the ratio of the values of $3/(Z-S)$ we find $r(K^+) = 1.33$ A, $r(Cl^-) = 1.81$ A. Proceeding in this way we obtain the set of univalent radii shown in Table 28.

TABLE 28. *Univalent crystal radii* (A)

Li+	0.60	H-	2.08
Na+	0.95	F-	1.36
K+	1.33	Cl-	1.81
Rb+	1.48	Br-	1.95
Cs+	1.69	I-	2.16

† See also P.-O. Löwdin, *Thesis*, 1948, Uppsala, for a slightly different and more refined partitioning of the total lattice energy. The experimental values for this and many other alkali halides are given in D. F. C. Morris, *Acta Cryst.*, 1956, **9**, 197.

With a few exceptions, to which we shall return in a moment, the interionic distance in the crystal is almost exactly equal to the sum of the appropriate entries in this table.

For divalent ions, or ions with larger valence, it is necessary to decrease the univalent radii, calculated as above, by a factor arising from the fact that the Coulomb forces increase as the square of the net charge. We shall be content to list a few important crystal radii in Table 29.† It will be noticed that the positive ions are always much smaller than the corresponding negative ions, and that the higher the positive charge, the smaller

TABLE 29. *Polyvalent crystal radii* (A)

Be^{++}	0·31	B^{3+}	0·20		
Mg^{++}	0·65	Al^{3+}	0·50	O^{--}	1·40
Ca^{++}	0·99	Sc^{3+}	0·81	S^{--}	1·84
Zn^{++}	0·74	Ga^{3+}	0·62		

is the ionic radius. It will also be seen that for given net charge the ionic radius increases with atomic number: the only exception to this rule occurs when, as in $Ca^{++} \rightarrow Zn^{++}$ or $Sc^{3+} \rightarrow Ga^{3+}$, the difference in atomic number is associated with the filling-up of inner d-shell orbitals.

The ionic radii given in Table 28 enable us to understand one important factor which determines the type of crystal structure with given atoms. This is the radius ratio of the ions. Suppose that, as in Li^+I^-, this ratio is much less than $\sqrt{2}-1 = 0·414$. (In Li^+I^- the ratio is actually $0·60/2·16 = 0·28$, but in Li^+F^- it is $0·60/1·36 = 0·44$). Then, as Fig. 7 shows, it is not possible for the positive and negative charges on adjacent corners of the fundamental unit cube to touch. Such contact as there is must be between the much larger anions. Consequently the interatomic distance is greater than the sum of the crystal radii (in LiI this is 3·02 A instead of the expected 2·76), and the positive cations fit into the interstices of the closely packed negative anions.

Another point arises in this connexion. So long as the ionic radii differ considerably the sodium chloride arrangement is the most stable for alkali-halide crystals. But when the radii become

† For further particulars see L. Pauling, *Nature of the Chemical Bond*, Cornell University Press, 3rd edn., 1960, chap. xiii.

more nearly comparable, as in CsCl (1·69 and 1·81 A respectively), the simple-cubic type of arrangement ceases to be the most effective way of packing, and the structure changes to the body-centred

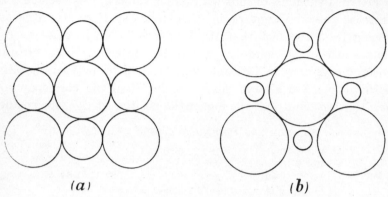

(a)   *(b)*

FIG. 11.7. The crystal structures of *(a)* LiF, and *(b)* LiI.

form shown in Fig. 8, where each ion is surrounded by as many oppositely charged ions as possible. In the caesium chloride lattice this is 8, instead of 6 as in the sodium chloride lattice. This

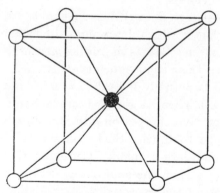

FIG. 11.8. The CsCl lattice. The open circles are Cs atoms, the closed circle is Cl.

situation applies to the chlorides, bromides, and iodides of caesium and rubidium.

We could summarize this discussion by saying that the crystal structure assumed by any given substance is chiefly determined by (a) the relative numbers of ions of each type, (b) the desire of ions of one kind to surround themselves with as many ions of different charge as possible, (c) the large repulsions that set in when the ions are closer together than the sum of their appropriate radii, and (d) the radius-ratio of the ions, which governs the most satisfactory way in which they can be packed together. Rules of this kind were developed first experimentally by Goldschmidt.

11.6. Ionic complexes

In our previous discussion we have treated the units as single atoms. But this is obviously not essential, and we could perfectly well suppose that they were complex ions such as CN^-, NO_3^- SO_4^{--}, or even larger units such as the ferricyanides and cobalt-ammines described in Chapter X. Here of course the assignment of a definite radius may not be possible if the complex is very un-symmetrical (e.g. the azide N_3^- which is linear, or the carbonate CO_3^{--} which is planar) and purely geometrical factors, not unlike those we met in § 2 when discussing molecular crystals, play a larger part in determining the structure. Not surprisingly, a very great variety of crystal forms is possible. But there are other cases, such as NH_4^+ and SO_4^{--}, which are tetrahedral, and where the resultant electric field at points outside the molecule is almost indistinguishable from that due to a central charge. In these molecules it is possible to assign an ionic radius just as in the monatomic systems of § 5. For example, the radius of ammonium is 1·48 A, about the same as rubidium, so that the salts of the two substances are frequently isomorphous. Thus at temperatures above 184°, 138°, and −18° C respectively, ammonium chloride, bromide, and iodide have the same NaCl structure as the corre-sponding rubidium halides. It is interesting, however, that at temperatures below these transition points the structures change to the CsCl form, illustrating the extreme delicacy of the balance that often exists in favour of one or the other type.

In all these cases the binding within any one group is of the valence kind discussed in Chapters I–X; but the binding between the groups is essentially ionic, governed by the same principles (a)–(d) which we enumerated at the end of § 5.

XII

METALS

12.1. The metallic bond

WE must now turn our attention to the fourth type of bond listed in § 11.1 as occurring in the solid state. This is the metallic bond. In a subject so extensive as the theory of metals and alloys, we can do nothing more than indicate some of the extremely interesting links that exist between it and our previous theory of molecular valence. At the very start of our discussion it is important to recognize two characteristic properties that bear directly on any later theory: (1) a metal is a conductor of electricity, (2) metals nearly always crystallize with a large coordination number. Thus the typical metallic structures are the body-centred cubic (b.c.c.), the face-centred cubic (f.c.c.), and the close-packed hexagonal (h.c.p.), shown in Fig. 1. In the first of these each atom is surrounded by fourteen near neighbours, eight at the distance of closest approach R and six more at $2R/\sqrt{3} = 1\cdot15R$; in the other two structures there are twelve equidistant neighbours.

From the first of the characteristic properties we infer that at least certain electrons are relatively free to roam over the crystal, and even under the influence of a small electric field, to flow in any chosen direction.

From the second property we infer that the bonds cannot be of the familiar localized type discussed in earlier chapters. When there are twelve neighbours it is obvious that the '8—N rule' of § 11.3 has broken down completely. There is, in fact, no conceivable way in which an atom could form twelve simultaneous covalent bonds. It is perfectly clear that metals present us with an extreme case of the delocalization of bonds which we described in Chapter IX.

We can get some guidance from a study of one very simple case. Let us consider the metal lithium, which crystallizes in the b.c.c. structure, with a distance of closest approach of the nuclei equal to 3·03 A. Now there are only three electrons in a lithium atom whose ground state is $(1s)^2(2s)$; and the ionic radius (Table 28 on p. 316) of $Li^+(1s)^2$ is only 0·60 A. Such closely bound electrons will be almost unaffected by the presence of other lithium atoms, so that we are led to the conclusion that there is one, and only one, valence electron per atom, to confer metallic property on the crystal. The bonding that exists between each atom and its fourteen near neighbours must be almost entirely due to these solitary electrons, one per atom, whose bonding power is therefore 'spread-out'. This follows equally well from a comparison of the bond length (2·67 A) in the diatomic molecule Li_2 with the distance

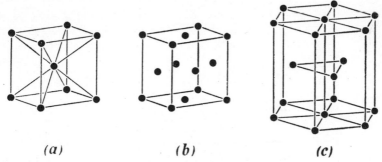

(a)   *(b)*   *(c)*

FIG. 12.1. Typical metallic structures.
(a) body-centred cubic: example, lithium; (b) face-centred cubic: example, copper; (c) hexagonal close-packed: example, zinc.

of closest approach (3·03 A) in the metal. The increased length in the metal implies that the 'bonds' are weaker: but of course there are more of them, with the result that the total binding energy per atom increases from 13 kcal/gm. atom in the molecule to 39 kcal/gm. atom in the metal. The valence, or conduction, electrons are therefore more tightly bound in the metal than in the molecule, but their bonding power has to be distributed more widely.

From this simple example we can already begin to see how our former theories will have to be applied. We shall find that both the m.o. and v.b. approximations can be generalized to explain a good deal of the metallic state; but in their generalizations they acquire some quite new features. These features contribute to our understanding in rather different ways, so that no proper account

of metals can at present be given without making use, from time
to time, of both methods. This situation, which we have already
met for molecules, becomes much more pronounced for metals.
For that reason we shall follow our usual custom, and deal with
the theories one by one, comparing them at the end. It will be
most convenient to take them in the order of their historical
development, which, interestingly enough, was the reverse of that
for the molecule. This means that we must start with the m.o.
theory.

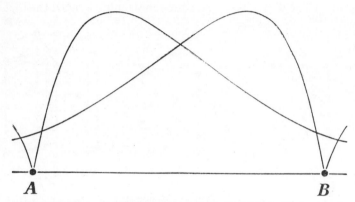

Fig. 12.2. The overlapping of two atomic 2*s* orbitals (Slater type)
on adjacent atoms of metallic lithium.

12.2. Bloch's molecular-orbital theory

The essential point in the m.o. theory of molecules was that each
electron was supposed to move in a potential field which extended
over all the atoms. By suitable averaging we were able to introduce a one-electron Hamiltonian and corresponding wave equation. The solutions of this equation were approximately described
in terms of linear combinations of a.o.'s.

The necessary condition that the m.o.'s should be delocalized
was that the a.o. for any one atom overlapped significantly with
those of more than one of its neighbours. In benzene, for example,
each π a.o. overlapped equally with both its neighbours, with the
result (§ 9.6) that the m.o.'s extended over all six carbons.

There is nothing to prevent us from following exactly the same
procedure, with very similar results, when we are dealing with an

infinite array of atoms instead of a finite array. It is clear that all the conditions for delocalization hold for an alkali metal, where we have seen that each central atom has one valence electron in an *s* orbital, which will overlap considerably with all its fourteen near neighbours. In such a case the 'molecular orbitals' of valence theory have become the 'conduction orbitals' of a metal. Everything depends on the degree of overlap, and as Fig. 2 shows for the particular case of Li, this is quite large. The numerical value of the overlap integral $\int \psi_A(2s)\psi_B(2s)\, d\tau$ for adjacent atoms has a magnitude 0·50 when the orbitals are described according to the Slater rules of § 2.8. We must, therefore, expect completely delocalized orbitals. These are generally known as 'Bloch' wave functions, after their originator.† The date of this work (1928) reminds us that the application to metals preceded that to molecules. It would not be entirely inappropriate to call the completely delocalized m.o.'s, such as in benzene, 'Bloch orbitals'.

However, the orbitals for an infinite array differ in one very important respect from the molecular ones with which we have so far been concerned in this book. We can see this most simply if we start with one atom (e.g. of lithium), and watch the way in which the allowed energies of the electrons change as we build up the infinite crystal by successive additions of one further atom. In § 4.7 we saw how, when a second atom B is added to the first one A, the a.o. ψ_A becomes the two diatomic orbitals $\psi_A \pm \psi_B$, each with its distinct energy. If we now add a third atom, we shall obtain three m.o.'s and their energies will be grouped around the original energy of ψ_A. This process may be continued. Each successive addition of a new atom adds one more energy value, at the same time slightly altering those of the previous set. The process is illustrated in Fig. 3, from which it will be seen that in the limit each a.o. gives rise to a band of energies. There will be one band from each of the allowed orbitals of the original atom, and the way

† *Z. Phys.*, 1928, **52**, 555. A full account of all this and much related work is given by N. F. Mott and H. Jones, *The Theory of the Properties of Metals and Alloys*, Clarendon Press, Oxford, 1936. There is a simpler account in M. A. Jaswon, *The Theory of Cohesion*, Pergamon Press, 1954, and W. Hume-Rothery, *Atomic Theory for Students of Metallurgy*, London, Institute of Metals, 3rd edn., 1960.

in which these bands are built up shows that the total number of levels in a band is equal to one per atom of the metal. If the total number of atoms is very large (order 10^{23} in a normal piece of metal, though irregularities and cracks will usually mean that each monocrystalline unit is a lot smaller than this), the levels are so close together that we are justified in calling them a continuum.

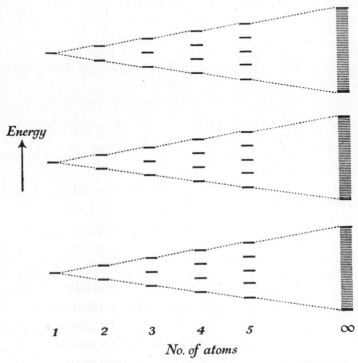

Energy

No. of atoms

FIG. 12.3. The building-up of energy bands by repeated addition of one more atom.

If the separate atomic energies (e.g. 2s and 2p of lithium) are well separated, or if the distance between adjacent atoms is so great that there is no appreciable overlapping between neighbouring a.o.'s, the separate bands of energies will remain distinct. But if the original atomic energies are close together, or if neighbouring atoms are sufficiently near to each other, then the bands may lose their individuality and merge into one another. In rough terms this means that the m.o.'s must not be regarded as composed solely of the one, or of the other, type of a.o., but both types have to be included.

If the starting a.o.'s are degenerate, as with p or d orbitals, the resulting band may split into several parts, depending on the crystal symmetry. But the total number of states in all these bands will be the equivalent of three per atom for p-bands, and five per atom for d-bands.

We may, therefore, describe the energy levels for a metal in the following terms. When the atoms are at infinite separation, the

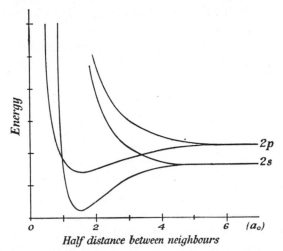

FIG. 12.4. Energy bands in metallic lithium (after Millman).

energies are merely the energies of separate a.o.'s. But as the lattice constant diminishes, interaction occurs, and each separate level splits into a band, whose width increases steadily. Ultimately the bands cross, as is shown in Fig. 4† for the case of metallic lithium. In order to calculate the total electronic energy of the metal, we must allow the available number of electrons to occupy the lowest of the levels, taking account of the exclusion principle, and of electron spin, exactly as in the *aufbau* principle developed for molecules in Chapter IV. This requires us to know the distribution of energies within the various bands—a matter with which we shall not here concern ourselves, except to say that

† N. H. Frank, *Phys. Rev.*, 1935, **47**, 282.

calculated equilibrium values of the lattice constant usually† agree very nicely with experiment.

The idea of bands, or zones, of allowed energies, separated by forbidden zones, is the most novel—and at the same time the most important—new feature of this method. But it is not entirely unexpected, as the following considerations show. Let us consider a block of metallic sodium. The ionization potential of a sodium atom is only 5·1 eV, so a fairly good picture of the metal is obtained if we imagine it to contain an assembly of electrons, one per atom, effectively free except that they are confined within the volume of the metal. This has sometimes been called the 'box model' of a metal. It was developed largely by Sommerfeld to explain conductivity and other characteristic metallic properties. Now free electrons such as those just described will be represented by de Broglie waves (§ 2.1) in which the wavelength λ is related to the energy E by the equation

$$\lambda = h/\sqrt{(2mE)}. \tag{1}$$

But in the metal itself there is a regular array of sodium ions Na^+, whose presence will perturb these electron waves. A situation arises not unlike that which occurs when X-rays traverse crystalline material. Such waves experience only a relatively small absorption except for certain special wavelengths—those which satisfy the Bragg relation. We may say that X-rays of these particular wavelengths cannot be transmitted through the crystal. The parallel with our de Broglie waves is immediate. For any chosen direction of propagation there are certain forbidden λ, and thus, by (1), certain forbidden energies. In this way we see how the zones of forbidden energy are related to the structure of the crystal. It is true that on account of the three-dimensional character of the metal, the discontinuities occur at different energies for different directions of propagation. Thus the matter is not quite so simple as the account we have just given. But a more refined treatment, associated with the name of Brillouin,† shows that the band-character of the energy levels follows from this type of analysis just as well as from our earlier reasoning.

† See Mott and Jones, loc. cit.

It should scarcely be necessary to add that all the discussion of this section applies only to valence orbitals (and higher ones). The inner-shell electrons of the atoms remain as much localized around their respective nuclei as in the case of simple molecules—and for precisely the same reasons (§ 4.10).

Our description of a band is not yet quite complete. For we require to know how the total number of allowed energies in any band varies with position in the band. This is given by the density of states function $N(E)$, where $N(E)\,dE$ is the number of energy

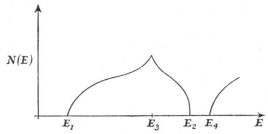

FIG. 12.5. The $N(E)$ curve for a typical discrete band.

levels per atom (sometimes per unit cell, or per unit volume) which lie in the range E, $E+dE$. The calculation of $N(E)$, which almost always vanishes at the top and bottom of each band, and often has a single maximum rather above its mid-point, is outside the scope of this book. A typical shape† is shown in Fig. 5, which shows a band with allowed energies between E_1 and E_2 and having a peak at E_3. A further, non-overlapping band starts at E_4. In more complicated cases, particularly where several bands overlap, considerable complexity in the $N(E)$ curve may easily arise. An example, for body-centred-cubic iron, is shown later in Fig. 9.

12.3. Conductors and insulators

It is obvious from the way in which the argument was developed, that our description of electron levels in terms of allowed and forbidden zones applies to all periodic systems, metallic or otherwise. Whether it is convenient to use it for non-metals, as well

---

† This is a simplified form of the $N(E)$ curve for lithium, as in J. F. Cornwell and E. P. Wohlfarth, *Nature*, 1960, **186**, 379.

as metals, depends upon the phenomenon being discussed. There is no doubt, however, that in the matter of deciding whether a given solid is a conductor or an insulator, the concept of zones is extremely valuable. Let us consider an idealized substance in which the bands are all distinct and well separated (Fig. 6). As usual, the available electrons are supposed to occupy the allowed levels, working upwards from the bottom. The shaded levels are those which are full: the unshaded ones are empty. In case (a) the

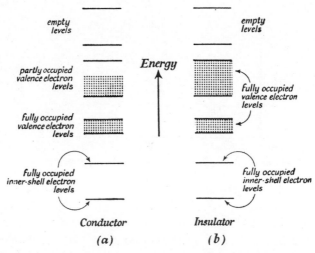

Fig. 12.6. Conductors and insulators. The partly-filled band in (a) makes the substance a conductor, but the filled bands of (b) make it an insulator.

top band is only partly filled. In case (b) it is completely full. Now each m.o. is completely delocalized, and we may, if we like, think of the energy levels as occurring in pairs, corresponding to electron waves travelling in opposite directions in the crystal. Suppose that we apply an external electric field by joining the two ends of the metal to the poles of a battery. The immediate effect will be to try to make more electrons flow in the one direction than in the other. This may be achieved in case (a) by giving the electrons flowing in the direction of the field more energy and thereby raising them into some of the previously empty levels of the band. As a result a current flows, and the substance is a metallic conductor.

Indeed the process would continue with an indefinitely great current developing, were it not for collisions of the electrons with the positive nuclei, just as in Drude's early classical theory of conductivity. In case (b), on the other hand, no such current can flow. For since the band is completely full, with equal numbers of electrons moving in all directions, we can never get any net flow in the direction of the field. The substance is therefore an insulator. Indeed the only way to get a current to flow is by applying

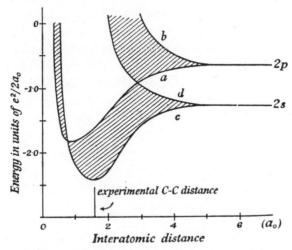

FIG. 12.7. Energy bands in diamond (after Kimball). In addition to the shaded bands, there are bands of zero width following curves (a) and (b) of the figure.

so intense an electric field that enough energy can be given to a few of the electrons to raise them to the next band, previously quite empty, but which may now be called the conduction band. This is the explanation of dielectric breakdown.

The argument above is easily generalized. If there are partly filled bands of electrons, the substance is a conductor: if there are only completely filled and completely empty bands, it is an insulator.

We may illustrate this in terms of lithium and diamond, of which the first is a metal and the second an insulator. The band structure of lithium has already been given in Fig. 4. The corresponding structure for diamond† is reproduced in Fig. 7. In the case of lithium there is only one valence electron per atom, so that the lowest band is only half-full: the crystal should therefore be a conductor. In the case of diamond there are four valence electrons per atom. The bands which are shown in the figure are such that two electrons per atom (with opposed spins) can fit into each of the shaded energy zones, and two also into the bands of zero width which follow curves (a) and (b). Thus at the equilibrium distance, as shown, the lower band (between a and c) is completely filled, and so is (a). The rest are completely empty. There is a large energy gap before any other allowed energy bands appear, thus providing us with an excellent interpretation of the insulating property of diamond. Although this description of diamond is perfectly proper and correct, it is still true that for most purposes the description in terms of localized σ-bonds (§ 11.3) is simpler and equally valid. The reader may recall a similar situation in the description of methane (§ 7.3, small type) in terms either of localized or delocalized m.o.'s.

Several other points are related to this distinction between metals and insulators. We must be content to list some of them and comment briefly upon them.

1. Our description of a metal leads us to regard each atom as ionized, and in a 'sea' of electrons. The binding is due to this approximately uniform electron cloud, and for that reason the internal forces in metals are different from those in, for example, polar crystals, where the individual units are nearly distinct positive and negative ions. Further, on account of the 'sea' of electrons, considerable movement of the positive ions is possible without great expenditure of energy. We have here an explanation of the plasticity of metals, and of the effects of work-hardening.

2. In order that the 'electron sea' may be formed it is desirable that in the separate atoms there should be one or more easily ionized electrons, for electrons that are too tightly bound to their

---

† G. E. Kimball, *J. Chem. Phys.*, 1935, **3**, 560. The $N(E)$ curve at the equilibrium distance has been calculated by G. G. Hall, *Phil. Mag.*, 1952, **43**, 338; by J. C. Slater and G. F. Koster, *Phys. Rev.*, 1954, **94**, 1498; and by L. Kleinman and J. C. Phillips, *Phys. Rev.*, 1959, **116**, 880.

particular nucleus will not readily be shared with the rest of the crystal. This is one reason why the earlier groups of the Periodic Table give metallic structures, and the later groups adhere to the 8—N rule.

3. One particularly important function of a second type of atom forming an alloy with a first is to add or remove electrons. The importance of the electron concentration, i.e. number of valence electrons per atom, can hardly be exaggerated, as Hume-Rothery[†] has pointed out.

4. The band structure explains how an insulator may acquire a photoconductivity if ultraviolet light shines upon it. All that is required is that the frequency v of the light shall be such that hv is at least equal to the energy gap between the top occupied band and the lowest unoccupied band. Absorption of such light carries electrons into the conduction band, where they may flow under the influence of an electric field.

5. Similarly it explains the semi-conductivity[‡] that arises when impurity atoms are present in the metal, and provide additional energy levels outside, but fairly close to, the allowed bands.

A particularly important application of this 'doping' of pure metals arises when, as in solid germanium, the electrical conductivity of the absolutely pure substance is low; but if a small impurity is present in such small proportions that it merely occupies a site otherwise reserved for the original type of atom, and if this impurity has one fewer valence electrons (e.g. gallium, which has 3 valence electrons, as compared with germanium, which has 4), then we have a p-type semi-conductor, in which the electrical conductivity is chiefly due to the positive 'holes' in the otherwise completely full valence band. Similarly, if the impurity has one additional valence electron (e.g. arsenic with 5, compared with germanium with 4), we have an n-type semi-conductor, in which the conductivity is due to the negative charge of the excess valence electrons, which begin to occupy the hitherto empty conduction band.

† A simple account is in Hume-Rothery's books *Atomic Theory for Students of Metallurgy*, Institute of Metals, London, 1960, or *The Metallic State*, Oxford University Press, 1931.

‡ See, e.g., A. H. Wilson, *Semi-conductors and Metals*, Cambridge, 1939.

After this introduction to the m.o. theory of metals we must now turn to the v.b., or resonance, theory.

12.4. Valence-bond theory of metals†

The essential character of the v.b. theory of metals is the same as for molecules: that is, we consider the various ways in which the electrons on the various atoms may be paired together. Each such scheme of pairing is a structure, and all possible structures contribute, in appropriate measure, to the complete wave function. But we can see at once one new feature. In colloquial language 'there are not enough electrons to go round'. For example, each lithium atom has one valence electron, but there are eight near neighbours and six others almost as close, with which it may be paired. This means that there is a very large number of possible structures in each of which bonds are drawn between adjacent Li atoms. Pauling‡ has shown that if we restrict ourselves simply to the eight nearest neighbours, a lithium crystal containing $2N$ atoms will have about $3 \cdot 14^N$ such structures, among which it may be said to resonate. So long as we confine ourselves to these non-ionic structures, this resonance will necessarily be of the 'synchronized' kind, represented by

$$\left\{ \begin{matrix} \text{Li—Li} \\ \text{Li—Li} \end{matrix} \right., \quad \left. \begin{matrix} \text{Li} & \text{Li} \\ | & | \\ \text{Li} & \text{Li} \end{matrix} \right\},$$

in which the shift of one bond necessitates the synchronous shift of at least one other bond. But we have no logical grounds for excluding ionic structures: rather is it the case that without such structures, corresponding to separation of positive and negative charge, there can be no possible hope of explaining the flow of electrons in metallic conduction. We are, therefore, led to introduce structures involving Li^+ and Li^- atoms. Now it may easily be seen that there are many more of these ionic structures than of the covalent ones. Pauling's argument leads to the conclusion that the number $3 \cdot 14^N$ of covalent structures is to be compared with

† L. Pauling, *Phys. Rev.*, 1938, **54**, 899; and *Nature of the Chemical Bond*, Cornell Univ. Press, 3rd edn., 1960, chap. 11.
‡ *Proc. Roy. Soc.* A, 1949, **196**, 343.

$(2 \cdot 32 \times 3 \cdot 14)^N$ ionic structures. The actual numerical values are approximate: but their ratio warns us that we must expect ionic structures to play a more important role in the metal than in the diatomic molecule. If we bear in mind that a Li^- atom may be treated as divalent, and a Li^+ as zero-valent, then resonance between covalent and ionic structures can be represented in the symbolic manner

$$\left\{ \begin{matrix} Li—Li \\ Li—Li \end{matrix} , \quad \begin{matrix} Li—Li^- \\ | \\ Li^+ Li \end{matrix} \right\}.$$

We could say, pictorially, that the lower bond in the covalent structure on the left had 'pivoted' around one of the two atoms which it joined. Resonance of this kind is uninhibited, since the shift of one bond no longer involves the simultaneous shift of any others.

This pivotal resonance is effectively confined to metals. For structures of the ionic type described above will only make a significant contribution to the total wave function if the atom which is to receive the additional charge has a relatively low-lying orbital, otherwise unoccupied, into which it may go. Such orbitals are called the 'metallic orbitals'. We can see at once why all the covalent solids which satisfy the $8—N$ rule are non-conductors. For if the $8—N$ rule is obeyed, every atom contrives to complete its octet of electrons by what are essentially covalent bonds, so that the only unoccupied a.o.'s belong to an outer shell, and will have considerably higher energy. Thus in diamond (Fig. 11.3) a total of eight electrons is involved in the bonds from any one carbon to its four neighbours: this completes the L-shell, and C^- structures could only occur through use of the more energetic M-shell orbitals. With lithium, on the other hand, there are $2p$ orbitals whose energy does not greatly exceed that of the $2s$ orbitals (if I denotes ionization potential,

$$I(2s) - I(2p) = 5 \cdot 37 - 3 \cdot 53 = 1 \cdot 84 \text{ eV}).$$

In fact there is always a choice of three p orbitals, $2p_x$, $2p_y$, and $2p_z$, so that, if the $2s$ orbital was already used in one of the original covalent bonds, we could still choose that particular $2p$ orbital that best suited the immediate need for maximum overlapping in the second bond. It seems likely, however, that the separation into pure s and p orbits no longer remains: and that hybridization, such as that described in Chapter VIII, occurs. In view of the relatively small energy difference between $I(2s)$ and $I(2p)$, this could be achieved without difficulty. Indeed, if we imagine hybridization of the digonal type (§ 8.2) in which s and p are replaced by $s+p$ and $s-p$, we allow considerably greater overlap both for the original covalent bond, and also for the second (pivotal) bond—at any rate if their directions are opposed to each other. In such a case there would be no distinction between the two bonds from each Li⁻ atom.

We may, therefore, expect that those metallic atoms which are electrically neutral would be hybridized similarly to the diatomic molecule: but that the negative bicovalent ions would be hybridized approximately digonally. The mean hybridization would then lie somewhere between 10 and 50 per cent. The final values, as estimated by Pauling,† both for Li and the other alkali metals, are shown in Table 30.

TABLE 30. *Hybridization in alkali metals and diatomic molecules*

Metal		Li	Na	K	Rb	Cs
Percentage p character	Metal	41	27	26	26	28
	Molecule	14	7	6	5	6

The description of a metal that we have just given for lithium, may be generalized to apply to other metals than the alkalis. For example, in the alkaline-earth metal beryllium, which has the hexagonal close-packed structure with twelve near neighbours, the valence electrons $(2s)^2$ must first be excited to the configuration $(2s)(2p)$, and then hybridized. But this still leaves no less than two other unoccupied $2p$ orbitals to serve as metallic orbitals. It is true that as a result of interplay between neutral bicovalent $Be(2s)(2p)$ and the negative trivalent $(2s)(2p)^2$, the hybridization is not exactly of the digonal type: nor indeed can it yet be calculated with any confidence. But at least a qualitative understanding of this and other similar metals is here available.

† 1949, loc. cit.

A similar generalization can be made for other metal types, but since many of these involve the use of d orbitals, we shall postpone any discussion till later (§ 7). In every case the essential property is the possession of a suitable metallic orbital, unoccupied in all non-ionic covalent structures. This raises the important question: what grounds have we for accepting this guiding principle, in order to discriminate between conductors and non-conductors?

The most important reason for believing in the existence of metallic orbitals is that without them no explanation of electrical conductivity is forthcoming from the v.b. theory. But a further justification may be found in the binding energy which, as we have already seen, is much greater for a metal than for the corresponding diatomic molecule. This requires a very large number of resonating structures, such as would be provided by the uninhibited resonance of pivoting bonds. In addition to all this, we shall see in § 5 that the whole problem of interatomic distances is made coherent on this theory; and also, in § 7, that many difficulties in the transition metals, where d electrons play a fundamental role, are cleared away. Finally, we can explain some of the polymorphisms so frequently encountered in this field. The example of tin will serve to illustrate this latter point.

Tin has fourteen electrons outside a stable krypton-like core. These electrons must occupy the $4d$, $5s$, and $5p$ orbits, whose energy probably increases in the sequence $4d < 5s < 5p$. This suggests that there are two configurations, SnA and SnB, which we should consider. In the diagram internally-paired atomic electrons are

shown by arrows, bonding electrons by dots, and metallic orbitals by circles. SnA has the maximum possible valency, and will form a crystal satisfying the $8—N$ rule, with tetrahedral hybridization sp^3. This is precisely the structure of non-conducting grey tin, which is stable below $18°$ C. The only resonance here is of the unimportant kind which occurs in the electronically similar diamond crystal. It is certainly true that we might hope to obtain greater coordination than 4 by placing more tin atoms around any given central atom, and by relying on resonance for their stability. Such resonance would occur, but it would necessarily be of the synchronous kind such as among the Kekulé structures of benzene; and the strongly tetrahedral character of the sp^3 hybrids would impose further limitations on the number of effective pairing schemes. Evidently the gain in energy which resulted would be insufficient to offset the repulsive energy between the non-bonded atoms which appears as soon as a greater coordination than 4 is introduced. SnB, on the other hand, is divalent; but it has a metallic orbital, and should be a conductor. Pauling[†] gives reasons for believing that it is the chief component of white tin, which is stable at higher temperatures. It is concluded that SnB and SnA here occur in the ratio 3:1, which leads to an average valency of 2·5. It is clear that in ways similar to this, fractional valences of all kinds may be interpreted.

12.5. Interatomic distances[‡]

In metallic lithium we have seen that the one valence electron per atom must serve to bind this atom to eight near neighbours and to six slightly more distant ones. The average number of electrons per 'bond' must be considerably less than for the single bond of a diatomic molecule, where it is 2. We may introduce a number n, called the fractional bond number, such that $2n$ is the total share of the valence electrons associated with the bond. In lithium the two types of bond will have different n-values, which we could write n_8 and n_6. Evidently these must satisfy the relation

$$8n_8 + 6n_6 = 1. \qquad (2)$$

The precise values of n_8 and n_6 are related to the interatomic distances found in the metal. Pauling has suggested that the atomic radius $R(n)$ for a metallic bond with bond number n is given (in A) by:

$$R(1) - R(n) = 0{\cdot}300 \log n. \qquad (3)$$

The logarithmic form of this equation is suggested by the fact that

---

† *J. Chem. Soc.*, 1948, p. 1461.

‡ L. Pauling, *J. Amer. Chem. Soc.*, 1947, **69**, 542; *Proc. Roy. Soc.* A, 1949, **196**, 343.

the single-, double-, and triple-bond radii for carbon and nitrogen fit an expression of type (3), though with a different coefficient 0·35 on the right-hand side. The resonance found in benzene and other aromatic molecules has the effect of decreasing $R(n)$ for large n. This may be incorporated by changing the coefficient 0·35 to 0·30. The expression (3) is thus suggested by theoretical considerations, but its final form is largely empirical. Very probably the coefficient 0·30 is not really a constant, but varies slightly with the kind of atom and the type of bond.

Now in lithium there are eight neighbours at a distance 3·032 A, and six at a distance 3·502 A. This means that $R(n_8) = 1·516$, $R(n_6) = 1·751$. With these values equations (2) and (3) give

$$n_8 = 1/9·0, \qquad n_6 = 1/54·6, \tag{4}$$

and $R(1) = 1·230$ A. It is clear from this that even a small increase in bond length makes a large difference in the bond number n.

In the example above we have used the observed distances to predict $R(1)$. But, as Pauling showed, values of $R(1)$ may often be estimated by other means, and then we may even be able to calculate expected interatomic distances and (see later) correlate them with bond type and total valence number of each atom.

12.6. Comparison of the two Bloch and Pauling theories

It is not possible at this stage to say which of the two theories that we have described is the better. But a few comments on their basic assumptions may be made.

In the first place the valence electrons are not completely independent, as supposed in the m.o. theory. Even if, as Wigner and Seitz† have shown, we insert a correlation energy, it appears rather as an afterthought. But, on the other hand, it is equally unsatisfactory, in v.b. theory, to discuss a metal in terms of various bond structures. For we cannot even enumerate these structures; much less can we compute their weights. This leads us to a further difficulty, in that the bond number n introduced in § 5 is not a very suitable parameter to use in order to measure a bond. For as

† *Phys. Rev.*, 1933, **43**, 804.

we saw in Chapter IX, with increasing size of conjugated molecule, the more highly excited structures become progressively more important, collectively.

It would be fair to say that by virtue of the extremely natural way in which the electrons are delocalized in the m.o. theory, this theory is chiefly suited to a discussion of conductivity, and the properties related to this. But on account of its association with bonds of molecular type, the v.b. theory is most effective in discussing interatomic distances, and bond types. Such numerical results as have so far been obtained by both theories confirm this general conclusion.

12.7. Introduction of d electrons

We have hitherto been concerned with atoms in which d electrons play no significant role. In the transition metals this is far from being the case, and extremely varied and interesting problems are introduced. It will only be possible in the space available here to indicate a few of the ways in which these electrons complicate the previous picture.

We may begin quite simply with a discussion of the noble metal copper. An isolated copper atom has an outer electron configuration $...(3d)^{10}(4s)$, so that there is one s electron outside a closed core. But in the metal the $3d$ electrons cannot be regarded simply as inner-shell non-bonding electrons, in the same way that in metallic Na the $(2p)^6$ inner-shell electrons of one atom were almost unaffected by the presence of neighbouring atoms. This is because the $3d$ charge-clouds in Cu overlap considerably more than the $2p$ charge-clouds in Na. As a result we can no longer speak of the binding as due solely to the $4s$ electron, but must include the $3d$ electrons as well.

In the simplest Bloch-type picture of this metal, due chiefly to Mott and Jones,[†] it is supposed that both the $3d$ and the $4s$ electrons form separate bands, similarly to the $2s$ and $2p$ bands of lithium in Fig. 4. Since the $4s$ a.o.'s overlap strongly, the

[†] For the calculations see K. Fuchs, *Proc. Roy. Soc.* A, 1935, **151**, 585; 1936, **153**, 622. More refined calculations involving hybridization of s and d are given by H. M. Krutter, *Phys. Rev.*, 1935, **48**, 664, and D. J. Howarth, *Proc. Roy. Soc.* A, 1953, **220**, 513.

s-band will be wide: and since the $3d$ orbitals overlap less strongly their band will be narrow. The situation is similar to that shown in Fig. 8 a. According to this view the d-band will be completely filled, and also one-half of the s-band, and copper would count as a monovalent metal. This situation may be compared with that in metallic Ni, where there is one fewer electron than in Cu, and for which, as a result, not all the d-band is filled. This is shown in Fig. 8 b, in which the shaded regions represent the levels that are filled. Explicit calculation shows that there are about 9·4 electrons in the d-band (giving 0·6 'holes'), and 0·6 electrons in the s-band.

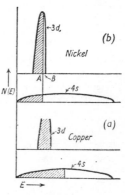

Fig. 12.8. The relative position of the s- and d-bands in copper and nickel.

The distinction between Cu and Ni shown in Figs. 8 a, b accounts very nicely for their magnetic properties. For electrons which are firmly engaged in bonds will have their spins paired with some other electrons, so that no resultant spin paramagnetism will arise from them. Electrons which are not engaged in binding and may be regarded as effectively 'atomic', will tend to obey Hund's rules (Ch. II). This will mean that a completed shell such as $(3d)^{10}$ will show no resultant magnetic moment, but an incomplete group such as $(3d)^{9·4}$ will do so. If, on the average, a fraction 0·6 of the Ni atoms has one d electron missing, then the saturation moment should be 0·6 Bohr magnetons per atom, in complete agreement with the experimental value. Copper, on the other hand, should be non-ferromagnetic.

A similar discussion can be given for the other ferromagnetics such as Fe and Co. But this explanation is unsatisfying because essentially it neglects all mixing of s and d orbitals. If their separate bands overlap so much as Fig. 8 would lead us to expect, then we should no longer treat them separately, but should set up Bloch wave functions in which s and d orbitals both appear simultaneously. When this is done, a total of six overlapping bands appears. Their total $N(E)$ curve is shown in Fig. 9 for the case of body-centred iron.† In this metal there are eight electrons per atom in the 3*d* and 4*s* shells. If we feed these electrons, two at a time, into the levels of Fig. 9 in order of increasing energy, all the levels in the shaded area will be filled, and all the others of higher energy will be empty. Quite evidently the simple explanation of 0·6 holes in a distinct *d*-band has now become much more complex. However, as earlier calculations had shown,‡ the top band of which Fig. 9 is composed, and which is about half-filled, is almost

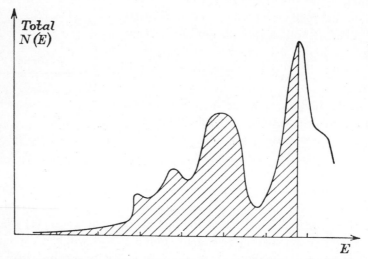

FIG. 12.9. The energy bands in body-centred iron (after J. H. Wood).

entirely composed of *s* orbitals. The other five bands, which are completely or almost completely filled, are composed chiefly of *d* orbitals. Thus there does remain something of the earlier simple interpretation of ferromagnetism.

This latter diagram suggests rather strongly that some sort of hybridization of *d* and *s* orbitals is really taking place, and will serve to introduce the v.b. account of these transition metals. Let us consider the two metals, copper and iron. The first of these illustrates very well the way in which *d* electrons are used in this

† Adapted by permission, from calculations by J. H. Wood, *Phys. Rev.*, 1962, **126**, 517.

‡ M. F. Manning, *Phys. Rev.*, 1943, **63**, 190; J. B. Greene and M. F. Manning, ibid., p. 203.

theory. It is supposed that instead of the expected outer atomic configuration $d^{10}s$, where d and s are abbreviations for $3d$ and $4s$, we promote two of the d electrons into p orbitals, to give a configuration $d^2d^2d^2d\ d\ s\ p\ p$ (in which we have listed the independent orbitals separately). In this configuration each atom has five unpaired electrons, which could hybridize to form strongly directed bonds. Alternatively we could have $d^2d^2ddd\ sppp$ with seven unpaired electrons: possibly both of these, and others involving Cu^+ and Cu^-, occur simultaneously, giving an average valence for each copper atom rather greater than 5. These hybrids of s, p, and d now form resonating bonds in which the metallic character of the substance is shown by the fact that many of the atoms have one or more unused 'metallic orbitals', in the language of § 4. Empirical evidence suggests that on the average 2·56 of the original set of five d orbitals take part in the hybrids, and that the remaining 2·44 d orbitals are effectively a.o.'s, showing only a weak interaction with the corresponding orbitals on adjacent atoms. It is interesting to notice that if we use the relation of § 5 relating bond number and interatomic distance, to infer the total valence of each copper atom, we find a value about 5·5, in very satisfactory agreement with our earlier interpretation of the bonds in terms of hybrids involving rather more than five s, p, and d electrons per atom.

The iron atom has three electrons fewer than the copper atom, so that we may expect outer atomic configurations d^8, and others related to it in the same way as in our earlier discussion of copper. In fact the average valence number of an iron atom, as determined from interatomic distances, is about 5·8, indicating roughly the same kind of hybridization as in copper. Now if 5·8 electrons per atom are involved in resonating bond formation, there will remain $8-5\cdot8 = 2\cdot2$ d electrons per atom which are atomic. If these are each able to occupy separate d orbitals, then Hund's rules suggest strongly that we should have a magnetic moment per atom equal to 2·2 magnetons. This agrees excellently with the saturation value 2·22 of the magnetic moment of iron. It seems highly probable that there are, in fact, sufficient available d orbitals to allow these 2·2 atomic electrons to have separate orbitals. But clearly, if further electrons are added, this will become increasingly more unlikely, and we should soon expect the saturation moment to diminish. This is precisely what happens. The greatest saturation moment occurs with an alloy of Fe and Co (26 per cent. cobalt) and then decreases through Co and Ni, until at Cu the number of atomic d electrons is so large that they are obliged to 'double-up', with paired spins; by this time ferromagnetism has disappeared.

It should hardly be necessary to add that the numerical values in this theory are to be regarded as averages, and that many of the details in the calculations and the final values are likely to be altered slightly with further development in the theory.

It may be asked why we feel free to use apparently highly excited atomic states in this discussion of the valence number of any given atom in the metal. The explanation is that in the transition metals the energies of $(n-1)d$, ns, np all lie close together. Thus in iron, the mean energies of the $3d$, $4s$, $4p$ are such that

$$E_{3d} - E_{4s} \approx 28 \text{ kcal/mole},$$
and
$$E_{4p} - E_{3d} \approx 32 \text{ kcal/mole}.$$

All three energies lie within about 60 kcal/mole. Now in our discussion of the tetravalence of carbon on p. 206 we found it worth while to use about 60 per cent. of sp^3 although the mean energy of a $2p$ electron is nearly 200 kcal/mole higher than that of a $2s$ electron. It is not at all surprising, therefore, that when the s, p, d range is less than a third of this, the advantages in terms of additional valences conferred by excitations from s and d to p lead such excited states to make a considerable contribution to the full wave function for the metal.

The question will naturally arise: can we say that one or other of these theories for the behaviour of d electrons is better than the other? It is not possible to answer this question satisfactorily at the moment. Just as in our earlier discussion of simple metals, the Pauling theory gives a particularly clear account of the interatomic distances, and by its insistence on the molecular character of the binding relates the whole discussion closely to the more familiar ground of molecular structure. But this is achieved at the expense of an adequate account of electrical conductivity. Such an account is provided with great elegance by the Bloch method. However, the energy of sublimation does suggest that more electrons take an active part in the binding than the simple m.o. method would lead us to believe. In this respect the v.b. method appears to have a definite, though small, advantage.

XIII

THE HYDROGEN BOND
AND OTHER
MISCELLANEOUS TOPICS

13.1. The hydrogen bond†

MOST of the bonds with which we have so far been concerned have an energy lying in the range 50–100 kcal/mole. But there is one very common bond, whose energy is very much less than this, and which we must now describe. In rough terms we can say that in this bond, usually called the hydrogen bond, a single hydrogen atom appears to be bonded to two distinct atoms, of which at least one is usually, though not always, oxygen. The hydrogen bond is particularly important because its energy is so small, of the order of 6 kcal/mole, and also because the hydroxyl group occurs so frequently in most biological systems.

The most obvious example of this bond is in ice, where the binding of the water molecules to each other may be represented by the dotted lines in Fig. 1 a. At sufficiently low temperatures there is practically complete coordination of this kind, giving rise to a relatively open tetrahedral structure around each oxygen atom. If it were not for the directional character of these dotted hydrogen bonds, it is hard to see how such an open structure could be stable. The process of melting may be thought of largely as the breaking of a certain number of these bonds, and at room temperature only about one-half of the maximum possible number of such bonds still remain unbroken.‡ The breaking of all these latter is associated with transition from the liquid to the gas phase (heat absorbed on melting = 1·44 kcal/mole, heat absorbed on sublimation = 12·2 kcal/mole). This argument suggests—as is indeed true —that highly associated liquids, with high dielectric constants, very often make use of this type of bond.

---

† Recent reviews are given by C. A. Coulson, *Research*, 1957, **10**, 159; and G. C. Pimentel and A. L. McClellan, *The Hydrogen Bond*, 1960, W. H. Freeman and Co.
‡ For a somewhat different model see J. A. Pople, *Proc. Roy. Soc. A*, 1951, **205**, 163.

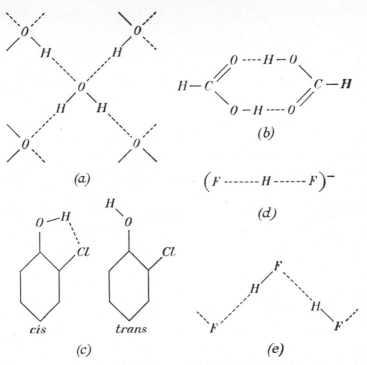

FIG. 13.1. Types of hydrogen bond.

(a) water, showing tetrahedral coordination around each oxygen atom.
(b) the dimer of formic acid,
(c) *cis*- and *trans*- *ortho*-chlorophenol; only the *cis* form shows hydrogen bonding,
(d) HF_2^- from the ionic crystal $K^+(HF_2)^-$.   (e) polymeric HF.

We can distinguish at least four distinct types of hydrogen bond. These are shown in Fig. 1, (a)–(d), and may be described as

(a) intermolecular, extending over many molecules,
(b) intermolecular, extending over two molecules, which form a dimer,
(c) intramolecular, in which the hydrogen is bonded to two atoms of the same molecule,
(d) (FHF)⁻, in which the anion of the polar crystal KHF_2 exists as a distinct charged unit in the solid. This ion must be distinguished (see later) from the hydrogen bond in liquid

HF where, as shown in (e), the angle between successive FHF directions is about 120°.†

The first question that arises concerns the position of the H atom. Is it, as was at first supposed, at the mid-point of the O···O line in (a) and (b), or is it so much more closely linked with one of the two atoms that we are justified in distinguishing between the two types of linkage, as we have done in Fig. 1? Until recently there was no satisfactory way of determining by experiment the precise positions of the hydrogen atoms (their contribution to X-ray or electron scattering was not sufficient to permit of them being really closely located by either of these techniques). It was therefore necessary to rely on infra-red absorption and Raman spectra. If it should turn out that the characteristic frequency of vibration along the direction of the bond—the valency vibration— is not greatly affected by association, we can safely infer that the bond itself is not much altered either. In many cases this is just what is found. Thus in the monomer of formic acid (see Fig. 1 b) the O—H stretching frequency is 3,570 cm^{-1} in the gas phase, and for the dimer it is 3,110 cm^{-1}. This decrease in frequency is not large enough to conclude that the bonding is entirely different. But it does agree nicely with a small increase in bond length, from 0·98 A in the monomer, to about 1·04 A in the dimer.‡ In ice the increase is even less, being from 0·96 A to 1·00 A. Since here the O···O distance is about 2·76 A, this means that one of the O—H distances is almost normal for an O—H bond, but that the other is much longer (by about 0·8 A).

This implies that in ice individual water molecules preserve their identity, though of course they may 'switch over' from one favoured position to another. Final evidence for the continuing identity of the water molecules was provided by Pauling's§ study of the residual entropy of ice at low temperatures. This entropy arises from the fact that although each O atom is surrounded by four H atoms in approximately tetrahedral directions, two of these

---

† M. Atoji and W. Lipscomb, *Acta Cryst.*, 1954, **7**, 173, in crystalline HF. In the gas phase electron diffraction measurements by R. A. Oriani and C. P. Smyth, *J. Chem. Phys.*, 1948, **16**, 1167, suggest an angle of about 144°.

‡ M. M. Davies and G. B. B. M. Sutherland, *J. Chem. Phys.*, 1938, **6**, 755.

§ *J. Amer. Chem. Soc.*, 1935, **57**, 2680.

are quite close to the O atom, the other two being further away. At sufficiently low temperatures the 'switching over' referred to earlier cannot take place, and one of the many possible configurations is 'frozen-in'. A simple calculation shows that the number of possible configurations in a crystal containing N water molecules is approximately $(3/2)^N$, so that there should be an entropy associated with this freedom, of magnitude $R \log(3/2) = 0.81$ cal/mole degree. The experimental value is 0.82. This astonishingly close agreement confirms the general picture of the hydrogen bonding as being between almost normal molecules. More recently Wollan, Davidson, and Schull[†] have studied the scattering of neutrons by heavy ice, in which the hydrogen atoms have been replaced by deuterium atoms. Their experimental results are only compatible with Pauling's picture of random distribution of D_2O units in which the bond angles are all approximately tetrahedral, and in which one D atom lies along every O...O line.

The arguments given above practically confirm that the H atoms lie along the O...O line. Further evidence for this comes from the FHF_2^- ion (Fig. 1 d) where Ketelaar[‡] has been able to identify and interpret the vibrational spectrum. Additional evidence may also be found from the ammonium fluoride crystal, where the separate units are F^- and NH_4^+. The latter ion is tetrahedral, just like methane, and it is found experimentally that in the crystal each N atom is surrounded tetrahedrally by four F atoms. As a result the structure is unusually open, a situation that would be particularly hard to understand if it were not for a strong directional character in the hydrogen bond F...H—N.

During recent years much progress has been made in determining the position of the H atoms and its relation to the length of the bond X—H, the change in frequency of the valence vibration, and the distance X...Y in the bond X—H...Y. Neutron diffraction methods[§] and nuclear magnetic resonance techniques[||] have revealed a general pattern in all such bonds. Fig. 2, taken from a useful survey by K. Nakamoto, M. Margoshes, and R. E. Rundle[††]

[†] *Phys. Rev.*, 1949, **75**, 1348.   [‡] *Rec. Trav. chim.*, 1941, **60**, 523.
[§] See G. E. Bacon, *Neutron Diffraction*, Clarendon Press, Oxford, 1955.
[||] See G. C. Pimentel and A. L. McClellan, loc. cit.. chap. 4.
[††] *J. Amer. Chem. Soc.*, 1955, **77**, 6480.

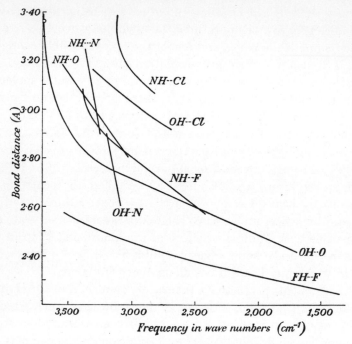

FIG. 13.2. X—H vibration frequency v_s plotted against the X...Y distance in solids containing the hydrogen bond system X—H...Y.

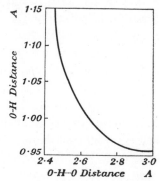

FIG. 13.3. Variation of O_1—H distance with O_1—H...O_2 distance.

shows the relation between vibration frequency v_s and total bond length X···Y. Also Fig. 3, adapted from the same paper, shows that for the particular case of O—H···O, the O—H distance increases as the O···O distance decreases. It would appear from this that when the O···O distance is as low as about 2·4 A, the proton is actually central. When this happens the bond has become quite different from a normal O—H bond. Some evidence,[†] from both X-ray and neutron diffraction, suggests that even with a bond length as large as 2·54 A, the H atom may sometimes be central (or may appear to be central).

13.2. Energy of the hydrogen bond

Table 31[‡] gives a few of the energies of hydrogen bonds between different atoms. Since, as we have seen, these bond lengths vary over a wide range, it is clear that so also will their energies. This is shown in the table, from which it can be seen that most of these energies are in the range 2–8 kcal/mole, about one-tenth of an average conventional bond energy. It is probable that there are other hydrogen bonds (e.g. —Cl···H—C⟨) which are weaker still. But these are of little interest in the theory of valence, though they may be important for a study of solutions and of intermolecular

TABLE 31. *Energies of hydrogen bonds*

Bond	O—H···O	C—H···O	O—H···N	N—H···O
Energy (—ΔH in kcal per mole-H bond)	3–7	2·6	4–7	3–4

Bond	N—H···N	N—H···F	C—H···N	F—H···F§
Energy (—ΔH in kcal per mole-H bond)	3–5	∼5	3–5	6–8

§ This is the value in $(HF)_n$ polymers. In $(FHF)^-$ the energy is about 27 kcal/mole.

---

† G. E. Bacon and N. A. Curry, *Acta Cryst.*, 1957, **10**, 524; 1960, **13**, 717, for the central bond in potassium hydrogen bisphenylacetate. See also D. Hadži and A. Novak, *Proc. Chem. Soc. (London)*, 1960, p. 241, for the central bond in di-*p*-chlorophenyl hydrogen phosphate.

‡ Taken largely from M. M. Davies, *Ann. Rep. Prog. Chem.*, 1946, **43**, 1, and Pimentel and McClellan, loc. cit., pp. 212 and 224. The O—H···N value is due to J. A. Ketelaar, *J. Chim. phys.*, 1949, **46**, 425. F—H···F values are from D. F. Smith, *J. Chem. Phys.*, 1958, **28**, 1040.

forces in the kinetic theory of gases. There are two possible ways in which we may attempt to account for these energies. They are by means of (a) resonance or (b) electrostatic forces. In saying this we have disregarded the view occasionally put forward, that H is sometimes divalent. This could only occur by use of $H(2s)$ or $H(2p)$ orbitals, whose energy is much too high relative to $H(1s)$ to make such a condition at all likely, or even stable. In earlier times the interpretation (a) was favoured, but this is not now regarded as adequate by itself, except perhaps in the $(FHF)^-$ ion (though even here the structure $F^-H^+F^-$ is calculated to have a much greater weight† than either covalent structure $F—H\ F^-$ or $F^-\ H—F$). For example, Gillette and Sherman‡ have discussed the formic acid dimer where the two resonating structures are

$$\text{H—C}\underset{\text{O—H}\cdots\text{O}}{\overset{\text{O}\cdots\text{H—O}}{\diagup\diagdown}}\text{C—H} \quad\text{and}\quad \text{H—C}\underset{\text{O}\cdots\text{H—O}}{\overset{\text{O—H}\cdots\text{O}}{\diagup\diagdown}}\text{C—H}$$

Such resonance can only provide 50 per cent. of the total energy required, even when the H atoms are placed in the most favourable symmetrical positions. We are obliged to fall back on hypothesis (b), in which the binding is regarded as essentially electrostatic. But we shall see later that certain ionic resonance structures may also help to build up the total distribution of positive and negative charges, whose mutual potential energy we shall have to calculate.

Confirmation of this view is soon obtained. In the first place effective hydrogen bonds are only noticed between electronegative atoms such as O, N, F, and S, so that there are strong dipoles already present. And in the second place, as was originally shown by Bernal and Fowler,§ approximately the correct energy of binding is obtained if, in ice, we regard each H_2O unit as consisting of a negative charge located at the O nucleus, and two compensating positive charges at the H nuclei; the magnitudes of these charges are such as to give the normal dipole moment of a water molecule, and the total electrostatic interaction between the charges on one

---

† Calculations are by G. Bessis and S. Bratož, *J. Chim. phys.*, 1960, **57**, 769; experimental charge density measurements are by T. R. R. McDonald, *Acta Cryst.*, 1960, **13**, 113.

‡ *J. Amer. Chem. Soc.*, 1936, **58**, 1135.

§ *J. Chem. Phys.*, 1933, **1**, 515.

molecule and the charges on all the other molecules measures directly the energy of the two hydrogen bonds associated with this molecule. It is true that† certain refinements are necessary to allow for the additional dipole moment induced in any one water molecule by the field of its neighbours, and for the van der Waals dispersion forces, and for the fact that the net negative charge should not be located exactly on the oxygen nuclei, but should be displaced towards the hydrogens. These are small points, and do not seriously disturb our conclusion that the bonds are essentially electrostatic in origin. A more serious difficulty is associated with the fact discussed in § 8.10 that the dipole moment in water resides chiefly in the four non-bonding electrons. If these occupy approximately tetrahedral orbitals, then it will be the negative charge rather than the positive charge in each H_2O molecule that should be located in two parts. It seems likely, however, that provided the total molecular dipole moment is correct, approximately the same electrostatic energy would be found whether we describe the bonds in terms of point charge-charge interactions, or charge-dipole interactions, or charge-charge cloud interactions.‡

We can soon see why only hydrogen (or deuterium) will serve as the middle atom of the bond. In order that the electrostatic energy of interaction shall be greatest, it is desirable that the units should approach as close together as possible. In this respect hydrogen possesses two favourable properties. Its atomic radius (0·3 A) is extremely small, and it possesses no inner-shell electrons. As a result the adjacent molecule can approach very closely without the introduction of large repulsive energy terms. It is, of course, necessary to have an electropositive atom in the centre, but if, for example, we tried to replace H by Na, the larger size of the Na atom and the presence of a complete inner L-shell would open out the structure to such an extent that the energy of binding would be inadequate. It is also necessary to have an electronegative atom at either end of the system: here again the relatively small

† E. J. Verwey, *Rec. Trav. chim.*, 1940, **60**, 887; 1942, **62**, 127; M. Magat, *Ann. de Phys.*, 1936, **6**, 108; J. S. Rowlinson, *Trans. Faraday Soc.*, 1951, **47**, 120.

‡ For further discussion of this matter for the case of ice, see J. E. Lennard-Jones and J. A. Pople, *Proc Roy. Soc.* A, 1951, **205**, 155; and J. A. Pople, *ibid.*, p. 163.

size of such atoms (Table 13 on p. 189) readily permits a close approach of the two molecules.

The fact that the energy of a hydrogen bond is essentially electrostatic does not mean that no resonance effects occur. If, for example, we consider a simplified model O—H···O, and disregard all other electrons except two for the bond O—H and two for a lone-pair on the other oxygen atom, we can anticipate that the following three main structures will participate:

$$(1) \quad -O-H \qquad\qquad O\langle$$

$$(2) \quad -\overset{-}{O}\ \overset{+}{H} \qquad\qquad O\langle$$

$$(3) \quad -\overset{-}{O}\ H \text{-------} \overset{+}{O}\langle$$

In (3) the right-hand oxygen atom becomes trivalent by giving up one of its electrons. Structures (1) and (2) would provide normal

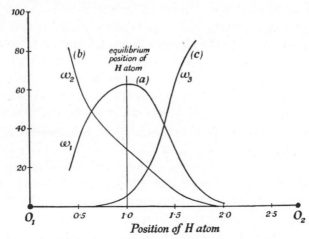

FIG. 13.4. Variation in the weights of the basic structures in the O—H···O bond, when the H atom moves along the O···O axis. The structures are
(a) —O—H O⟨   (b) —O⁻ H⁺ O⟨
(c) —O⁻ H—O⁺⟨.
The O···O distance is taken as 2·78 A.

electrostatic interaction: structure (3) corresponds to covalent resonance involving one rather long bond. It was first suggested by Pauling[†] that the weights w_1, w_2, w_3 of these structures could

† J. Chim. phys., 1949, **46**, 435.

be estimated by essentially the same methods as those used in § 12.5 for metals. From a knowledge of the O—H and H...O distances, the ratio of the bond orders is computed: and this, coupled with the known dipole moment of O—H, allows w_1, w_2, and w_3 to be separately determined. Some calculations of this type have been made by C. A. Coulson and O. Danielsson,[†] who also investigated how the weights altered when the proton was moved in one direction or the other along the O...O line. Some of their results are shown in Fig. 4, from which it appears that in the equilibrium configuration

$$w_1 = 65 \text{ per cent.,} \quad w_2 = 31 \text{ per cent.,} \quad w_3 = 4 \text{ per cent.}$$

The small value of w_3 provides yet further confirmation of the general picture that we have been describing, even though, on account of the many different approximations involved, and the rather idealistic character of the model used, not too great reliance can be placed on the precise values of the w's.[‡]

In certain systems, such as the β-form of oxalic acid

$$\text{H—O} \diagdown \overset{}{\underset{...\text{O}\diagup}{}} \text{C—C} \overset{\diagup\text{O}...\text{H—O}}{\underset{\diagdown\text{O—H}...\text{O}\diagup}{}} \text{C—C} \diagup$$

in which the hydrogen bonding stretches continuously over many molecules, the O...O distance is decreased from 2·8 A to about 2·5 A, and the bond energy is nearly doubled (10 kcal/mole instead of 5 or 6). In the equilibrium configuration Coulson and Danielsson now show that

$$w_1 = 60 \text{ per cent.,} \quad w_2 = 28 \text{ per cent.,} \quad w_3 = 12 \text{ per cent.,}$$

suggesting that these short hydrogen bonds are not so completely electrostatic as the long ones.

The case of $(FHF)^-$ appears to be rather different from those of the other molecules discussed, and even from the polymeric strings $(HF)_n$ which occur in liquid hydrogen fluoride. For there is only one minimum in the potential energy curve corresponding to movement of the H atom along the F...F line, and in the equilibrium configuration the proton lies at the mid-point of the

[†] *Ark. Fys.*, 1954, **8**, 239, 245.
[‡] Thus H. Tsubomura, *Bull. Chem. Soc. Japan*, 1954, **27**, 445, includes more structures than (1)–(3), and finds rather different weights w_r.

line joining the two fluorine atoms. This conclusion follows from the complete lack of any residual entropy† such as that found in ice. The differences between (FHF)⁻ and (HF)$_n$ are well illustrated in Table 32,† which gives the fundamental vibration frequency and the F...F distance as well as the energy.

TABLE 32. *Characteristics of* F...H...F *bonds*

	Frequency (cm⁻¹)	F...F distance (A)	Energy (kcal/mole)	Dielectric constant
(HF)$_n$ gas phase	3,440	2·55	6–8	Large, temperature dependent
(FHF)⁻ .	1,450	2·26	27	Small (4·1) and temperature independent
Free HF .	4,140	..	..	..

The much reduced F...F distance in (FHF)⁻ suggests, in conformity with Danielsson's calculations for the O...H...O bond, that the binding involves a much greater resonance between the covalent structures (I) and (II) than in the other molecules which we have discussed in this chapter. Indeed, the contributions from

(I)   F⁻ H—F⁻
(II)   F—H F⁻
(III)   F⁻ H⁺ F⁻

(I), (II), and (III) may easily be of the same order of magnitude. The symmetrical nature of the ion shows at once that the weights of (I) and (II) are equal. Further evidence for the importance of the covalent structures is provided by the H...F distance which is only 0·21 A greater in the ion (1·13 A) than in the isolated HF molecule (0·92 A). It is not yet possible to say, with any certainty, just how much of the binding energy is electrostatic and how much is resonance.‡

It would be satisfying if it were possible to calculate reasonably accurate energies for hydrogen bonds; or even for the various contributions to any one of them. But unfortunately there are

† E. F. Westrum and K. S. Pitzer, *J. Amer. Chem. Soc.*, 1949, **71**, 1940.

‡ A calculation of the electrostatic energy made by M. M. Davies, *J. Chem. Phys.*, 1947, **15**, 739, gives 47·3 kcal/mole, a value which seems rather too high. For more recent work see Bessis and Bratož, loc. cit.

very few really good measurements of ΔH for any hydrogen bond, and good calculations of the electrostatic energy, etc., depend on a knowledge of better wave functions than we yet possess. The best information at present available is for the case of ice. The figures in Table 33 compare the experimental bond energy as determined from the heat of sublimation, with the calculated energy, when this latter is split up into its various major component parts. These component energies are not known very

TABLE 33. *Estimated energy contributions to each separate H-bond in ice (kcal)*

(A) Electrostatic	+6
(B) Delocalization (e.g. ionic resonance)	+8
(C) Repulsive overlap of charge-clouds on non-bonded atoms	−8·4
(D) Dispersion forces	+3
Total (theoretical)	+8·6
Experimental heat of sublimation	+6·1 kcal

reliably, and future analysis is almost certain to change them; but it is perfectly clear from the table that in this particular case no completely satisfactory account can be given without including several factors not normally required in discussing conventional chemical bonds. The recognition that these factors will change from one bond to another, and also when any one given bond is extended or compressed, provides part of the fascination in the study of this type of link.

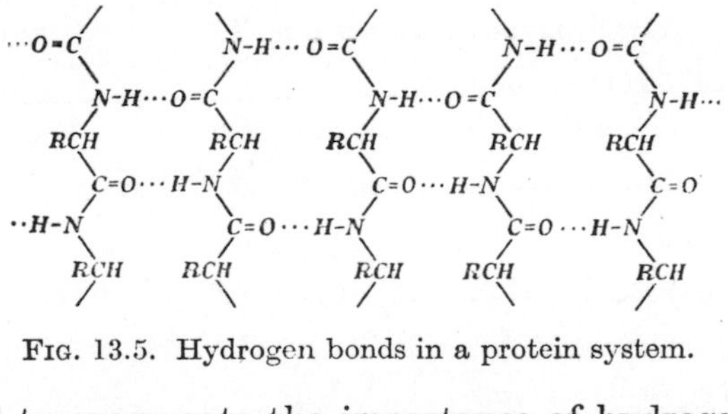

FIG. 13.5. Hydrogen bonds in a protein system.

It is hard to exaggerate the importance of hydrogen bonding. The abnormally high dielectric constants of liquids such as CH_3OH, H_2O, and HCN compared with other liquids where the individual dipole moments are of the same order of magnitude; the association which frequently occurs in liquids; the mutual orientation of the molecules in many organic crystals such as the purines and pyrimidines;[†] the process of attaching of ordinary 'dirt' to the skin of the human body; the regular arrangement of polypeptide chains in a protein structure in some such manner[‡] as that illustrated in Fig. 5; the cross-linking in the double-helix of a nucleic acid, and its significance for the duplication of gene structure; the fact that nearly all biological processes seem to involve the hydrogen bond at some stage; all these show that this type of binding is outstandingly important.

13.3. Hyperconjugation—experimental aspects[§]

Several distinct lines of evidence suggest that a methyl group —CH_3, when attached to a resonating system, or even to a single atom which contains π electrons, behaves as if it were conjugated to the attached group. To a lesser degree this is also true for —$CH_2 . CH_3$ and other alkyl radicals, as well as for $\diagdown CH_2$. Earlier evidence was largely derived from the effects of alkyl substitution on the reaction rates of benzyl bromide and benzyl chloride; it appeared that alkyl substitution caused electronic charge to flow into the benzene nucleus, and that this charge transfer was most effective with the methyl radical as substituent. Evidence from reaction rates is always difficult to interpret in an unambiguous way; and fortunately there are plenty of other effects which reveal the phenomenon. Following Mulliken[‖] we refer to the phenomenon itself as hyperconjugation, i.e. an additional conjugation beyond that ordinarily recognized.

In the first place the *ortho-para* directing property of the methyl group in toluene is shown by the existence of a dipole moment 0·4 D for this molecule. Now —CH_3 in methane is obviously equivalent to $\diagdown CH$, since CH_4 has no net dipole moment. But when C—H in benzene is replaced by C—CH_3 a moment appears.

† See, for example, C. J. B. Clews and W. Cochran, *Acta Cryst.*, 1949, **2**, 46.
‡ W. T. Astbury, *Trans. Faraday Soc.*, 1940, **36**, 871.
§ For a general review see V. A. Crawford, *Quart. Rev.*, 1949, 3, 226; and a series of articles collected in *Tetrahedron*, 1959, 5, 105–274. A complete account of the experimental work is in *Hyperconjugation*, by J. W. Baker, Clarendon Press, Oxford, 1952; and in *Hyperconjugation*, by M. J. S. Dewar, Ronald Press Company, New York, 1962.   ‖ *J. Chem. Phys.*, 1939, **7**, 339.

Comparison of the moments of nitrobenzene (I) and nitrotoluene (II) shows that the moment of the methyl group in the latter molecule is in the same direction as that of the nitro group and that the two contributions are practically additive. This confirms that in toluene (III) the methyl group is positive with respect to the benzene ring.

It appears from the above that certain electrons are able to

$\mu = 4{\cdot}0$ D	$\mu = 4{\cdot}5$ D	$\mu = 0{\cdot}4$ D

All moments in benzene solution.

(I)   (II)   (III)

migrate in and out of the benzene ring; they are therefore delocalized and we should accordingly expect a resonance energy stabilizing the molecule. This is precisely what is found. Accurate heats of combustion show that toluene is about 1·5 kcal/mole more stable than would be expected on the basis of the usual bond additivity rules. This is evidently a kind of delocalization energy (see Chapter IX), though its magnitude is much smaller than with conventional π-electron molecules such as benzene or naphthalene. The effect is not confined to toluene, however, for Mulliken, Rieke, and Brown[†] have shown from a comparison of the heats of combustion of a large number of hydrocarbons, including those containing methylated double bonds but no ordinary conjugation, that the total binding energy of a molecule may be predicted to about ± 1 kcal/mole by use of the additivity relations provided that a quantity 1·5 kcal/mole is included for each methyl group. Energy differences of this magnitude may be quite important in determining reaction rates. In this way hyperconjugation seems to be significant in the oxidation of hydrocarbons.[‡] There is also evidence that the charge displacements previously described are involved in the carcinogenic activity of certain aromatic hydrocarbons.[§]

[†] R. S. Mulliken, C. A. Rieke, and W. G. Brown, *J. Amer. Chem. Soc.*, 1941, **63**, 41.
[‡] C. F. Cullis, C. N. Hinshelwood, and M. F. R. Mulcahy, *Proc. Roy. Soc.* A, 1949, **196**, 160.
[§] A. Pullman, *Ann. Chim.*, 1947, **2**, 5; and A. and B. Pullman, *Cancérisation par les substances chimiques et structure moléculaire*, Masson, Paris, 1955.

Since the total energy of the molecule is altered by the replacement of H by CH_3, we should expect that the same would be true of the excited levels and therefore also of the spectrum. This is the case. Table 34† shows in the first two rows the ionization potentials of various methylated ethylenes both in the ground state and in

TABLE 34. *Ionization potentials in eV of methyl-substituted ethylenes* ($C_2H_{4-n}Me_n$)

No. of methyl groups (n)	0	1	2§	3	4
Ionization potential:					
ground state	10·51	9·73	9·13	8·68	8·30
excited state	2·9	2·6	2·2	1·9	1·7
Difference	7·6	7·1	6·9	6·8	6·6

§ These figures refer to *cis*-butene.

the first excited singlet state, which corresponds to a transition $\pi \rightarrow \pi^*$ (§ 4.7). The difference between these rows is shown in the bottom row, which gives the approximate position of the first absorption band. Quite evidently there is a shift to the red with each successive methylation. This shift is also usually found in methylated aromatic and conjugated systems,‡ and plays an important part in the design of new dye molecules.

We must be careful not to attribute the whole of the effects described in Table 34 to hyperconjugation. For in addition there is an inductive effect. This latter effect arises because, in methyl ethylene for example, the trigonal carbon of the double bond is more electronegative than the tetrahedral carbon of the methyl group (§ 8.9), and consequently the σ-bond between the two carbons will have a small polar character in which the σ-charge flows to the ethylenic carbon. This extra charge will repel the π electrons of the double bond and reduce their ionization potential

† Adapted from R. S. Mulliken, *Rev. Mod. Phys.*, 1942, **14**, 265, and R. Brailsford, P. V. Harris, and W. C. Price, *Proc. Roy. Soc.* A, 1960, **258**, 459; the original values were determined by W. C. Price and W. T. Tutte.

‡ This rule breaks down when the distribution of π electrons on the various nuclei is not uniform. This includes non-alternant hydrocarbons such as azulene, where there is at least one ring with an odd number of carbon atoms; and also heteronuclear aromatics, such as pyridine. For details see C. A. Coulson, *Proc. Phys. Soc.* A, 1952, **65**, 933, and H. C. Longuet-Higgins and R. G. Sowden, *J. Chem. Soc.*, 1952, p. 1404.

just as in the carbonyl bonds of Table 15 (p. 195). Without doubt this is one of the reasons why, on passing from ethylene to propylene, the ionization potential drops from 10·51 to 9·73 eV. But it is unlikely to be the only reason, as the following argument shows.

Let the methyl group be attached to carbon A of the ethylenic bond A—B. Then in the language of § 4.3 the allowed m.o.'s for the π electrons are $c_1 \psi_A + c_2 \psi_B$, where ψ_A and ψ_B are π a.o.'s, and c_1, c_2 are chosen to satisfy the secular equations. The energies of these m.o.'s satisfy the equation (4.5). If we neglect the overlap integral S, and put $E_A = E_B + \delta$, so that δ measures the inductive effect on A, these energies are

$$E = E_B \pm \beta + \tfrac{1}{2}\delta + \text{terms in } \delta^2 \text{ and higher powers.}$$

For the unsubstituted ethylene $\delta = 0$, and so

$$E = E_B \pm \beta.$$

Hence the inductive effect changes the allowed energies of the π and π^* orbitals by $\tfrac{1}{2}\delta + \text{terms in } \delta^2$. Thus if δ is small, both the ground state and excited state should be affected in nearly the same way. But Table 34 shows that whereas the ionization potential in the ground state is decreased by 0·8 eV, in the excited state the decrease is only 0·3 eV. We are therefore obliged to conclude that hyperconjugation plays a significant role as well as the inductive effect; and further, since increased delocalization would be expected to lower the energies, it appears likely that hyperconjugation affects the excited state more than it affects the ground state.

Before we explain how the m.o. and v.b. theories account for hyperconjugation, we must refer to a further effect. In toluene, for example, the methyl group acts as a donor bond, and the C—H bond length should be slightly increased. Mulliken, Rieke, and Brown† calculate this increase to be 0·001 A, which is quite inappreciable. On the other hand, the C—Me bond is an acceptor and its length should decrease. It has often been claimed that there is evidence for such a decrease in methyl acetylene CH_3—$C'{\equiv}C''H$,

† Loc. cit.

where the effect should be enhanced since (see § 13.4) there is hyperconjugation in both the y and z directions. In this molecule the length C—C' is 1·46 A, considerably less than the normal value 1·54 A for carbon–carbon single bonds. But part of this decrease must be attributed to a change of atomic radius from tetrahedral to digonal carbon at the end C' of the bond C—C': indeed, if we use the C—H bond lengths in Table 17 (p. 210) to infer the corresponding change in covalent radius of carbon, we should conclude that there was a decrease of about 0·03 A on passing from tetrahedral to digonal hybridization. This is only about one half of the observed shortening of 0·08 A, and would lead us to suppose that the rest was due to hyperconjugation.

13.4. Hyperconjugation—theoretical

The explanation of hyperconjugation is a little different, according to our choice of m.o. or v.b. language. Let us choose toluene as our example. In v.b. terms the molecule would be described as a resonance hybrid of the structures (I)–(V), in which (I) is taken to include all five normal structures for benzene as in Figs. 9.2 and

(I)   (II)   (III)   (IV)   (V)

9.4; (II) and (III) represent covalent structures with one long bond; and finally (IV) and (V) are typical ionic structures. It will be seen that (II)–(V) all provide a partial double-bond character for the C—Me bond, and therefore explain how bond length changes arise. They also show that charge flows from the H atoms into the *ortho*- and *para*- positions in the ring. It is unfortunate that at present no satisfactory ways exist for determining the relative weights of the various structures, so that this account is descriptive only. It should also be pointed out that what appears as a double bond in the C—Me link in (II)–(V) is not a conventional

π-bond, since it arises from the pairing of a tetrahedral orbital directed towards one of the H atoms with a π orbital on C_1 of the benzene ring.

This type of explanation shows us at once why the dipole moment of acetaldehyde (2·72 D) is greater than that of formaldehyde (2·27 ± 0·1 D). For in acetaldehyde there are hyperconjugation structures such as (VI) which have no counterpart in formaldehyde, and in which the positive and negative charges are considerably separated. Similarly if the CHO group of acetaldehyde

is replaced by a Cl atom to give CH_3Cl, there will be structures such as (VII) analogous to (VI) except that the use of a chlorine π orbital for the formation of a double bond requires that the Cl shall be positively charged, and the H negative. Pauling originally suggested resonance with this type of structure to explain certain bond contractions such as would occur if the C—Cl bond partook of some double-bond character. However, structures such as (VII), which require the removal of an electron from an electronegative atom and its addition to an electropositive one, are not energetically favourable. It seems possible that at least part of the bond contractions observed are due to hybridization effects (Chapter VIII) in the C or Cl atoms,† or in both.

Structure (VII) in which the C—Cl bond appears double, may not be very important for methyl chloride. But similar structures (e.g. (VIII)) become much more important if the methyl group is replaced by a vinyl group, to give vinyl chloride. Here the opportunities for π-electron delocalization are more favourable, with the result that C—Cl acquires a distinct double-bond character, and, as a necessary corollary, the Cl atom loses π electrons. The first of these phenomena is shown by a shortening of the C—Cl bond length (1·69 A in vinyl chloride as compared with 1·77 A in methyl chloride—though part of this difference will be due to a hybridiza-

† J. Duchesne, *Trans. Faraday Soc.*, 1950, **46**, 187.

tion change from sp^2 to sp^3): and the second is shown† by the much reduced reactivity of the chlorine in substituted aromatic and conjugated molecules as compared with similar substituted aliphatic compounds.

Discussions of this kind justify the inclusion of ionic structures such as (IV) and (V) in our account of hyperconjugation.

The m.o. description of this phenomenon requires us to show how electrons of a methyl group can acquire a delocalization into the π orbitals of, for example, a benzene ring. Now the symmetry

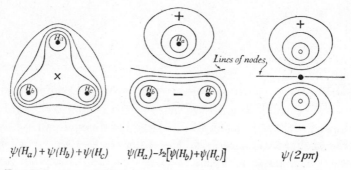

$$\psi(H_a) + \psi(H_b) + \psi(H_c) \qquad \psi(H_a) - \tfrac{1}{2}[\psi(H_b) + \psi(H_c)] \qquad \psi(2p\pi)$$

FIG. 13.6. Group orbitals in toluene. H_a, H_b, and H_c are the three hydrogen atoms of the methyl group.

arguments of Chapter IV tell us that this is only possible if, in the CH_3 group, we can find orbitals of π-character. So far as the C atom is concerned this is easy, for they are simply suitable $2p$ a.o.'s; and for the H atoms it may be achieved by treating H_3 as a single group. Let us call the three hydrogens H_a, H_b, H_c, with a.o.'s ψ_a, ψ_b, ψ_c. Then we may form 'group orbitals' of the type

$$\psi_a + \psi_b + \psi_c, \qquad \psi_a - \tfrac{1}{2}(\psi_b + \psi_c). \tag{1}$$

Approximate contours of these group orbitals are shown in Fig. 6.‡ It is obvious that the first of these orbitals is approximately symmetrical around the axis perpendicular to the paper through the point marked with a cross. This axis is the Me—C bond. We could say that the orbital has σ-type symmetry relative to this bond,

† Quadrupole coupling measurements by J. H. Goldstein, *J. Chem. Phys.*, 1956, **24**, 106, suggest that in vinyl chloride approximately 0·06 π electrons have left the chlorine nucleus, presumably in a manner similar to that represented by (VIII).

‡ C. A. Coulson, *Quart. Rev.*, 1947, **1**, 144.

and any delocalization in which it could take part would be σ hyperconjugation. Such delocalizations do take place in all paraffin molecules.† They are always present and are implicitly included in tables of bond energies. The second group orbital in (1), which is shown in the middle of Fig. 6, is evidently closely similar to a normal π-type orbital, such as is shown on the right. Thus there are regions in which ψ is positive and negative, with a nodal surface separating them, which corresponds very well with the nodal plane in a $2p\pi$ a.o. It is because the H_3 group can function like this that π delocalization, or hyperconjugation, can take place. We may therefore think of the H_3 group as being represented by some kind of pseudo-atom, with a π orbital that could conjugate with the benzene ring.

There is, in fact, a third group orbital in addition to the two shown in (1). All three are mutually orthogonal, as they should be if they are to have any simple physical significance, and the third one has a wave function

$$\psi_b - \psi_c. \tag{2}$$

This corresponds to a π orbital at 90° to the former one. Thus in toluene, which we could draw symbolically as (I), we have one species of π hyperconjugation; and in methyl acetylene (II) we have both π_y and π_z hyperconjugation, where the y- and z-directions

(I)   (II)   (III)

are both at right-angles to the axis of the molecule. In the same way, as was first shown by Mulliken,‡ cyclopentadiene (III) should receive additional stabilization by hyperconjugation involving the H_2 group in the form (2).

(IV)   (V)

---

† For details in the case of methane, see C. A. Coulson, *Trans. Faraday Soc.*, 1942, **38**, 433. The presence of these delocalizations is partly responsible for the differences in energy between straight-chain and branched paraffins.

‡ *J. Chem. Phys.*, 1939, **7**, 339.

When making calculations by the m.o. method we therefore treat toluene as if it were (IV) and assign reasonable Coulomb terms and resonance integrals to the pseudo-atom X and the pseudo-bond X—C. The total effective number of π electrons is taken to be 8. When plausible values are assumed for the various parameters, the final charge distribution (V) is obtained.† These figures give the observed molecular dipole moment 0·39 D. According to these calculations the charge migrations to the *ortho-* and *para-* positions are quite small, and the greater part of the polarity resides in the region of the methyl group itself. The small size of the charge migrations into the ring is in agreement with nuclear magnetic resonance measurements when the chemical shifts, of the *ortho-*, *meta-*, and *para-*protons appear to be almost equal.‡

It might be thought from this that the phenomenon of hyperconjugation was fully understood. This is far from being the case. Thus Dewar and Schmeising§ list five types of experiment commonly quoted as evidence for it. These are:

    (*a*) the shortening of σ-bonds, as in methyl acetylene,

    (*b*) greater stability than is obtained from the addition of normal bond energies; and correspondingly lower heats of hydrogenation per double bond,

    (*c*) dipole moments in molecules such as toluene,

    (*d*) absorption of light in the ultra-violet,

    (*e*) difference in chemical reactivity between hyperconjugated molecules and their unconjugated analogues.

But not one of these provides unequivocal evidence for hyperconjugation in the ground state of the isolated molecule. For (*a*) the shortening of the bonds is at least partly due to changes of hybridization; (*b*) σ-bonds between two sp^2-carbon atoms, or between one sp^2-carbon and another sp^3-carbon, will not be expected to have quite the same energy as between two sp^3-atoms; (*c*) the sp^2-atom will be more electronegative than the sp^3-atom,

† C. A. Coulson and V. A. Crawford, *J. Chem. Soc.*, 1953, p. 2052. More recent estimates of the charge distribution are due to A. Streitwieser and P. M. Nair, *Tetrahedron*, 1959, **5**, 149.

‡ See J. A. Pople, W. G. Schneider, and H. J. Bernstein, *High Resolution Nuclear Magnetic Resonance*, McGraw-Hill, 1959.

§ M. J. S. Dewar and H. N. Schmeising, *Tetrahedron*, 1959, **5**, 166.

so that we should expect some small dipole moment in the σ-bonds,† without the need to introduce π delocalization; (d) absorption of light refers to an energy difference between the ground and an excited state, so that no definite conclusions can be drawn with regard to either alone; (e) reactivity is determined only in part by the isolated unperturbed molecule, but depends very considerably on the ease with which the molecule may be perturbed away from its stationary ground state, many of the characteristics of the transition state being quite different from those of the isolated reactants.

In view of these criticisms, the status of hyperconjugation in the ground state of a molecule cannot be regarded as completely established. But the following conclusions do appear to be substantiated:‡

(i) hyperconjugation is usually more extensive in excited states than in ground states;

(ii) hyperconjugation is usually more effective in cations (carbonium ions) and anions than in neutral molecules;

(iii) hyperconjugation is usually more important in radicals than in neutral molecules.

With this rather abbreviated introduction to a very confused situation we must now leave this topic.

13.5. Hindered rotation around a single bond

In all our discussions of σ-bonds we have supposed that there was an exact axial symmetry around the bond direction. This would imply, as originally postulated by van 't Hoff, that there was no intrinsic resistance to rotation of the two groups at either end of the bond relative to each other. In this respect there is a sharp distinction between σ- and π-bonds, for, as we showed in § 8.2, the reduced overlapping of π orbitals in a double bond when they are no longer parallel leads to reduced binding; this implies that work has to be done in order to rotate one end relative to the

† A. J. Petro, *J. Amer. Chem. Soc.*, 1958, **80**, 4230.
‡ See, for example, N. Muller and R. S. Mulliken, *J. Amer. Chem. Soc.*, 1958, **80**, 3489; R. S. Mulliken, *Tetrahedron*, 1959, **5**, 253, where the concepts of isovalent and sacrificial hyperconjugation are developed

other. No such condition obtains with σ-bonds, and we might therefore expect free rotation around them. In fact, as entropy studies and (sometimes) spectroscopic and microwave analysis show, there are frequently barriers of the order of 1 to 4 kcal/mole opposing such rotation. Table 35 gives some experimental barrier heights.

TABLE 35. *Barrier heights*† *(kcal/mole) for internal rotation in molecules* CH_3X

X =	CH_3	C_2H_5	CF_3	OH	CHO
Barrier height =	2·8	3·3	1·5	1·07	1·15

The explanation of these surprisingly high values presents some difficulty. Let us consider the ethane molecule as an example. In this case the barrier is high, despite the fact that the polarity of the C—H bonds is low. Indeed we can discount any possible explanation in terms of purely Coulombic forces due to point charges on the various nuclei: for if the six H atoms were in fact completely denuded of electrons, so that they were simply bare protons, the barrier height—which here corresponds to the change in energy when one CH_3 group is rotated through 60°—would only be 5·2 kcal/mole. Now the effective charge on the H atoms is much less than this—crude dipole moment calculations suggest a value less than $e/10$, leading to a barrier height $1/100 \times 5·2$ kcal/mole. This is less than 2 per cent. of the observed value.

Further confirmation of this comes from the fact (Table 35) that replacing the nearly neutral H atoms of CH_3 by the more strongly charged F atoms, as in $H_3C.CF_3$, appears to reduce, and not to increase, the barrier height.

Another possibility is that some kind of exchange interaction might provide a suitable barrier. However, a simple application of the formula of perfect pairing (7.25) soon shows us, as we should expect, that the only terms in the energy which depend on the

† All except the first two heights are obtained by microwave analysis (see E. B. Wilson, *Advances in Chemical Physics*, Interscience, 1959, **2**, 367, and K. S. Pitzer, *Discussions Faraday Soc.*, 1951, **10**, 66). It has been shown by Blade and Kimball (*J. Chem. Phys.*, 1950, **18**, 630) that many of the earlier values in the literature are seriously wrong when they are obtained by thermodynamic methods. But the thermodynamic value for ethane is confirmed spectroscopically by D. R. Lide, *J. Chem. Phys.*, 1958, **29**, 1426.

mutual angle between the two CH_3 groups are those representing H...H interactions. It has been calculated by Eyring[†] that these interactions contribute only about 0·4 kcal/mole to the barrier: they have the further disadvantage that they predict a condition of lowest energy in the *cis* position, where the methyl groups face one another along the direction of the C—C bond, whereas the observed equilibrium is in the *trans*, or staggered, position, where the mutual angle of twist is 60°.

There are three other possible ways in which the resistance to rotation might conceivably arise. They are

(i) asymmetry of the C—C σ-bond,

(ii) hyperconjugation,

(iii) forces between non-adjacent bonds.

Let us discuss these in turn, keeping to ethane as our example.

It was suggested by Gorin, Walter, and Eyring[‡] that the central σ-bond in ethane was not composed solely of $2s$ and $2p\sigma$ a.o.'s, but that there was an admixture of $4f$. This is the lowest orbital which would certainly permit a non-axially symmetrical distribution of charge in the C—C bond, and would therefore provide some resistance to twisting. In a rough way this admixture of $4f$ orbitals could be thought of as an allowance for the polarization of the C—C bond by the aggregate of C—H bonds. Explicit calculation, however, shows that, owing to the high energy of $4f$ a.o.'s relative to $2s$ and $2p$ orbitals, the amount of $4f$ that is likely to be present is so small as not to provide more than a small fraction of the observed barrier height. Another possibility is to include some $3d$ a.o.'s in the tetrahedral hybrids at each carbon atom. Table 19 (p. 230) shows that this may be done. It appears to lead to a barrier not exceeding 0·6 kcal/mole, and, even then, probably with the *trans* position the more stable.

The second suggestion invokes hyperconjugation. In addition to the normal structure (I) there will be other structures such as (II) and (III) which will all provide a small double-bond character for the central C—C bond, and consequently lead to a barrier. The height of the barrier is not easy to calculate, but since (§ 3) the

[†] *J. Amer. Chem. Soc.* 1932, 54, 3191.   [‡] *Ibid.*, 1939, 61, 1876.

total hyperconjugation energy of two CH_3 groups is only about 3 kcal/mole, it seems extremely unlikely that such an explanation

$$
\begin{array}{ccc}
\mathrm{H} \diagdown \quad \diagup \mathrm{H} & \mathrm{H} \qquad \mathrm{H} & \mathrm{H}^+ \qquad \mathrm{H}^- \\
\mathrm{H-C-C-H} & \mathrm{H-C=C-H} & \mathrm{H-C=C-H} \\
\mathrm{H} \diagup \quad \diagdown \mathrm{H} & \mathrm{H} \diagup \quad \diagdown \mathrm{H} & \mathrm{H} \diagup \quad \diagdown \mathrm{H} \\
\text{(I)} & \text{(II)} & \text{(III)}
\end{array}
$$

as this could provide more than a small fraction, perhaps 0·3 kcal/mole, of the observed value.

The final suggestion is that there are significant forces between each pair of C—H bonds. Only the C—H bonds at opposite ends of the molecule can influence the potential barrier. Their mutual interaction will consist partly of exchange forces and partly of purely classical electrostatic forces. Two distinct proposals have been made, both of which still allow the charge distribution of each C—H bond to preserve axial symmetry. The suggestion made by E. N. Lassettre and L. B. Dean[†] is that in addition to a small dipole moment, each C—H bond has a quadrupole moment. As we have seen, the interaction of the C—H dipole moments is too small to produce the required barrier height. But it is now proposed that the quadrupole moments are sufficiently large to do so. Higher multipole moments could be considered also (e.g. octupole), but they would be most unlikely to be effective if both dipole and quadrupole moments failed. All exchange forces are neglected. Unfortunately our present knowledge of the details of the charge distribution in C—H bonds is inadequate to calculate the quadrupole moment with any great precision, though the rough calculations of Lassettre and Dean show that their suggestion is not absurd.

More recently, however, Linus Pauling[‡] has urged further consideration of the detailed shape of the charge-cloud for each C—H bond. He shows that if we add small amounts of d- and f-type orbitals to the primary sp^3 tetrahedral hybrids at each carbon atom, we may be able to build up a sufficiently strong interaction between the two methyl groups. We must not add too much

† *J. Chem. Phys.*, 1949, **17**, 317.   ‡ *Proc. Nat. Acad. Sci.*, 1958, **44**, 211.

because of the promotion energy required. But even a small amount will increase the overlapping and so strengthen the bond. His calculations suggest that the actual weight of these higher orbitals is about sufficient to provide the observed barrier for internal rotation. The final form obtained by Pauling† may be written

$$\psi = 0{\cdot}50s + 0{\cdot}83p + 0{\cdot}20d + 0{\cdot}14f,$$

where s, p, d, f denote atomic orbitals of type $2s, 2p, 3d, 4f$ and all possess cylindrical symmetry (e.g. the $3d$ function is the $3d_{z^2}$ orbital of page 42, with the z-axis lying along the C—H bond direction). This orbital ψ could be interpreted as implying 4 per cent. d-character ($0{\cdot}20^2 = 0{\cdot}04$), and 2 per cent. f-character. Exchange repulsions of the type $-\tfrac{1}{2}\Sigma J_{ij}$ in equation (7.25) lead to a zero barrier from the s and p contributions to ψ; but the d and f contributions do not vanish. The chief difficulties with this theory are that the method of estimating the d- and f-weights is not rigorous, and also that many other factors, such as polarity and quadrupole interactions, are neglected.

In view of the situation described above, it must be admitted that no entirely satisfactory explanation of the barrier to internal rotation has yet been provided. It seems likely that almost all of the factors we have described play some part, with no one of them so dominant as to be effectively the sole cause, but with modifications of the charge-cloud in each C—H bond as the most important.

It should be added, to avoid misunderstanding, that barriers of the height shown in Table 35 are still sufficiently low to permit the fast interconversion of isomers with deuterium replacing one or more hydrogens.

13.6. Electron-deficient molecules‡

The coordination around atoms in groups IV–VII is dominated by the $8-N$, or octet, rule (§§ 7.6 and 11.3). For atoms in group I, where there is only one loosely bound valence electron in an orbit of type ns, the tendency is to share this electron with as many other adjacent atoms as possible by the formation of a metal.

† *Nature of the Chemical Bond*, Cornell University Press, 3rd edn., 1960, p. 127.
‡ For a review see H. C. Longuet-Higgins, *Quart. Rev.*, 1957, **11**, 121.

Atoms of the remaining groups II and III may be expected to show both kinds of behaviour, according to circumstances. For this reason they are more difficult to systematize.

Group II atoms have a ground state $(ns)^2$, and, as suggested by Table 5 (p.102), they would thus be inert. For example, the ground state of Be_2 would be described as $(2s\sigma)^2(2s\sigma^*)^2$. According to the argument of § 6.1 this would be unstable. But by excitation of the type $s^2 \to sp$ they acquire a divalent character. A case in which this configuration occurs is BeO, which is evidently $\sigma^2\pi^2$, with a double bond similar to that in ethylene, except for the polarity induced by the difference in electronegativities of the two atoms. More usually, however, atoms of this group form triatomic molecules and then, as suggested in § 8.13, the sp configuration is replaced by digonal hybrids (cf. § 8.2) of form $s \pm p$. This will cause the molecule to be linear. Examples of this behaviour are the dichlorides and dibromides of Hg, Zn, and Cd. It is possible to write these molecules in a purely ionic form, as for example, $Cl^-Hg^{++}Cl^-$. No doubt such structures play a part, but they must be energetically less favourable than the structure involving hybrids. Furthermore, since the centre of mean position in a hybrid (cf. Fig. 8.2) is some distance away from the central nucleus, there is a very real sense in which the polarity represented by the ionic formula is already included in the bond diagram.

Even when this type of bonding occurs there are empty spaces in the valence shell of the group II atom. For that reason we may refer to these as electron-deficient molecules. In ionic crystals it is possible to fill up these empty spaces; this is partly why, in solids, atoms like Be are usually tetravalent. The ion BeF^{--} is tetrahedral, and although this can also be formulated as a purely ionic complex $Be^{++}(F^-)_4$, it is better to say that the Be atom makes use of four tetrahedral orbitals, whose centres of position are so far from the Be nucleus that the Be—F bonds have a considerable polarity $\overset{+\longrightarrow}{\text{Be—F}}$. A similar situation occurs in the ion BF_4^-.

Group III atoms behave in much the same way. In the unexcited form s^2p they should be monovalent. But relatively little energy is needed to excite to a valence-state sp^2. This would be expected to lead to trigonal plane bonds. In fact, both spectro-scopic and dipole measurements confirm that all the three known trihalogen compounds BF_3, BCl_3, BBr_3 are planar. In these mole-cules there is an incomplete octet round the boron atom, and consequently there are fewer repulsions than usual between elec-trons not actually paired together. This reduces the bond length, showing once again (cf. § 7.7) the importance of these non-bonding repulsions. Pauling† gives reasons for believing that this bond shortening is as large as 0·09 A. It may be called the sextet correction.

There is a further reason for this sextet correction. Our previous description concerns only σ-bonds. These leave a vacant π orbital on the central atom. Now if the outer atoms are halogens, they will each have two π electrons, which could therefore flow from the halogen atoms on to the central atom. This would be favoured by the fact that the molecule was planar, and that the three σ-bonds would tend to remove charge from the group III atom, and so increase its effective electronegativity. We might represent this, in v.b. language, by allowing resonance between structures such as (I), which is covalent, and (II), which is ionic. As a result the bonds acquire a partial double-bond character. This explanation

$$
\begin{array}{cc}
\underset{F}{\overset{F}{\diagdown}}\!\!\!B\!\!-\!\!F & \underset{F}{\overset{F}{\diagdown}}\!\!\!B^+\!\!=\!\!F^+ \\
\text{(I)} & \text{(II)}
\end{array}
$$

helps us to see why, although BH_3 does not exist (see next section: there are no π electrons on the H atoms), BMe_3 does, and has the plane trigonal character of BCl_3. Presumably the electron-donor property of the methyl group, discussed in § 13.4, provides suf-ficient π electrons by a species of hyperconjugation to allow the boron atom more nearly to complete its octet.

If the metaborate ion BO_2^- existed alone, it would be linear, as O^-—B^+—O^-. However, no such linear BO_2^- has been substanti-ated. The desire of the boron atom to complete its octet is shown by the fact that in water solution BO_2^-. $2H_2O$ forms tetrahedral

† *Nature of the Chemical Bond*, 1st edn., 1939, p. 160.

$B(OH)_4^-$. Anhydrous metaborates polymerise to increase the co-ordination. Similarly the complex $BH_3.CO$ exists and is tetra-hedral. Now in our account of CO in § 8.11 we showed that there are two lone-pair electrons at the carbon atom with orbitals strongly directed away from the oxygen atom. These two electrons can be used to provide a donor bond between the C and B atoms, without any serious dislocation of charge, since they can 'fall into' the empty tetrahedral orbitals of boron. A precisely similar explanation fits the formation of BH_3NMe_3, where the boron atom uses the strongly directed lone-pair electrons (§ 8.10) of NMe_3. Another way in

(III)   (IV)

which boron can complete its octet is by sharing π electrons in a similar fashion to that discussed in Chapter IX for aromatics. This is why, when B_2H_6 and NH_3 are heated to 200° C there results the compound borazole,† with formula $B_3N_3H_6$. On account of its structure (III) this is sometimes called 'inorganic benzene'. The boron atom is in a trigonal state, and there are six π electrons, two from each N atom. Resonance with Kekulé-like structures such as (IV) helps to complete the boron octets. As a result the B—N distance is only 1·44 A, considerably less than the expected normal single-bond distance 1·58 A. $B_3O_3Me_3$ has a similar hexagonal nucleus with B and O atoms alternating round the ring.

The recognition that a boron and a nitrogen atom can replace two carbon atoms has led to the development of an interesting new group of hetero-aromatic molecules, of which the boron aza-deriva-tive of phenanthrene‡ (V) is a particular example. An extreme

† Also sometimes called borazine. Molecular-orbital calculations for borazole have been made by D. W. Davies, *Trans. Faraday Soc.*, 1960, **56**, 1713.

‡ M. J. S. Dewar, V. P. Kubba, and R. Pettit, *J. Chem. Soc.*, 1958, p. 3073.

form occurs in the layer-lattice of boron nitride (VI), where each plane resembles a graphite layer plane.†

(V)   (VI)

In the field of saturated molecules a similar replacement-situation occurs. We have already met it earlier in this section in the formation of $H_3B.NMe_3$ analogous to $H_3C.CMe_3$. There is also a most interesting tetrahedral boron nitride, entirely similar to the tetrahedral diamond lattice but with alternate boron and nitrogen atoms.‡

13.7. Boron hydrides

Our discussion in § 6 has omitted what is almost certainly the most interesting type of binding involving boron. This occurs in the boron hydrides, § with which we shall couple certain aluminium and beryllium hydrides. We have already stressed the fact that the borine radical BH_3 does not exist; but diborane B_2H_6 does exist and is quite stable. For many years it was believed that B_2H_6 had the same structure as ethane C_2H_6, and it was often written as $BH_3.BH_3$. The fact that there were not enough valence electrons to complete the bonds was interpreted in terms of resonance between structures containing one-electron bonds, or even with one bond missing, so that on the average each bond had a strength 6/7 of a normal single bond. But careful spectroscopic analysis of its rotation-vibration spectrum by W. C. Price|| makes it clear that the molecule has a twofold axis of symmetry along the line joining

† See R. Taylor and C. A. Coulson, *Proc. Phys. Soc.* A, 1952, **65**, 834, for calculations; R. S. Pease, *Nature*, 1950, **165**, 722, for structure determination.

‡ See L. Kleinman and J. C. Phillips, *Phys. Rev.*, 1960, **117**, 460, for calculations; R. H. Wentorf, *J. Chem. Phys.*, 1957, **26**, 956, for preparation.

§ Reviews are given by R. P. Bell and H. J. Emeleus, *Quart. Rev.*, 1948, **2**, 132; and H. C. Longuet-Higgins, *Quart. Rev.*, 1957, **11**, 121.

|| *J. Chem. Phys.*, 1947, **15**, 614.

the two boron atoms. The structure which is proposed† is shown in (I), in which the two terminal BH_2 groups are coplanar, and the two central hydrogens lie symmetrically above and below this plane. We shall shortly have to discuss the nature of the bonds

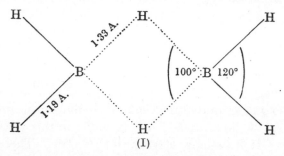

(I)

joining these two hydrogen atoms to the boron atoms, but for the present we represent them by dotted lines, as in (I). Structures of this type are called 'Bridge Structures'. The bridge structure (I), in which four of the hydrogens are different from the other two, is in agreement with chemical evidence that any number up to but not exceeding four of the hydrogens in B_2H_6 may be substituted without great difficulty. It also gives a satisfactory explanation‡ of the vibrational spectrum, and in the case of bromodiborane B_2H_5Br,§ of the rotational fine structure. Finally, in the case of B_2H_6, using the boron isotope of mass 11, whose nucleus has a spin $\frac{3}{2}$, it has been shown‖ by J. N. Shoolery that the complicated nuclear magnetic resonance spectrum is only compatible with a bridge structure. It may therefore be regarded as established.

Once having admitted the possibility of bridge structures such as (I), it is not difficult to find other examples. The next two elements in group III are Al and Ga, which form hydrogen bridge structures†† such as (II) and (III). The aluminium system is interesting because it stretches over the whole of the plane, each pair

---

† Originally proposed by W. Dilthey, *Z. angew. Chem.*, 1921, **34**, 596, but revived by B. V. Nekrassov, *J. Gen. Chem. URSS*, 1940, **10**, 1021, 1156, and by Y. K. Syrkin and M. E. Dyatkina, *Acta Physicochim. URSS*, 1941, **14**, 547.

‡ W. C. Price, loc. cit.; H. C. Longuet-Higgins and R. P. Bell, *J. Chem. Soc.*, 1943, p. 250.

§ C. D. Cornwell, *J. Chem. Phys.*, 1950, **18**, 1118.

‖ *Discussions Faraday Soc.*, 1955, **19**, 215.

†† H. C. Longuet-Higgins, *J. Chim. phys.*, 1949, **46**, 268.

of adjacent Al atoms being bridged by two H atoms above and below the plane. There is also an aluminium borohydride† (IV)

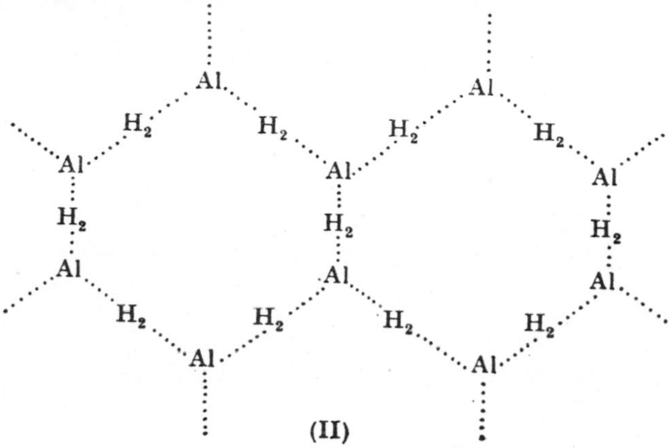

(II)

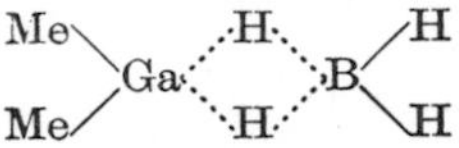

(III)

with octahedral coordination around the Al atom, and, interestingly enough, a beryllium compound (V). However, when we continue this sequence to the alkali compound lithium borohydride (VI), the structure goes over into an ionic lattice involving Li^+ and BH_4^-. Furthermore a whole series of higher borohydrides exist, of

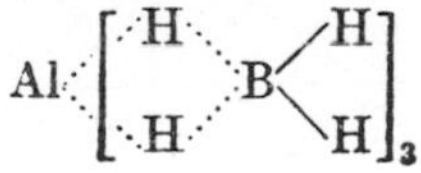

(IV)

(V)

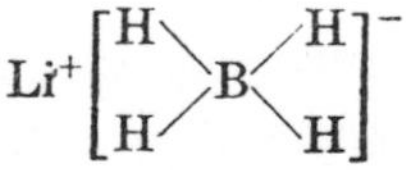

(VI)

which (VII) is a simple example; and the dimer of $AlCl_3$ is often written in what is essentially the same form (VIII).

† W. C. Price, *J. Chem. Phys.*, 1949, **17**, 1044.

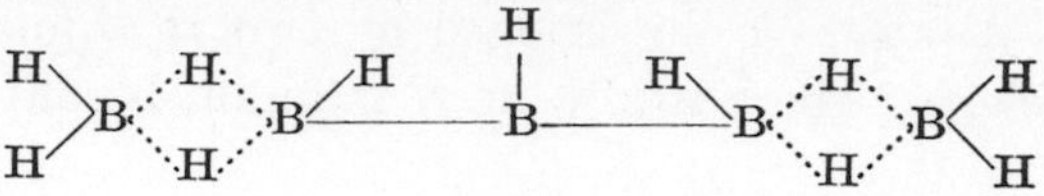

(VII)

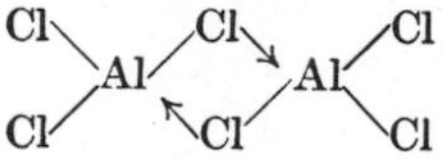

(VIII)

Bridge molecules are not confined to group III elements. Thus there is a $BeCl_2$ polymer† represented by (IX) as well as the mixed

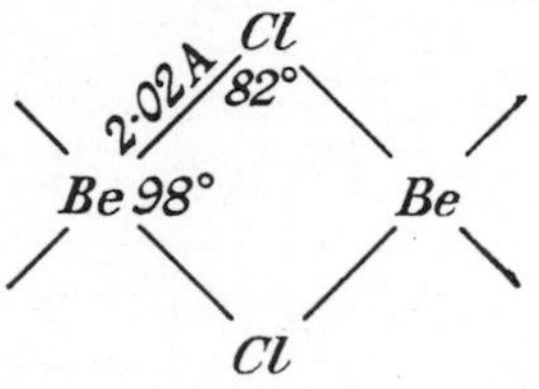

(IX)

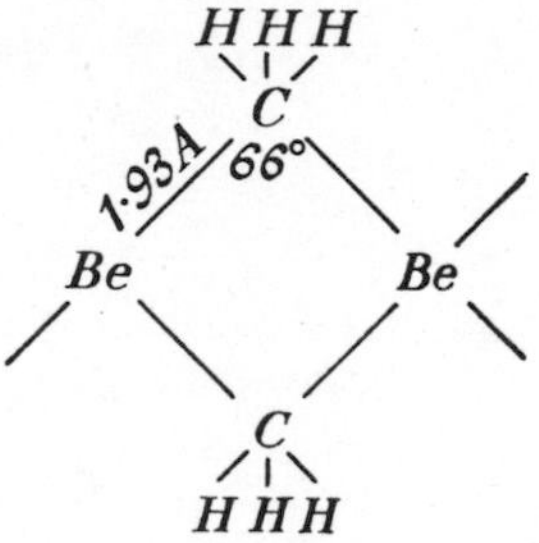

(X)

boron-beryllium compound (V). There is also a similar polymer (X) with methyl groups‡ replacing the chlorine atoms. From the geometry of this molecule it would seem as if the role of the $1s$ orbital of a bridge hydrogen can equally be taken by a $3p$ orbital of chlorine, or a tetrahedral sp^3 hybrid of carbon. So also an amino group NH_2 may replace one of the bridge hydrogen atoms in diborane.

Bridge molecules are therefore not uncommon. We must now discuss the interpretations put forward to explain this valence situation.

13.8. Theoretical interpretation of bridge structures

A large number of different interpretations have been proposed. We shall discuss these one by one.

(i) *Hydrogen bond.* Since hydrogen appears to join two atoms together, there is a certain similarity to the hydrogen bond

† R. E. Rundle and P. H. Lewis, *J. Chem. Phys.*, 1952, **20**, 132.
‡ A. I. Snow and R. E. Rundle, *Acta Cryst.*, 1951, **4**, 348.

described earlier in this chapter. This similarity is only formal, however, because the B—H bond is almost without any dipole moment. (On Pauling's electronegativity scale

$$x_B = 2 \cdot 0, \qquad x_H = 2 \cdot 1.)$$

We may therefore neglect the possibility of such an electrostatic origin for the bridge.

(ii) *Covalent resonance.* We may write two covalent structures (I) and (II) between which resonance might occur, leading to a

(I)   (II)

symmetrical molecule. This interpretation is inadequate because, as Syrkin and Dyatkina showed,[†] the resulting resonance energy is insufficient to offset the unfavourable valence angles and the repulsion of non-paired electrons. In addition, the B···B distance is so short that (see later) it seems essential to include some form of B—B bonding.

(iii) *Ionic resonance.* Syrkin and Dyatkina next suggested that ionic structures such as (III) might contribute to the resonance.

(III)

Once more the valence angles are not favourable, and the calculations of Syrkin and Dyatkina, although they gave a fairly large stabilization, completely neglected some of the known repulsions between non-paired electrons.[‡]

(iv) *Protonated double bond.* It was suggested by K. S. Pitzer[§] that diborane was essentially similar to ethylene, except that the two bridge protons were embedded in the charge-cloud of the π-bond, as shown in (IV). This is in agreement with the close

(IV)

† Loc. cit.   ‡ Longuet-Higgins and Bell, loc. cit.
§ *J. Amer. Chem. Soc.*, 1945, **67**, 1126.

similarity in the two u.v. absorption spectra,† and is supported by
the fact that the B···B separation of 1·77 A is only 0·15 A greater
than would be expected for a double bond on the basis of a single-
bond covalent radius (Table 13, p.189) of 0·81 A. So also, Mulliken‡
finds that at this distance there is a substantial overlap between
the two boron $2p\pi$ a.o.'s. An objection to this description, which
otherwise is quite attractive, is that none of the hydrogens is labile.
Experimentally the chemical reactions of diborane§ and other
electron-deficient compounds suggest very strongly that they contain the hydride ion H^- rather than the proton H^+. Thus the
evidence for relatively bare, and therefore acidic, protons as in
(IV) is not convincing.

(v) *Three-centre bonds.* It was observed by Longuet-Higgins‖
that when the full wave function corresponding to Pitzer's ethylene model is written in the proper determinantal form (cf. equation 5.36), its terms may be rearranged, without in any way
altering the complete expansion, in such a manner as to describe
the bonding in the bridge by means of two similar three-centre
bonds. The boundary contours of these bonds are shown schematically in (V), and the orbitals, which are necessarily m.o.'s, are
compounded of approximately tetrahedral hybrids at the two
boron atoms and a $1s$ orbital at the appropriate hydrogen.

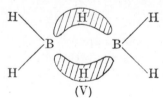

(V)

(vi) *Donor bonds.* It was suggested by Walsh and Eistert†† that
the B—H bonds, which are not particularly strong bonds, might
donate part of their density into the vacant B orbitals, as sug-

† W. C. Price, *J. Chem. Phys.*, 1948, **16**, 895.

‡ *Chem. Rev.*, 1947, **41**, 207.

§ A. E. Finholt, A. C. Bond, and H. I. Schlesinger, *J. Amer. Chem. Soc.*, 1947,
69, 1199.

‖ *J. Chim. phys.*, 1949, **46**, 275.

†† A. D. Walsh, *J. Chem. Soc.*, 1947, p. 89; B. Eistert, *Z. angew. Chem.* A, 1947,
59, 170.

gested by the formulation (VI). However, if there was no resonance with the mirror-image structure to (VI) this would give an

(VI)

unsymmetrical molecule, in which the two BH_2 groups were not
coplanar, and which would therefore be different from that
observed. If resonance is allowed, this merely becomes another
way of describing some of the earlier models.

(vii) *Introduction of d orbitals*. It has been proposed[†] that in the
case of the beryllium compounds (IX) and (X) of § 7 the chlorine
atom and the carbon atom might make use of $3d$ orbitals as well
as the more conventional $3p$ and sp^3 hybrids. It is certainly true
that such orbitals could be used, and could be employed in combination with the other orbitals in such a way as to give two
bridge bonds from each of these groups. But the excitation energy
in either case is very large, of the order of 10 eV. We should not
therefore expect such excited orbitals to play much part in the
binding. Further, even if we used them, their size (cf. p. 228)
would be so much larger than that of the other orbitals that effective hybridization would be very improbable. Even if this explanation were valid for (IX) and (X) it could not be expected to apply
to diborane, for the lowest d orbital in hydrogen is the $3d$ orbital,
whose size (see equation 2.12) is nine times as large as the fundamental $1s$ orbital. We therefore reject this introduction of
d orbitals as the main explanation of these bridged molecules.

It will be evident from the above that no completely satisfactory
account of these bridges has yet been given; (iv) and (v) appear to
be the most satisfactory. The first of these two fails because it
appears to suggest positive bridge atoms and a too-strong B—B
bond. The second fails because it does not appear to suggest any
direct B—B interaction. Yet Snow and Rundle[‡] show that if we
use Pauling's relation (equation 12.3) between bond number and
bond distance in dimethyl beryllium (X) we should expect bond

[†] R. J. Gillespie, *J. Chem. Soc.*, 1952, p. 1002.   [‡] Loc. cit.

numbers 0·35 and 0·31 for the Be—C and Be—Be bonds respectively. This would imply an almost equal bonding in metal-bridge atom and metal-metal bonds. Perhaps, therefore, (v) is the closest that we can get without becoming too detailed.

This is precisely the conclusion reached by molecular-orbital analysis.† Hamilton, for example, shows that if we desire one single simple representation, then the wave function associated

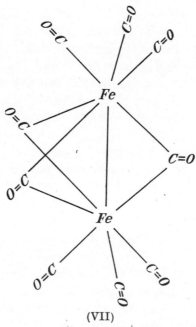

(VII)

with (v) is the closest that we can get. This is in agreement with the fact that the 'outer' B—H bonds are very normal, as judged by their calculated force constant.‡ But of course a more accurate calculation would need to include a good deal of configurational interaction, thus modifying the simple picture represented by (V).

It may be worth remarking here that situations such as that described above for dimethyl beryllium (X), where there is cross-

† W. Hamilton, *Proc. Roy. Soc.* A, 1956, **235**, 395; *J. Chem. Phys.*, 1958, **29**, 460; H. Brion, in *Calcul des Fonctions d'Onde Moléculaires*, Centre National de la Recherche Scientifique, Paris 1958, p. 85; M. Yamazaki, *J. Chem. Phys.*, 1957, **27**, 1401.

‡ R. P. Bell and H. C. Longuet-Higgins, *Proc. Roy. Soc.* A, 1945, **183**, 357.

ring bonding between two metal atoms, is by no means confined to this example; many other cases have been found. A particularly interesting situation occurs in di-iron enneacarbonyl,[†] $Fe_2(CO)_9$, where, as (VII) shows, in addition to the central 'cage' of Fe—C—Fe bonds, there is also direct Fe—Fe bonding. This is confirmed by the fact that the spins of the odd electrons on the Fe atoms are opposed, and also by the Fe—Fe distance. This is 2·46 A, almost the same as in metallic iron, 2·48 A.

Considerable success has been achieved, chiefly by Lipscomb[‡] and colleagues, in interpreting all the known borohydrides in terms of suitable combinations of conventional two-centre bonds, three-centre bonds of the 'open' type represented by (V), and—in some

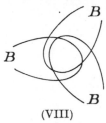

(VIII)

cases—three-centre bonds of a 'closed', or triangular, type involving the simultaneous symmetrical overlapping of orbitals on three boron atoms, where all three orbitals are hybrids, directed towards the centre of the boron triangle, as in (VIII). These three-centre bonds are a type of partly delocalized molecular orbital. In every case there are just enough valence electrons in the molecule to allot two to each of the bonding m.o.'s, and none to any of the other possible m.o.'s. In electron-deficient molecules of this kind it is clear that the idea of an old-fashioned electron-pair bond has broken down. The nearest that we can reach to maintaining the idea of paired electrons is by the use of these three-centre (and, occasionally, four-centre) molecular orbitals. The reason for this is quite simple to see. When we have more orbitals on the atoms than there are electrons to fill them by normal sharing, we have a situation very similar to that which we have already met in

† H. M. Powell and R. V. G. Ewens, *J. Chem. Soc.*, 1939, p. 286.
‡ W. N. Lipscomb, *J. Chem. Phys.*, 1954, **22**, 985; W. H. Eberhardt, B. Crawford and W. N. Lipscomb, ibid., 989.

metals: and the characteristic 'metallic orbital' of § 12.4 appears. In one sense, therefore, there is a close parallel between diborane and a tiny element of metal. This is why there is no hope of describing such molecules in terms of localized electron-pair bonds. This concept is now entirely inappropriate.

13.9. Inorganic π-electron rings

There is another type of three-centre bond which has now been discovered.† This occurs in ring systems built up from inorganic atoms such as phosphorus, sulphur, and nitrogen. We shall discuss the best-known of these, the phospho-nitrilic chlorides, formed from the molecule PCl_2N by bringing together three, or four, or more units in the manner represented by the trimer (I). But other

(I)   (II)   (III)

examples of the same type of situation‡ are provided by the tetramer ring system (II), and the trimer (III): and in (I) the chlorines may be replaced by F, NH_2, or CH_3. There is obviously a new type of bonding in all these molecules. The bond diagrams incorporated in (I)–(III) show possible ways in which we might attempt to account for this bonding. The analogy with aromatic molecules such as those discussed in Chapter IX is very tempting, and it has often been suggested that there is resonance between the structures shown in these diagrams and others, which differ in the location of the single and double bonds. Indeed, these molecules have sometimes been called 'inorganic aromatics'. However, we shall see later that this is not a very suitable description.

† D. P. Craig and N. L. Paddock, *Nature*, 1958, **181**, 1052.
‡ For a review of these compounds see M. Goehring, *Quart. Rev.*, 1956, **10**, 437: and A. G. Sharpe, *Ann. Rep. Chem. Soc.*, 1959, **56**, 112.

It will be noticed that in drawing the diagrams (I)–(III) we have treated nitrogen as trivalent, phosphorus as pentavalent, and sulphur as tetravalent. In the cases of P and S this can only be achieved by the use of d orbitals. Thus the outer shell of an isolated phosphorus atom consists of $(3s)^2(3p^3)$, and is associated with trivalence, as in the familiar phosphine PH_3. Pentavalence can only arise by excitation of one of the $3s$ electrons, to give $(3s)(3p)^3(3d)$. In sulphur the corresponding excitation is either $(3s)^2(3p^4) \rightarrow (3s)(3p)^4(3d)$ or $(3s)^2(3p)^4 \rightarrow (3s)^2(3p)^3(3d)$. It seems inevitable that we should have to use d orbitals: the only way to avoid them in (I), for example, would be to regard the molecule as an almost purely ionic one (IV). This structure may play a part,

(IV)

but it is quite unreasonable to treat it as a complete account of the molecule. The major difficulty now arises from the need to decide just which of the five possible d orbitals (see § 2.8) should be used, and in what way.

Let us consider the trimer (I). If we form approximately tetrahedral hybrids from the phosphorus $3s3p^3$ orbitals, we can establish a set of σ-bonds, of conventional type, for the P—Cl and P—N bonds. We should then be left with six unallocated electrons, one from each of the six atoms of the ring. The lowest available atomic orbitals with which we must seek to form molecular orbitals are the $2p\pi$ orbitals on each N atom and a choice from among all five $3d$ orbitals on each P atom. Now there are circumstances† in which a suitable d orbital could enter into resonance conjugation with adjacent $p\pi$ orbitals. Consider (V) the case of a $d\pi$ orbital on atom B placed between two $p\pi$ orbitals on A and C. With the directions of the axes as shown, the d orbital (see § 2.8) is the d_{xz}.

† First proposed in this form by H. C. Longuet-Higgins for thiophene, in *Trans. Faraday Soc.*, 1949, **45**, 173.

This orbital overlaps equally both A and C, and so we have the necessary condition for delocalized π-type m.o.'s. The chief difference is that, as is shown by the signs in the various lobes of the orbitals, the overlap is positive for B and C, but negative for A and B. This shows itself in the distinction between bonding and anti-bonding m.o.'s. Thus, if all three orbitals had been $p\pi$ orbitals, a bonding m.o. would be similar in general form to $\phi_A + \phi_B + \phi_C$; but in (V) this would give anti-bonding in the region A—B and bonding

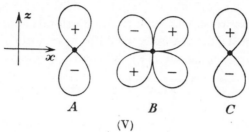

(V)

in B—C. Bonding in both regions would come from $-\phi_A + \phi_B + \phi_C$. In an actual problem, of course, the coefficients of the orbitals would not be exactly ± 1. But the relation between their bonding and anti-bonding character and the relative signs of the coefficients in an orbital $c_1 \phi_A + c_2 \phi_B + c_3 \phi_C$ would remain.

Now if (I) had possessed a planar central ring, we could have extended this discussion by allowing the delocalization of (V) to stretch round the ring, in just the same general way as the 'double-streamers' of Fig. 9.3 in benzene. Craig† has shown that, in such a case, the order of the m.o. levels is the inverse of that shown in Fig. 9.7. But according to this interpretation the π electrons would be fully delocalized, and we should have an aromatic type of molecule.

Recent analysis‡ has led to a modification of this picture in which the 'double-streamers' all round the ring are replaced by three-centre bonds. Consider (VI), the trimer (which for the moment we suppose to be planar), with the atom N_1 lying between P_1 and P_2. Let the z-axis be perpendicular to the molecular plane, and draw lines $P_1 x_1$, $P_1 y_1$, $P_2 x_2$, $P_2 y_2$, etc., as shown. Then there

† *J. Chem. Soc.*, 1959, p. 997; *Chem. Soc. Special Publ.*, 1958, no. 12, p. 343.
‡ M. J. S. Dewar, E. A. C. Lucken, and M. A. Whitehead, *J. Chem. Soc.*, 1960, p. 2423.

is very good overlapping of the $2p\pi$ orbital of N_1 with the $3d_{x_1z_1}$ and $3d_{x_2z_2}$ orbitals of P_1 and P_2. By choosing the signs of the linear combinations correctly, a strong three-centre π-bond can be formed. Its LCAO expression would be

$$\chi_1 = c_1\,(d_{x_1z_1}+d_{x_2z_2})+c_2\,p_{N_1}.$$

Presumably on account of the slightly greater electronegativity of p_{N_1} than $d_{x_1z_1}$ the coefficient c_2 will be a little greater than c_1. A

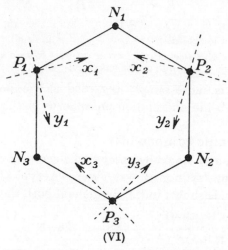

(VI)

similar three-centre π-bond χ_2 is formed from $d_{y_2z_2}$, p_{N_2}, and $d_{y_3z_3}$. Finally, a third such bond χ_3 is formed from $d_{x_3z_3}$, p_{N_3}, and $d_{y_1z_1}$. The π-electron description is then $\chi_1^2\,\chi_2^2\,\chi_3^2$. Dewar *et al.*† show that further mixing of χ_1, χ_2, χ_3 lowers the energy very little. It can also be shown that, provided that $P_1\,N_1\,P_2$ are kept fixed, the bonds P_1—N_3 and P_2—N_2 may be bent out of the plane $P_1\,N_1\,P_2$ without any loss of overlap energy. Thus the molecule is free to assume a buckled form. Experiment reveals a chair conformation. The tetramer and higher polymers must be at least equally buckled.‡ A rather schematic representation of the three-centre molecular orbital χ_1 is shown in (VII).

† Loc. cit.
‡ The tetramers $P_4N_4(NMe_2)_8$ and $P_4N_4Cl_8$ are known to be buckled in a boat-like configuration. See G. J. Bullen, *Proc. Chem. Soc.*, 1960, p. 425. However, $P_4N_4F_8$ is planar (or nearly); see H. McD. McGeachin and F. R. Tromans, *J. Chem. Soc.*, 1961, p. 4777.

c c

A similar discussion will apply to other inorganic ring molecules, such as (II) and (III). Their electronic distribution is not strictly

$$P'_1 \qquad N_1 \qquad P_2 \qquad\qquad P_1 \qquad N_1 \qquad P_2$$

(a)   (VII)   (b)

separate atomic orbitals   molecular orbital

Formation of three-centre molecular orbitals from a sequence of atomic orbitals $d\pi—p\pi—d\pi$.

aromatic, but is more simply regarded as composed of allylic regions, which begin and end on phosphorus or sulphur atoms.

13.10. Meso-ionic compounds†

In 1935 Earl and Mackney‡ prepared a series of compounds, to which the name 'sydnones' was given. A typical example, N-phenylsydnone, is shown in (I). In general both the phenyl group

(I)   (II)

(III)

and the hydrogen atom may be replaced by other similar substituents. The chief peculiarity of these partially aromatic conjugated compounds is that no possible covalent bond structure can be drawn to represent the electronic pairings. As Wilson Baker has pointed out, the closest analogies are provided by the aliphatic diazo-compounds, which are resonance hybrids of the ionic forms $\text{>C}=\text{N}^+=\text{N}^-$ and $\text{>C}^-—\text{N}^+\equiv\text{N}$, and the organic azides, which involve similar resonance between $\text{R}—\text{N}=\text{N}^+=\text{N}^-$ and $\text{R}—\text{N}^-—\text{N}^+\equiv\text{N}$. In the case of the sydnones, (II) and (III)

† For a review see Wilson Baker and W. D. Ollis, *Quart. Rev.*, 1957, **11**, 15.
‡ *J. Chem. Soc.*, 1935, p. 899.

represent some of the very large number of possibilities† among which we may suppose resonance to take place. Dipole moment measurements‡ show that for this particular sydnone $\mu = 6\cdot5$ D, with the positive pole at the phenyl end of the molecule. This value is considerably less than that which would be expected for any of the various ionic structures separately, so that, if we use v.b. language, we are obliged to regard the system as a resonance hybrid of about twenty distinct ionic structures. By analogy with the term mesomerism used for aromatic systems such as benzene, these are called meso-ionic molecules.† It was at one time believed that the difficulty of having no covalent structures could be avoided by means of the bicyclic structure (IV), but this must be

$$Ph-N\begin{array}{c} CH-C=O \\ | \qquad | \\ N-\!-\!-O \end{array}$$

(IV)

largely discounted since the cross-link C—N is too long to admit being described as a normal single bond. In molecules of this type there cannot obviously be any normal localization of the π electrons; and, since the five-ring is either exactly, or nearly, planar, we may expect considerable delocalization. This would be most easily described by a m.o. calculation such as explained in § 9.8, and in which, excluding conjugation with the phenyl group, there are eight π electrons, occupying four m.o.'s extending over the pentagon and the outer oxygen atom. Such a calculation has been made by H. C. Longuet-Higgins,§ who obtained both the net

$$Ph-N\begin{array}{c} {}^{1\cdot65}\;CH-{}^{1\cdot37}C-O \\ {}^{1\cdot64}\quad | 1\cdot52 \\ {}^{1\cdot64}\;N-\!-\!-O \\ \quad 1\cdot41 \end{array}$$

(V)

$$Ph-N\begin{array}{c} {}^{-0\cdot01}CH-{}^{+0\cdot08}C-{}^{-0\cdot35}O \\ {}^{+0\cdot30}\quad | \\ N-\!-\!-O \\ {}^{-0\cdot14}\quad{}^{+0\cdot13} \end{array}$$

(VI)

$$Ph-N\begin{array}{c} CH-C=O \\ \pm\;| \\ N-\!-\!-O \end{array}$$

(VII)

---

† Wilson Baker, W. D. Ollis, and V. D. Poole, *J. Chem. Soc.*, 1949, p. 307.
‡ R. A. W. Hill and L. E. Sutton, *J. Chim. phys.*, 1949, **46**, 244; *J. Chem. Soc.*, 1949, p. 746.
§ *J. Chim. phys.*, 1949, **46**, 246.

charges on the atoms and the fractional bond orders. The bond orders are shown in (V) and indicate considerable resonance within the ring, but a relatively small contribution from structures possessing a carbonyl structure $\diagdown C{=}O$. The net charges (in units of the electronic charge), scaled to give approximately the correct dipole moment, are shown in (VI). This suggests that (III) is one of the most important of the many structures that are involved.

A convenient symbolic representation of these meso-ionic structures is shown in (VII), where the $\pm$ denotes that a large number of ionic structures are necessary, in which the same atom may sometimes appear with a positive and sometimes with a negative charge.†

The sydnones are not by any means the only types of meso-ionic compound. There is, for example, the betaine (VIII), where Am denotes the amyl group. The only structures possible for this type of molecule are ionic ones. It is not surprising that the dipole

(VIII)

(IX)

(X)

(XI)

(XII)

moment is large (approx. 6 D). Such a value is rather less than half that which would have been expected (15 D) if the formal charge distribution had really been as in (VIII). The difference may be interpreted either as implying the presence of other structures, or as evidence that the electric field of the zwitterion distribution of charge in (VIII) induces a powerful 'back-polarization' on the σ electrons. The matter is not yet settled.

Another type of meso-ionic molecule is shown in (IX), where

† This notation was introduced by J. C. E. Simpson, *J. Chem. Soc.*, 1946, p. 95.

X = O, S, or Se, and Y = H or Cl. Once again the dipole moment†
(4·03 D for benzfurazane, where X = O, Y = H) shows that ionic
structures such as (X) must be quite important, and justify us in

(XIII a)   (XIII b)

classifying these as meso-ionic compounds, which could be written
symbolically as (XI). Another such compound is the reagent
nitron (XII).

Finally we must mention a series of aromatic systems which
are also meso-ionic, and which includes the dyestuff Besthorn's
Red‡ (XIII). No Kekulé-like structure is possible for this molecule.

† R. W. Hill and L. E. Sutton, *J. Chim. phys.*, 1949, **46**, 244.
‡ F. Krollpfeiffer and K. Schneider, *Annalen*, 1937, **530**, 34.

AUTHOR INDEX

INDEX OF SUBSTANCES

INDEX OF SUBJECTS

*Roman numerals refer to chapters, other references are to pages.
Where quantities occur repeatedly only the first reference is usually
given*